the source

the definitive worship collection compiled by
Graham Kendrick

First published in Great Britain in 1998 by
KEVIN MAYHEW LIMITED
Buxhall
Stowmarket
Suffolk IP14 3BW

Words Only   ISBN   1 84003 121 2
                              Catalogue No. 1470101

Full Music   ISBN   1 84003 120 4
                              Catalogue No. 1470104

Complete Acetate Masters   ISBN   1 84003 119 0
                              Catalogue No. 1470201

Printed and bound in Great Britain

the source Production Team

KATHERINE LAIDLER
Managing Editor

DONALD THOMSON
Music Editor

CHRIS HINKINS
VERNON TURNER
Music Setters

LOUISE SELFE
Text Setter

JANE RAYSON
Copyright Manager

JAQUETTA SERGEANT
Cover Designer

GEOFF PEACHEY
Proof Reader

SARA ALLERTON
JANET SIMPSON
Project Co-ordinators

ALAN SPICER
Indexer

Foreword

Let the word of Christ dwell in you richly as you teach and admonish one another with all wisdom, and as you sing psalms, hymns and spiritual songs with gratitude in your hearts to God. And whatever you do, whether in word or deed, do it all in the name of the Lord Jesus, giving thanks to God the Father through him.

Colossians 3:16-17

It is to encourage the realisation of this kind of worship lifestyle that we have compiled and published **the source**, not least to facilitate the singing of psalms, hymns and spiritual songs, of which you will find here over six hundred of the best.

As an editorial panel we have sought to discharge our responsibilities as faithfully and generously as possible, believing that diversity was vital to the breadth and richness of the material we were considering. The songs in this book restate the teachings of our faith, explore new insights, proclaim hope, protest, express solidarity with the poor, call ourselves and others to repentance and faith; and in all this we celebrate our God and Saviour Jesus Christ, who, in the words of the writer to the Hebrews, 'became the source of eternal salvation for all who obey him'.

the source has, we believe, several claims to uniqueness.

The content of each hymn and song has been carefully assessed and, while we have still included some material that may be described as 'lighter', we believe that the *overall* balance is more substantial than in previous collections. This attention to substance and breadth has also enabled us to produce a book that will appeal to a broad church constituency.

While compiling **the source** we have been keenly aware of its prophetic dimension. For the first time we were making choices unencumbered by copyright or any other restrictions: the world was our oyster and we have made full use of the freedom offered to us, including songs both new and old which we expect to take their place (or re-take in the case of the older songs) among those loved by congregations everywhere. In this sense we have aspired to be like the kind of teacher Jesus affirmed who 'is like a householder who brings both new things and old out of his treasure-store' (Matthew 13:52).

There is also a sense in which we have been like harvesters; reaping and gathering what has been growing in the 'fields' of diverse worshipping communities. The variety of soils has produced a rich variety of styles and indeed emphasis which we hope will excite, intrigue and challenge the user to appreciate and benefit from the many facets of the jewel of worship expression which seeks to reflect the glory of God in the world today.

We have been careful to use inclusive language in referring to the human race wherever possible. Exceptions were made for clear reasons and after much deliberation. Non-copyright texts have been amended whilst those by living authors were referred back. We are grateful to the authors concerned for their willingness to co-operate.

Another fundamental aim was to make **the source** as *complete* as possible to help congregations integrate the material contained in it into their own worship. Thus, besides the main music book, there is also a words copy, instrumental arrangements for all 610 songs and hymns, a complete set of acetate masters and a recording programme.

the source is also the first major new publication to which the new CCL photocopying licence applies, making its accessibility even more valuable.

It is impossible to undertake a project of this magnitude without the help of many people. We wish to express our immense gratitude to all those whose opinions and assistance we have sought during the compilation of **the source**. We mention especially Chris Mitchell who has made keyboard arrangements of over 150 of the songs; he has brought enormous skill and dedication to this task.

We hope that in this diverse and approachable worship collection we have sown some seeds; that is all we can do. It is in the overflow of worship from hearts which are united in a passionate love for Jesus Christ that these seeds must be brought to glorious fruition.

GRAHAM KENDRICK
Compiler

JONATHAN BUGDEN
Adviser

MATTHEW LOCKWOOD
Assistant Adviser

The man brought me back to the entrance of the temple, and I saw water coming out from under the threshold of the temple towards the east (for the temple faced east). The water was coming down from under the south side of the temple, south of the altar. He then brought me out through the north gate and led me round the outside to the outer gate facing east, and the water was flowing from the south side.

As the man went eastward with a measuring line in his hand, he measured off a thousand cubits and then led me through water that was ankle-deep. He measured off another thousand cubits and led me through water that was knee-deep. He measured off another thousand and led me through water that was up to the waist. He measured off another thousand, but now it was a river that I could not cross, because the water had risen and was deep enough to swim in – a river that no one could cross. He asked me, 'Son of man, do you see this?'

Then he led me back to the bank of the river. When I arrived there, I saw a great number of trees on each side of the river. He said to me, 'This water flows towards the eastern region and goes down into the Arabah, where it enters the sea. When it empties into the sea, the water there becomes fresh. Swarms of living creatures will live wherever the river flows. There will be large numbers of fish, because this water flows there and makes the salt water fresh; so where the river flows everything will live.

Fruit trees of all kinds will grow on both banks of the river. Their leaves will not wither, nor will their fruit fail. Every month they will bear, because the water from the sanctuary flows to them. Their fruit will serve for food and their leaves for healing.

Ezekiel 47:1-9, 12

1 Abba, Father, let me be

Words and Music: Dave Bilbrough arr. Christopher Tambling

2 Abide with me

EVENTIDE 10 10 10 10

1. A - bide with me, fast falls the e - ven - tide; the dark-ness deep - ens; Lord, with me a - bide: when o - ther help - ers fail, and com-forts flee, help of the help-less, O a - bide with me.

2. Swift to its close ebbs out life's little day;
   earth's joys grow dim, its glories pass away;
   change and decay in all around I see;
   O thou who changest not, abide with me.

3. I need thy presence ev'ry passing hour;
   what but thy grace can foil the tempter's pow'r?
   Who like thyself my guide and stay can be?
   Through cloud and sunshine, Lord, abide with me.

4. I fear no foe with thee at hand to bless;
   ills have no weight, and tears no bitterness.
   Where is death's sting? Where, grave, thy victory?
   I triumph still, if thou abide with me.

5. Hold thou thy cross before my closing eyes;
   shine through the gloom, and point me to the skies;
   heav'n's morning breaks, and earth's vain shadows flee;
   in life, in death, O Lord, abide with me.

Words: Henry Francis Lyte
Music: William Henry Monk

3 Above the clash of creeds
(No other way)

1. A-bove the clash of creeds, the ma - ny voi - ces

that call on so ma - ny names,

in - to these fi - nal days our God has spo - ken

by send - ing his on - ly Son.

Chorus

There is no o-ther way by which we must be saved;
his name is Je-sus, the on-ly Sa-viour; no o-ther sin-
-less life, no o-ther sac-ri-fice, in all cre-
a-tion no o-ther way.

2. Before we called he came
   to earth from heaven,
   our maker became a man;
   when no one else could pay,
   he bought our freedom,
   exchanging his life for ours.

3. Beneath the cross of Christ
   let earth fall silent
   in awe of this mystery;
   then let this song arise
   and fill the nations:
   O hear him call, 'Come to me.'

Words and Music: Graham Kendrick

4 Alleluia, alleluia, give thanks to the risen Lord

2. Spread the good news o'er all the earth,
   Jesus has died and has risen.

3. We have been crucified with Christ,
   now we shall live for ever.

4. God has proclaimed the just reward,
   life for us all, alleluia!

5. Come let us praise the living God,
   joyfully sing to our Saviour.

Words and Music: Donald Fishel

5 All hail King Jesus!

Worshipfully with strength

All hail King Je - sus! All hail Em - ma - nu - el!

King of kings, Lord of lords, bright morn - ing star.

And through - out e - ter - ni - ty I'll sing your prai - ses,

and I'll reign with you through-out e - ter - ni - ty.

Words and Music: Dave Moody

To him who is able to keep you from falling
and to present you before his glorious presence
without fault and with great joy –
to the only God our Saviour
be glory, majesty, power and authority,
through Jesus Christ our Lord, before all ages,
now and for evermore! Amen.

Jude 24-25

6 All hail the Lamb

With awe

All hail the Lamb, en-throned on high;
his praise shall be our bat-tle cry;
he reigns vic-to-ri-ous, for e-ver glo-ri-ous,
his name is Je-sus, he is the Lord.

Words and Music: Dave Bilbrough

7 All hail the power of Jesus' name (Tune 1)

MILES LANE CM

7a All hail the power of Jesus' name (Tune 2)

DIADEM 86 86 extended

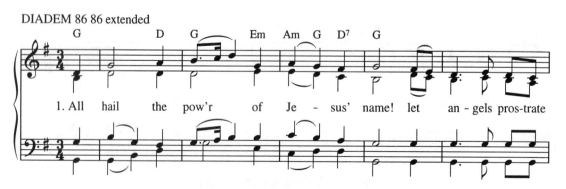

2. Crown him, ye martyrs of your God,
who from his altar call,
who from his altar call;
praise him whose way of pain ye trod,
and crown him, crown him, crown him,
crown him Lord of all.

3. Ye prophets who our freedom won,
ye searchers, great and small,
ye searchers, great and small,
by whom the work of truth is done,
now crown him, crown him, crown him,
crown him Lord of all.

4. Ye seed of Israel's chosen race,
ye ransomed of the fall,
ye ransomed of the fall,
hail him who saves you by his grace,
and crown him, crown him, crown him,
crown him Lord of all.

5. Let ev'ry tribe and ev'ry tongue
to him their hearts enthral,
to him their hearts enthral;
lift high the universal song,
and crown him, crown him, crown him,
crown him Lord of all.

6. O that, with yonder sacred throng,
we at his feet may fall,
we at his feet may fall,
join in the everlasting song,
and crown him, crown him, crown him,
crown him Lord of all.

Words: Edward Perronet
Music – Tune 1: William Shrubsole
Tune 2: James Ellor

Worthy is the Lamb, who was slain,
to receive power and wealth and
wisdom and strength
and honour and glory and praise!

Revelation 5:12

8 All heaven declares

Majestically

1. All heav'n de-clares the glo-ry of the ri-sen Lord.

Who can com-pare with the beau-ty of the Lord?

For-e-ver he will be the Lamb up-on the throne.

I glad-ly bow the knee and wor-ship him a-lone.

2. I will proclaim
the glory of the risen Lord.
Who once was slain
to reconcile us to God.
Forever you will be
the Lamb upon the throne.
I gladly bow the knee
and worship you alone.

Words and Music: Noel and Tricia Richards

9 All heaven waits

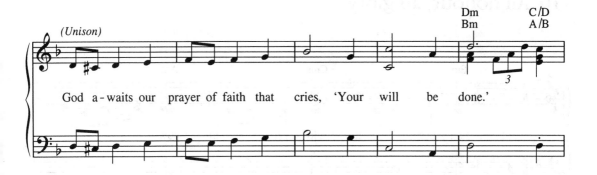

God a-waits our prayer of faith that cries, 'Your will be done.'

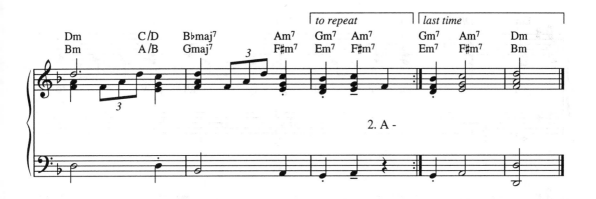

to repeat | last time

2. A -

2. Awake, O church, arise and pray,
   complaining words discard.
   The Spirit comes to fill your mouth
   with truth, his mighty sword.
   Go place your feet on Satan's ground
   and there proclaim Christ's name,
   in step with heaven's armies march
   to conquer and to reign!

   (Women)
3. Now in our hearts and on our lips
   the word of faith is near,
   let heaven's will on earth be done,
   let heaven flow from here.
   (Men)
   Come, blend your prayers with Jesus' own
   before the Father's throne,
   and as the incense clouds ascend,
   God's holy fire rains down.

4. Soon comes the day when with a shout
   King Jesus will appear,
   and with him all the church,
   from ev'ry age, shall fill the air.
   The brightness of his coming shall
   consume the lawless one,
   as with a word the breath of God
   tears down his rebel throne.

5. One body here, by heav'n inspired,
   we seek prophetic power;
   in Christ agreed, one heart and voice,
   to speak this day, this hour,
   in ev'ry place where chaos rules
   and evil forces brood;
   let Jesus' voice speak like the roar
   of a great multitude.

Words and Music: Graham Kendrick and Chris Rolinson

10 All honour, all glory

Words and Music: Chris Falson

11 All I once held dear
(Knowing you)

1. All I once held dear, built my life up - on, all this

world re - veres, and wars to own, all I once thought gain I have

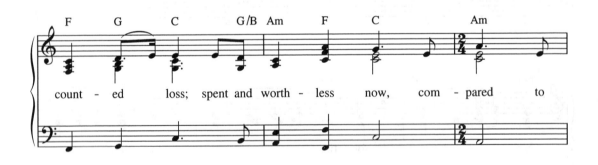

count - ed loss; spent and worth - less now, com - pared to

this. Know-ing you, Je-sus, know-ing you, there

2. Now my heart's desire
   is to know you more,
   to be found in you
   and known as yours.
   To possess by faith
   what I could not earn,
   all-surpassing gift
   of righteousness.

3. Oh, to know the pow'r
   of your risen life,
   and to know you in
   your sufferings.
   To become like you
   in your death, my Lord,
   so with you to live
   and never die.

Words and Music: Graham Kendrick

12 All over the world

2. Your banner is lifted, your praises are sung,
   your Spirit is moving all over the world.
   Divisions are falling, you're making us one,
   your Spirit is moving all over the world.
   Divisions are falling, you're making us one,
   your Spirit is moving all over the world.

Words and Music: Terry Butler

Praise him with the sounding of the trumpet,
praise him with the harp and lyre,
praise him with tambourine and dancing,
praise him with the strings and flute,
praise him with the clash of cymbals,
praise him with resounding cymbals.

Psalm 150:3-5

13 All people that on earth do dwell

OLD HUNDREDTH LM

1. All peo - ple that on earth do dwell, sing

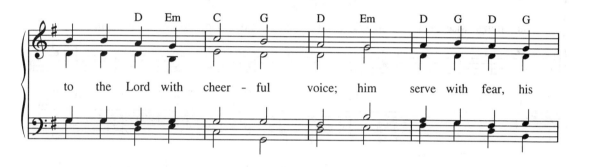

to the Lord with cheer - ful voice; him serve with fear, his

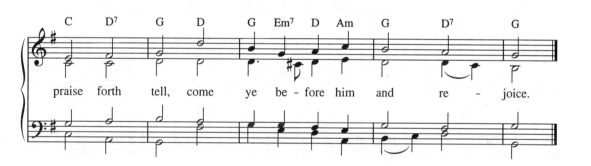

praise forth tell, come ye be - fore him and re - joice.

2. Know that the Lord is God indeed,
   without our aid he did us make;
   we are his flock, he doth us feed,
   and for his sheep he doth us take.

3. O enter then his gates with praise,
   approach with joy his courts unto;
   praise, laud and bless his name always,
   for it is seemly so to do.

4. For why? the Lord our God is good:
   his mercy is for ever sure;
   his truth at all times firmly stood,
   and shall from age to age endure.

5. Praise God from whom all blessings flow,
   praise him, all creatures here below,
   praise him above, ye heav'nly hosts:
   praise Father, Son and Holy Ghost.

Words: William Kethe from *Day's Psalter* alt.
Music: from the *Genevan Psalter*

14 All things bright and beautiful (Tune 1)

ROYAL OAK 76 76 and Refrain

1. All things bright and beau-ti-ful, all crea-tures great and small,
all things wise and won-der-ful, the Lord God made them all.

Verse

1. Each lit-tle flow'r that o-pens, each lit-tle bird that sings, he
made their glow-ing co-lours, he made their ti-ny wings.

This arrangement © Copyright 1998 Kevin Mayhew Ltd.

14a (Tune 2)

ALL THINGS BRIGHT AND BEAUTIFUL 76 76 and Refrain

1. All things bright and beau - ti-ful, all crea -tures great and

2. The purple-headed mountain,
   the river running by,
   the sunset and the morning
   that brightens up the sky.

3. The cold wind in the winter,
   the pleasant summer sun,
   the ripe fruits in the garden,
   he made them ev'ry one.

4. He gave us eyes to see them,
   and lips that we may tell
   how great is God almighty,
   who has made all things well.

Words: Cecil Frances Alexander
Music – Tune 1: traditional English melody
Tune 2: William Henry Monk

15 All to Jesus I surrender
(I surrender all)

1. All to Jesus I surrender, all to him I freely give; I will ever love and trust him, in his presence daily live. I surrender all,

I surrender all, all to thee, my blessed Saviour, I surrender all.

2. All to Jesus I surrender,
   humbly at his feet I bow;
   worldly pleasures all forsaken,
   take me, Jesus, take me now.

3. All to Jesus I surrender,
   make me, Saviour, wholly thine;
   let me feel the Holy Spirit,
   truly know that thou art mine.

4. All to Jesus I surrender,
   Lord, I give myself to thee;
   fill me with thy love and power,
   let thy blessing fall on me.

5. All to Jesus I surrender,
   now to feel the sacred flame;
   O, the joy of full salvation!
   Glory, glory to his name!

Words: J.W. Van De Venter
Music: W.S. Weedon

Words © Copyright HarperCollins Religious. Administered by CopyCare,
P.O. Box 77, Hailsham, East Sussex, BN27 3EF, UK. Used by permission.

16 Almighty God, we bring you praise

Worshipfully

Al-migh-ty God, we bring you praise for your Son,
the Word of God, by whose pow'r the world was made,
by whose blood we are re-deemed. Morn-ing star, the Fa-ther's
glo-ry, we now wor-ship and a-dore you. In our
hearts your light has ri-sen; Je-sus, Lord, we wor-ship you.

Words and Music: Austin Martin

17 Almighty God, my Redeemer
(All things are possible)

Words and Music: Darlene Zschech

For the Lord is good and his love endures for ever;
his faithfulness continues through all generations.

Psalm 100:5

18 Amazing grace

AMAZING GRACE CM

2. 'Twas grace that taught my heart to fear,
   and grace my fears relieved.
   How precious did that grace appear
   the hour I first believed.

3. Through many dangers, toils and snares
   I have already come.
   'Tis grace that brought me safe thus far,
   and grace will lead me home.

4. The Lord has promised good to me,
   his word my hope secures;
   he will my shield and portion be
   as long as life endures.

5. Yes, when this heart and flesh shall fail,
   and mortal life shall cease,
   I shall possess within the veil
   a life of joy and peace.

6. When we've been there a thousand years,
   bright shining as the sun,
   we've no less days to sing God's praise
   than when we first begun.

Words: vs. 1–4: John Newton alt, v.5: John Rees
Music: American folk melody arr. Richard Lloyd
This arrangement © Copyright 1993 Kevin Mayhew Ltd.

19 Among the gods
(You alone are God)

With strength

Verse

1. A-mong the gods there is none like you, O Lord, O
2. You are so good and for-giv-ing, O Lord, O

Lord.   There are no deeds to com-pare with yours, O
Lord.   You're rich in love to all who call to you, O

Lord.   All the na-tions you have made will come;
Lord.   All the na-tions you have made will come;

they'll wor-ship be-fore you, O Lord, O
they'll glo-ri-fy your name, O Lord, O

Chorus

Lord.
Lord.   For you are great and do mar-vel-lous deeds.

Words and Music: Carol Owen

20 An army of ordinary people

Words and Music: Dave Bilbrough

21 And can it be

SAGINA 88 88 88 extended

Verse

1. And can it be that I should gain an in - t'rest in the Sa - viour's blood? Died he for me, who caused his pain? For me, who him to death pur - sued? A - maz - ing love! How can it be that thou, my God, shouldst die for

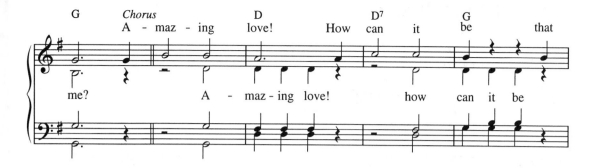

2. 'Tis myst'ry all! th'Immortal dies:
   who can explore his strange design?
   In vain the first-born seraph tries
   to sound the depths of love divine!
   'Tis mercy all! Let earth adore,
   let angel minds inquire no more.

3. He left his Father's throne above
   so free, so infinite his grace;
   emptied himself of all but love,
   and bled for Adam's helpless race;
   'tis mercy all, immense and free;
   for, O my God, it found out me.

4. Long my imprisoned spirit lay
   fast bound in sin and nature's night;
   thine eye diffused a quick'ning ray,
   I woke, the dungeon flamed with light;
   my chains fell off, my heart was free;
   I rose, went forth, and followed thee.

5. No condemnation now I dread;
   Jesus, and all in him is mine!
   Alive in him, my living Head,
   and clothed in righteousness divine,
   bold I approach the eternal throne,
   and claim the crown, through Christ my own.

Words: Charles Wesley
Music: Thomas Campbell

22 And he shall reign

2. He was given sov'reign power,
   glory and authority.
   Every nation, tribe and tongue
   worshipped him on bended knee.

3. On the throne for ever,
   see the Lamb who once was slain;
   wounds of sacrificial love
   for ever shall remain.

Words and Music: Graham Kendrick

23 A new commandment

A new com-mand-ment I give un-to you, that you love one a-
no-ther as I have loved you, that you love one a-no-ther as
I have loved you. By this shall all know that you are my dis-ci-ples if
you have love one for a-no-ther. By this shall all know that
you are my dis-ci-ples if you have love one for a-no-ther.

Words and Music: unknown

24 Anointing, fall on me

With a 'gospel' feel

25 Ascribe greatness

Thoughtfully with strength

As - cribe   great - ness to our   God,   the Rock,

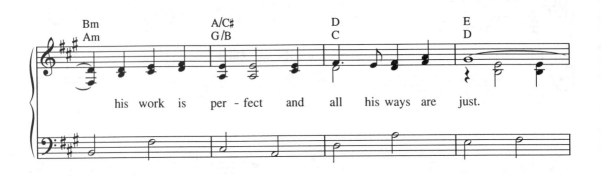

his   work   is   per - fect   and   all   his ways are   just.

As - cribe   great - ness to   our   God,   the Rock,

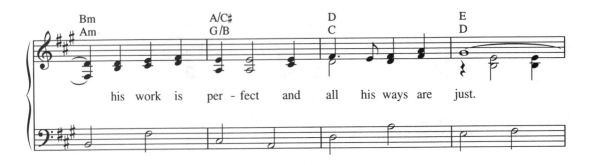

his   work   is   per - fect   and   all   his ways are   just.

A God of faith-ful-ness and with-out in-

jus - tice, good and up - right is he;

a God of faith-ful-ness and with-out in-

jus - tice, good and up - right is he.

Words and Music: Peter West, Mary Lou Locke and Mary Kirkbridge

26 As I come into your presence
(Awesome in this place)

As I come in-to your pre-sence, past the gates of praise,

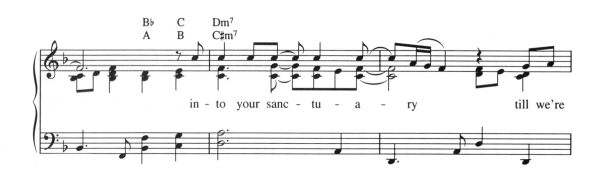

in-to your sanc-tu – a – ry till we're

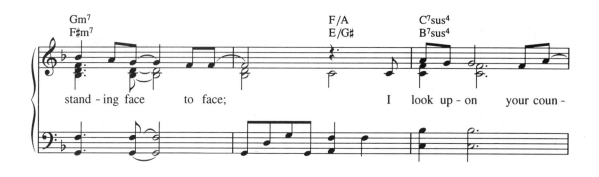

stand-ing face to face; I look up-on your coun-

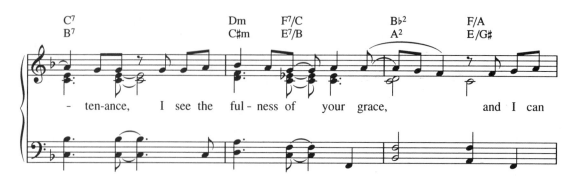

-ten-ance, I see the ful-ness of your grace, and I can

Words and Music: Dave Billington

27 As the deer pants

Flowing

Verse

1. As the deer pants for the wa-ter, so my soul longs af - ter you.

You a -lone are my heart's de - sire and I long to wor - ship you.

Chorus

You a -lone are my strength, my shield, to you a -lone may my spi - rit yield.

You a - lone are my heart's de - sire and I long to wor - ship you.

2. I want you more than gold or silver,
only you can satisfy.
You alone are the real joy-giver
and the apple of my eye.

3. You're my friend and you are my brother,
even though you are a King.
I love you more than any other,
so much more than anything.

Words and Music: Martin J. Nystrom

28 As the deer pants
(Your waves of love)

Rhythmically

As the deer pants for the wa - ter, so my soul, it thirsts for you, for you, O God, for you, O God.

1. As the
2. When can I come be-fore you and see your face? My

Words and Music: Richard Lewis

God, who has called you into fellowship
with his Son Jesus Christ our Lord, is faithful.

1 Corinthians 1:9

29 As we are gathered

As we are gathered, Jesus is here;
one with each other, Jesus is here; joined by the
Spirit, washed in the blood, part of the body, the
church of God. As we are gathered, Jesus is
here; one with each other, Jesus is here.

Words and Music: John Daniels

© Copyright 1979 Springtide/Word Music. Administered by CopyCare,
P.O. Box 77, Hailsham, East Sussex, BN27 3EF, UK. Used by permission.

30 As we lift up your name
(Revival fire, fall)

(Leader)
1. As we lift up your name, as we lift up your name, let your
(All)
2. As we lift up your name, as we lift up your name, let your
(Leader)

fire fall, let your fire fall; send your wind and your rain, send your
king-dom come, let your king-dom come; have your way in this place, have your

wind and your rain, on your wings of love, on your wings of love.
way in this place, let your will be done, let your will be done.

Pour out from hea-ven your pas-sion and pre-sence,

bring down your burn-ing de-sire. Re-vi-val fire,

Words and Music: Paul Baloche

Ascribe to the Lord the glory due to his name;
bring an offering and come into his courts.
Worship the Lord in the splendour of his holiness;
tremble before him, all the earth.

Psalm 96:8-9

31 As we seek your face

2. Move among us now,
   come, reveal your pow'r,
   show your presence, acceptance,
   move among us now.

3. At your feet we fall,
   sov'reign Lord,
   we cry 'holy, holy',
   at your feet we fall.

Words and Music: Dave Bilbrough

© Copyright 1990 Kingsway's Thankyou Music, P.O. Box 75, Eastbourne,
East Sussex, BN23 6NW, UK. Used by permission.

32 At the foot of the cross

Words and Music: Derek Bond

33 At the name of Jesus

2. At his voice creation
   sprang at once to sight,
   all the angel faces,
   all the hosts of light,
   thrones and dominations,
   stars upon their way,
   all the heav'nly orders
   in their great array.

3. Humbled for a season,
   to receive a name
   from the lips of sinners
   unto whom he came,
   faithfully he bore it,
   spotless to the last,
   brought it back victorious
   when from death he passed.

4. Bore it up triumphant,
   with its human light,
   through all ranks of creatures
   to the central height,
   to the throne of Godhead,
   to the Father's breast,
   filled it with the glory
   of that perfect rest.

5. All creation, name him,
   with love as strong as death;
   but with awe and wonder,
   and with bated breath.
   He is God the Saviour,
   he is Christ the Lord,
   ever to be worshipped,
   trusted and adored.

6. In your hearts enthrone him;
   there let him subdue
   all that is not holy,
   all that is not true;
   crown him as your captain
   in temptation's hour;
   let his will enfold you
   in its light and pow'r.

7. Truly, this Lord Jesus
   shall return again,
   with his Father's glory,
   with his angel train;
   for all wreaths of empire
   meet upon his brow,
   and our hearts confess him
   King of glory now.

Words: Caroline Maria Noel alt.
Music: Michael Brierley

For to us a child is born,
to us a son is given,
and the government will be on his shoulders.
And he will be called
Wonderful Counsellor, Mighty God,
Everlasting Father, Prince of Peace.

Isaiah 9:6

34 At this time of giving
(The giving song)

Accelerating with each verse

Chorus

At this time of giv-ing, glad-ly now we bring gifts of good-ness and mer-cy from a heav'n-ly King.

Verse

1. Earth could not con-tain the trea-sures hea-ven holds for you, per-fect joy and last-ing trea-sures, love so strong and true.

2. May his tender love surround you
   at this Christmastime;
   may you see his smiling face
   that in the darkness shines.

3. But the many gifts he gives
   are all poured out from one;
   come, receive the greatest gift,
   the gift of God's own Son.

   Last two choruses and verses:
   Lai, lai, lai . . . etc.

Words and Music: Graham Kendrick

35 At your feet we fall

2. There we see you stand, mighty risen Lord,
   clothed in garments pure and holy, shining bright.
   Eyes of flashing fire, feet like burnished bronze,
   and the sound of many waters is your voice.

3. Like the shining sun in its noonday strength,
   we now see the glory of your wondrous face.
   Once that face was marred, but now you're glorified,
   and your words like a two-edged sword have mighty pow'r.

Words and Music: David Fellingham

An angel of the Lord appeared to them,
and the glory of the Lord shone around them,
and they were terrified.
But the angel said to them, 'Do not be afraid.
I bring you good news of great joy
that will be for all the people.
Today in the town of David
a Saviour has been born to you;
he is Christ the Lord.
This will be a sign to you:
You will find a baby wrapped in cloths
and lying in a manger.'

Suddenly a great company of the heavenly host
appeared with the angel, praising God and saying,
'Glory to God in the highest,
and on earth peace to all on
whom his favour rests.'

Luke 2:9-14

36 Away in a manger

CRADLE SONG 11 11 11 11

2. The cattle are lowing, the baby awakes,
   but little Lord Jesus no crying he makes.
   I love thee, Lord Jesus! Look down from the sky,
   and stay by my side until morning is nigh.

3. Be near me, Lord Jesus; I ask thee to stay
   close by me for ever, and love me, I pray.
   Bless all the dear children in thy tender care,
   and fit us for heaven, to live with thee there.

Words: William James Kirkpatrick
Music: William James Kirkpatrick arr. Richard Lloyd
This arrangement © Copyright 1996 Kevin Mayhew Ltd.

37 Beauty for brokenness
(God of the poor)

1. Beau-ty for bro-ken-ness, hope for des-pair, Lord, in the suff-er-ing this is our prayer. Bread for the child-ren, jus-tice, joy, peace, sun-rise to sun-set your king-dom in-crease. your king-dom in-crease. speak.

to next verse

to chorus

Chorus

God of the poor, friend of the weak, give us com-pas-

sion, we pray, melt our cold hearts, let tears fall like rain. Come, change our love from a spark to a flame.

2. Shelter for fragile lives,
   cures for their ills,
   work for the craftsmen,
   trade for their skills.
   Land for the dispossessed,
   rights for the weak,
   voices to plead the cause
   of those who can't speak.

3. Refuge from cruel wars,
   havens from fear,
   cities for sanctu'ry,
   freedoms to share.
   Peace to the killing fields,
   scorched earth to green,
   Christ for the bitterness,
   his cross for the pain.

4. Rest for the ravaged earth,
   oceans and streams,
   plundered and poisoned,
   our future, our dreams.
   Lord, end our madness,
   carelessness, greed;
   make us content with
   the things that we need.

5. Lighten our darkness,
   breathe on this flame,
   until your justice
   burns brightly again;
   until the nations
   learn of your ways,
   seek your salvation
   and bring you their praise.

Words and Music: Graham Kendrick

Who may ascend the hill of the Lord?
Who may stand in his holy place?
He who has clean hands and a pure heart,
who does not lift up his soul to an idol
or swear by what is false.

Psalm 24:3-4

38 Be bold, be strong

Words and Music: Morris Chapman

39 Because of your love

Words and Music: Russell Fragar

40 Before the world began
(So you would come)

Be - fore the world be-gan
you were on his mind,
and
Noth-ing you can do
could make him love you more,
and

ev - 'ry tear you cry
is pre - cious in his eyes.
Be -
no-thing that you've done
could make him close the door.

cause of his great love,
he gave his on - ly Son;

Be -

ev - 'ry-thing was done
so you would come.

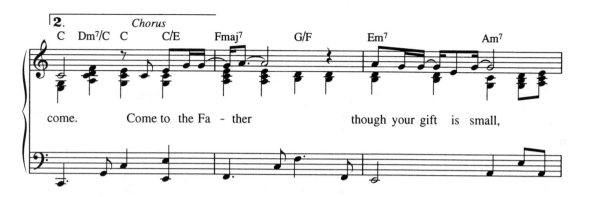

2. *Chorus*

come. Come to the Fa – ther though your gift is small,

bro-ken hearts, bro-ken lives, he will take them all. The

pow – er of the Word, the pow – er of his blood,

ev – 'ry-thing was done so you would come.

Words and Music: Russell Fragar

41 Be free

Be free in the love of God; he has made us whole.

1. For his pur-pose he has called us, in his hands he
gent-ly holds us. He will keep us and sus-tain us
in the Fa-ther's love.

2. God is gracious, he will lead us
   through his pow'r at work within us.
   Spirit, guide us, and unite us
   in the Father's love.

Words and Music: Dave Bilbrough

42 Be glorified

2. Worship the Lord, worship the Lord.
   Worship the Lord, worship the Lord.
   Worship the Lord in the heavens,
   worship the Lord in this earth;
   worship the Lord in this temple,
   Jesus, Jesus, be thou glorified,
   Jesus, Jesus, be thou glorified.

Words and Music: Billy Funk

43 Behold his love

Words and Music: Geoff Baker

44 Behold the Lord

1. Be-hold the Lord up-on his throne; his face is shin-ing like the sun. With eyes blaz-ing fire, and feet glow-ing bronze, his voice like migh-ty wa-ter roars. Ho - ly, ho - ly, Lord God Al-migh-ty. Ho - ly, ho - ly, we stand in awe of you.

2. The first, the last, the living One,
   laid down his life for all the world.
   Behold, he now lives for evermore,
   and holds the keys of death and hell.
   Holy, holy, Lord God Almighty.
   Holy, holy, we bow before your throne.

3. So let our praises ever ring
   to Jesus Christ, our glorious King.
   All heaven and earth resound as we cry:
   'Worthy is the Son of God!'
   Holy, holy, Lord God Almighty.
   Holy, holy, we fall down at your feet,

Words and Music: Noel Richards and Gerald Coates

45 Beneath the cross of Jesus

SAINT CHRISTOPHER 76 86 86 86

1. Be-neath the cross of Je-sus I fain would take my stand, the sha-dow of a migh-ty rock with-in a wea-ry land; a home with-in a wil-der-ness, a rest up-on the way, from burn-ing heat at noon-tide and the bur-den of the day.

2. O safe and happy shelter!
O refuge tried and sweet!
O trysting place where heaven's love
and heaven's justice meet!
As to the holy patriarch
that wondrous dream was giv'n,
so seems my Saviour's cross to me
a ladder up to heav'n.

3. There lies, beneath its shadow
but on the farther side,
the darkness of an awful grave
that gapes both deep and wide;
and there between us stands the cross,
two arms outstretched to save;
a watchman set to guard the way
from that eternal grave.

4. Upon that cross of Jesus
mine eye at times can see
the very dying form of One
who suffered there for me;
and from my stricken heart, with tears,
two wonders I confess –
the wonders of redeeming love,
and my unworthiness.

5. I take, O cross, thy shadow
for my abiding place!
I ask no other sunshine than
the sunshine of his face;
content to let the world go by,
to reckon gain as loss –
my sinful self, my only shame,
my glory all – the cross.

Words: Elizabeth C. Clephane alt.
Music: Frederick C. Maker

46 Be patient, be ready
(White horse)

Be pa - tient, be rea - dy, look up – the Lord is near. Be faith - ful, be fruit - ful, un - til the day that he ap - pears. Though all things are sha - ken and hearts are filled with fear,

Words and Music: Graham Kendrick

47 Be still, for the presence of the Lord

Be still, for the pre-sence of the Lord, the Ho-ly One is here.
Come, bow be-fore him now, with re-ver-ence and fear.
In him no sin is found, we stand on ho-ly ground.
Be still, for the pre-sence of the Lord, the Ho-ly One is here.

2. Be still, for the glory of the Lord is shining all around;
   he burns with holy fire, with splendour he is crowned.
   How awesome is the sight, our radiant King of light!
   Be still, for the glory of the Lord is shining all around.

3. Be still, for the power of the Lord is moving in this place;
   he comes to cleanse and heal, to minister his grace.
   No work too hard for him, in faith receive from him.
   Be still, for the power of the Lord is moving in this place.

Words and Music: David J. Evans

48 Be still and know

1. Be still and know that I am

God, be still and know that I am

God, be still and know that I am God.

2. I am the Lord that healeth thee . . .

3. In thee, O Lord, do I put my trust . . .

Words and Music: unknown
This arrangement © Copyright 1998 Kevin Mayhew Ltd.

49 Be still, my soul

FINLANDIA 10 10 10 10 10 10

Harmony

1. Be still, my soul: the Lord is on your side; bear pa-tient-ly the cross of grief and pain; leave to your God to or-der and pro-vide; in ev-'ry change he faith-ful will re-main. Be still, my soul: your best, your heav'n-ly friend, through thor-ny ways, leads to a joy-ful end.

2. Be still, my soul: your God will undertake
to guide the future as he has the past.
Your hope, your confidence let nothing shake,
all now mysterious shall be clear at last.
Be still, my soul: the tempests still obey
his voice, who ruled them once on Galilee.

3. Be still, my soul: the hour is hastening on
when we shall be for ever with the Lord,
when disappointment, grief and fear are gone,
sorrow forgotten, love's pure joy restored.
Be still, my soul: when change and tears are past,
all safe and blessèd we shall meet at last.

Words: Katharina Von Schlegal trans. Jane L. Borthwick, alt.
Music: Jean Sibelius

50 Be thou my vision

SLANE 10 10 10 10

1. Be thou my vi-sion, O Lord of my heart, naught be all else to me save that thou art; thou my best thought in the day and the night, wa-king or sleep-ing, thy pre-sence my light.

2. Be thou my wisdom, be thou my true word,
   I ever with thee and thou with me, Lord;
   thou my great Father, and I thy true heir;
   thou in me dwelling, and I in thy care.

3. Be thou my breastplate, my sword for the fight,
   be thou my armour, and be thou my might,
   thou my soul's shelter, and thou my high tow'r,
   raise thou me heav'nward, O Pow'r of my pow'r.

4. Riches I need not, nor all the world's praise,
   thou my inheritance through all my days;
   thou, and thou only, the first in my heart,
   high King of heaven, my treasure thou art!

5. High King of heaven, when battle is done,
   grant heaven's joys to me, O bright heav'n's sun;
   Christ of my own heart, whatever befall,
   still be my vision, O Ruler of all.

Words: Irish (c. 8th century) trans. Mary Byrne and Eleanor Hull
Music: traditional Irish melody arr. Colin Hand

51 Bind us together

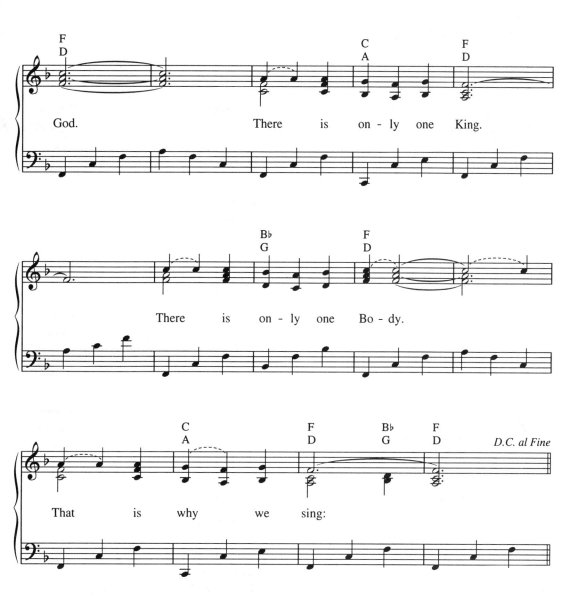

2. Made for the glory of God,
   purchased by his precious Son.
   Born with the right to be clean,
   for Jesus the vict'ry has won.

3. You are the fam'ly of God.
   You are the promise divine.
   You are God's chosen desire.
   You are the glorious new wine.

Words and Music: Bob Gillman

52 Blessed assurance, Jesus is mine

BLESSED ASSURANCE Irregular

1. Bless-ed as - sur - ance, Je-sus is mine: O what a fore - taste of glo - ry di - vine! Heir of sal - va - tion, pur-chase of God; born of his Spi - rit, washed in his blood.

Chorus

This is my sto - ry, this is my song, prais-ing my Sa - viour all the day long. This is my sto - ry, this is my song, prais-ing my Sa - viour all the day long.

2. Perfect submission, perfect delight,
   visions of rapture burst on my sight;
   angels descending, bring from above
   echoes of mercy, whispers of love.

3. Perfect submission, all is at rest,
   I in my Saviour am happy and blessed;
   watching and waiting, looking above,
   filled with his goodness, lost in his love.

Words: Frances Jane van Alstyne (Fanny J. Crosby)
Music: Phoebe Palmer Knapp

53 Blessed be the name of the Lord

With awe

1. Bless-ed be the name of the Lord.
Bless-ed be the name of the Lord. For
he is our Rock, for he is our
Rock, he is the Lord. For

2. Jesus reigns on high in all the earth.
Jesus reigns on high in all the earth.
Jesus reigns on high in all the earth.
Jesus reigns on high in all the earth.
The universe is in the hands of the Lord.
The universe is in the hands of the Lord.

Words and Music: Kevin Prosch and Danny Daniels

54 Blessing and honour
(Ancient of Days)

With an 'island' feel

Words and Music: Gary Sadler and Jamie Harvill

55 Blessing, honour, glory to the Lamb
(Glory to the Lamb)

Bless - ing, ho - nour, glo - ry to the Lamb. Ho - ly, right - eous, wor - thy is the Lamb.

1. Lamb.
2. Lamb. Death could not hold him down for he is ri - sen. Seat - ed up - on the throne he is the Lamb of God.

Words and Music: Geoff Bullock and Dave Reidy

© Copyright 1990 Word Music Inc. Administered by CopyCare,
P.O. Box 77, Hailsham, East Sussex, BN27 3EF, UK. Used by permission.

56 Bless the Lord, my soul

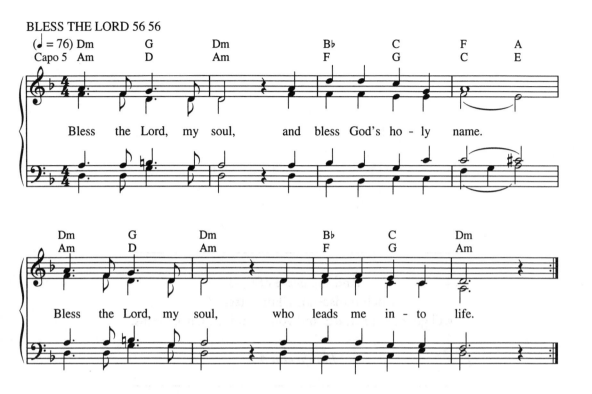

BLESS THE LORD 56 56

Bless the Lord, my soul, and bless God's ho-ly name.

Bless the Lord, my soul, who leads me in-to life.

Words: from Scripture
Music: Jacques Berthier

And the peace of God,
which transcends all understanding,
will guard your hearts and your minds in Christ Jesus.

Philippians 4:7

57 Breathe on me, Breath of God (Tune 1)

CARLISLE SM

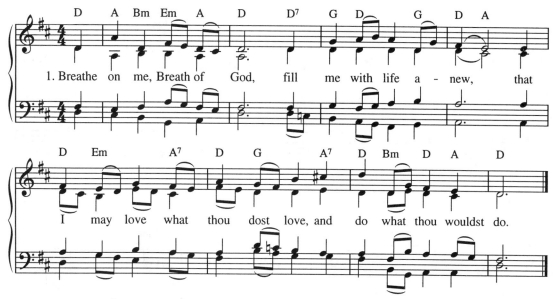

1. Breathe on me, Breath of God, fill me with life a-new, that
I may love what thou dost love, and do what thou wouldst do.

57a Breath on me, Breath of God (Tune 2)

TRENTHAM SM

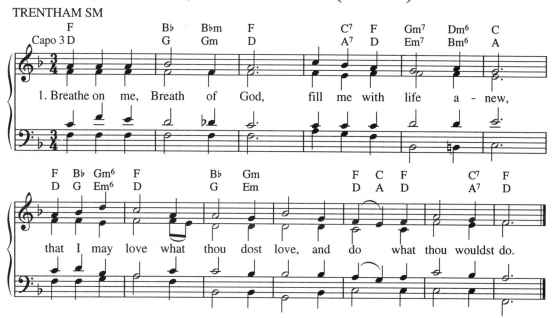

1. Breathe on me, Breath of God, fill me with life a-new,
that I may love what thou dost love, and do what thou wouldst do.

2. Breathe on me, Breath of God,
until my heart is pure:
until with thee I have one will
to do and to endure.

3. Breathe on me, Breath of God,
till I am wholly thine,
until this earthly part of me
glows with thy fire divine.

4. Breathe on me, Breath of God,
so shall I never die,
but live with thee the perfect life
of thine eternity.

Words: Edwin Hatch
Music – Tune 1: Charles Lockhart
Tune 2: Robert Jackson

58 Broken for me

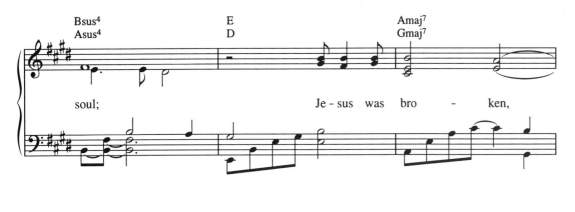

soul; Je - sus was bro - ken,

that we might be whole.

CODA

bro - ken for you.

2. Come to my table and with me dine;
   eat of my bread and drink of my wine.

3. This is my body given for you;
   eat it rememb'ring I died for you.

4. This is my blood I shed for you,
   for your forgiveness, making you new.

Words and Music: Janet Lunt

Therefore, if anyone is in Christ,
he is a new creation;
the old has gone, the new has come!

2 Corinthians 5:17

59 By his grace

By his grace I am re - deemed, by his blood I am made clean, and I now can know him face to face. By his pow'r I have been raised, hid-den now in Christ by faith. I will praise the glo - ry of his grace.

Words and Music: Steven Fry

60 By your side

Tenderly

By your side I would stay; in your arms I would lay. Je-sus, lo-ver of my soul, no-thing from you

Words and Music: Noel and Tricia Richards

61 Called to a battle
(Thunder in the skies)

Driving
Verse

1. Called to a bat - tle, hea - ven - ly war;
though we may strug - gle,
vic - to - ry is sure. Death will not tri - umph,
though we may die; Je -
- sus has pro - mised our e - ter - nal life.

2. Standing together, moving as one;
   we are God's army, called to overcome.
   We are commissioned, Jesus says go;
   in ev'ry nation, let his love be known.

Words and Music: Noel and Tricia Richards

62 Can a nation be changed?

With awe

Verse

1. Can a na-tion be changed? Can a na-tion be saved?

Can a na-tion be turned back to you?

Chorus

We're on our knees, we're on our

knees a-gain. We're on our knees, we're on our

last time

knees a - gain.

2. Let this nation be changed,
   let this nation be saved,
   let this nation be turned back to you.
   (Repeat)

Words and Music: Matt Redman

63 Can I ascend
(I'm coming up the mountain)

Words and Music: Matt Redman

64 Can we walk upon the water

Verse
Capo 3

1. Can we walk up-on the wa — ter if our
walk in-to the pro — mise of a-

eyes are fixed on you? There's an air of faith with-in
bun-dance in the land? Take us on, be-yond the ri —

us for a time of break — ing through. Can we
— ver, for the har-vest you have planned: let us

fly a lit-tle high — er, can we soar on ea-gle's wings?
see your king-dom com — ing in a mea-sure we've not seen.

Words and Music: Matt Redman

O Lord, our Lord,
how majestic is your name in all the earth!
You have set your glory
above the heavens.

Psalm 8:1

65 Can you see what we have made
(Song for Christingle)

1. Can you see what we have made, for this very
2. Count the sea-sons as we sing, sum-mer, au-tumn,
5. There's a world I'm dream-ing of, where there's peace and

spe - cial day? An o - range for our pla - net home
win - ter, spring. Sing to God who sends the rain,
joy and love. Light of Je - sus ev - 'ry - where,

cir - cl - ing a - round the sun.
mak - ing all things new a -
this is my Christ - in - gle

verse 1

verses 2 & 5

2. gain.
5. prayer.

Words and Music: Graham Kendrick

66 Celebrate, celebrate
(Seven reasons to celebrate)

Ce-le-brate,

ce-le-brate, ce-le-brate, O ce - le-brate Je-sus.

(Leader)
From the far cor-ners of earth we hear mu - sic.

(All)
O ce - le-brate. *(Leader)* E-cho-ing o-ver the land and sea. *(All)* O ce - le-brate.

(Leader)
Sound of the drums a-wakes a new morn-ing. *(All)* O ce - le-brate.

Words and Music: Graham Kendrick

67 Celebrate Jesus

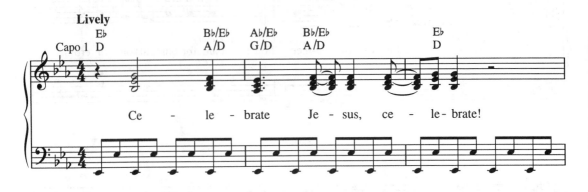

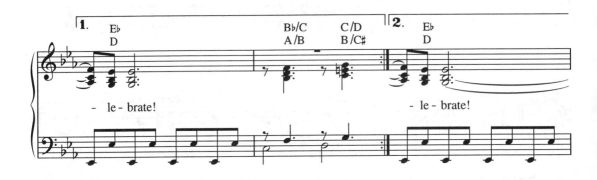

Words and Music: Gary Oliver

68 Change my heart, O God

69 Colours of day
(Light up the fire)

Flowing

Verse

1. Co-lours of day dawn in-to the mind, the sun has come up, the night is be-hind. Go down in the ci-ty, in-to the street, and let's give the mes-sage to the peo-ple we meet. So light up the fire and let the flame burn, o-pen the door, let Je-sus re-turn. Take seeds of his Spi-rit, let the fruit grow, tell the peo-ple of Je-sus, let his love show.

2. Go through the park, on into the town;
the sun still shines on; it never goes down.
The light of the world is risen again;
the people of darkness are needing a friend.

3. Open your eyes, look into the sky,
the darkness has come, the sun came to die.
The evening draws on, the sun disappears,
but Jesus is living, his Spirit is near.

Words and Music: Sue McClellan, John Paculabo and Keith Ryecroft

70 Come and see
(We worship at your feet)

2. Come and weep, come and mourn
   for your sin that pierced him there;
   so much deeper than the wounds of thorn and nail.
   All our pride, all our greed,
   all our fallenness and shame;
   and the Lord has laid the punishment on him.

3. Man of heav'n, born to earth
   to restore us to your heav'n.
   Here we bow in awe beneath your searching eyes.
   From your tears comes our joy,
   from your death our life shall spring;
   by your resurrection power we shall rise.

Words and Music: Graham Kendrick

Speak to one another
with psalms, hymns and spiritual songs.
Sing and make music in your heart to the Lord,
always giving thanks to God the Father for everything,
in the name of our Lord Jesus Christ.

Ephesians 5:19-20

71 Come down, O Love divine

DOWN AMPNEY 66 11 D

1. Come down, O Love divine, seek thou this soul of mine, and vi-sit it with thine own ar-dour glow-ing; O Com-for-ter, draw near, with-in my heart ap-pear, and kin-dle it, thy ho-ly flame be-stow-ing.

2. O let it freely burn,
   till earthly passions turn
   to dust and ashes in its heat consuming;
   and let thy glorious light
   shine ever on my sight,
   and clothe me round, the while my path illuming.

3. Let holy charity
   mine outward vesture be,
   and lowliness become mine inner clothing;
   true lowliness of heart,
   which takes the humbler part,
   and o'er its own shortcomings weeps with loathing.

4. And so the yearning strong,
   with which the soul will long,
   shall far outpass the pow'r of human telling;
   nor can we guess its grace,
   till we become the place
   wherein the Holy Spirit makes his dwelling.

Words: Bianco da Siena trans. Richard F. Littledale, alt.
Music: Ralph Vaughan Williams

72 Come, let us return

Words and Music: Graham Kendrick

73 Come, let us worship Jesus
(King of the nations)

(Women)

2. Lavish our heart's affection,
   deepest love and highest praise.
   Voice, race and language blending,
   all the world amazed.

4. Come, Lord, and fill your temple,
   glorify your dwelling-place,
   till nations see your splendour
   and seek your face.

(Men)

3. Bring tributes from the nations,
   come in joyful cavalcades.
   One thund'rous acclamation,
   one banner raised.

5. Fear God and give him glory,
   for his hour of judgement comes.
   Creator, Lord Almighty,
   worship him alone.

Words and Music: Graham Kendrick

74 Come on, all us singers, sing
(Singers' song)

Come on, all us sing - ers, sing that Je - sus Christ is Lord.

Come on, all us sing - ers, sing that Je - - sus Christ is Lord.

1. As your peo - ple, Lord, we now stand be - fore your throne.
2. As your peo - ple, Lord, we will sing with thank - ful - ness.

A sac - ri - fice of praise will be our song.
We want our lives to be a song of praise.

As your sing - ers, Lord, we will shout
Ban-ners we will wave to pro - claim

Words and Music: Martin Smith

75 Come on and celebrate
(Celebrate)

Very lively   G

Come on and ce-le-brate his gift of love, we will

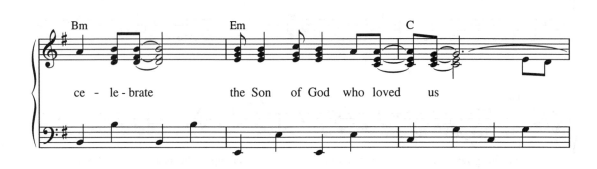

Bm   Em   C

ce - le - brate the Son of God who loved us

Am   Dsus⁴   D

and gave us life.   We'll shout your

G   Bm

praise, O King, you give us joy no-thing else can bring,

Words and Music: Patricia Morgan and Dave Bankhead

76 Come, Spirit, come

Breathe up-on me, blow, O wind of Spi - rit.

Breathe up-on me, blow, O wind of God.

2. Come, Spirit, come.
   Come, holy rain,
   fall on the dry ground of my life.
   O come, Spirit, come,
   O mighty flood,
   O loving stream and source of life.
   Flow over me, flow over me, Spirit.
   Flow over me, flow over me, Spirit.
   Flow over me, flow, O rain of God.

3. Come, Spirit, come.
   Come, holy fire,
   consume the offering of my life.
   O come, Spirit, come,
   O blazing fire,
   O burning love and flame of life.
   Burn in my heart, burn in my heart, Spirit.
   Burn in my heart, burn in my heart, Spirit.
   Burn in my heart, burn, O fire of God.

Words and Music: Elizabeth Bourbourze

77 Crown him with many crowns

DIADEMATA DSM

1. Crown him with ma-ny crowns, the Lamb up-on his throne; hark, how the heav'n-ly an-them drowns all mu-sic but its own: a-wake, my soul, and sing of him who died for thee, and hail him as thy match-less King through all e-ter-ni-ty.

2. Crown him the Lord of life,
who triumphed o'er the grave,
and rose victorious in the strife
for those he came to save.
His glories now we sing,
who died and rose on high,
who died eternal life to bring,
and lives that death may die.

3. Crown him the Lord of love;
behold his hands and side,
rich wounds, yet visible above,
in beauty glorified:
no angel in the sky
can fully bear that sight,
but downward bends each burning eye
at mysteries so bright.

4. Crown him the Lord of peace,
whose pow'r a sceptre sways
from pole to pole, that wars may cease,
and all be prayer and praise:
his reign shall know no end,
and round his piercèd feet
fair flow'rs of paradise extend
their fragrance ever sweet.

5. Crown him the Lord of years,
the Potentate of time,
Creator of the rolling spheres,
ineffably sublime.
All hail, Redeemer, hail!
for thou hast died for me;
thy praise shall never, never fail
throughout eternity.

Words: Matthew Bridges
Music: George Job Elvey

78 Day of favour

Words and Music: David Fellingham

79 Dear Lord and Father of mankind

REPTON 86 88 6

1. Dear Lord and Fa - ther of man-kind, for - give our fool-ish ways! Re - clothe us in our right-ful mind, in pur — er lives thy ser - vice find, in deep - er rev - 'rence praise, in deep - er rev - 'rence praise.

2. In simple trust like theirs who heard,
   beside the Syrian sea,
   the gracious calling of the Lord,
   let us, like them, without a word,
   rise up and follow thee,
   rise up and follow thee.

3. O Sabbath rest by Galilee!
   O calm of hills above,
   where Jesus knelt to share with thee
   the silence of eternity,
   interpreted by love,
   interpreted by love!

4. Drop thy still dews of quietness,
   till all our strivings cease;
   take from our souls the strain and stress,
   and let our ordered lives confess
   the beauty of thy peace,
   the beauty of thy peace.

5. Breathe through the heats of our desire
   thy coolness and thy balm;
   let sense be dumb, let flesh retire;
   speak through the earthquake, wind and fire,
   O still small voice of calm,
   O still small voice of calm!

Words: John Greenleaf Whittier
Music: Charles Hubert Hastings Parry

80 Did you feel the mountains tremble?

Words and Music: Martin Smith

81 Don't let my love grow cold
(Light the fire again)

Words and Music: Brian Doerksen

Create in me a pure heart, O God,
and renew a steadfast spirit within me.

Psalm 51:10

82 Do something new, Lord

With feeling

Chorus

Do some-thing new, Lord, in my heart, make a start;

do some-thing new, Lord, do some-thing new. *Fine*

Verse

1. I o-pen up my heart, as much as can be
2. I lay be-fore your feet, all my hopes and de-
3. I on-ly want to live for your plea-sure

known; I o-pen up my will
sires; un-re-ser-ved-ly sub-mit
now; I long to please you, Fa-ther—

to con-form to yours a-lone. *D.C. al Fine*
to what your Spi-rit may re-quire.
will you show me how?

Words and Music: Chris Bowater

83 Down the mountain the river flows
(The river is here)

With joy

1.   Down the moun - tain the
2. The ri - ver of God is
3. Up to the moun - tain we

ri - ver flows,   and it brings re - fresh - ing wher -
teem - ing with life,   and all who touch it can
love to go   to find the pre - sence

e-ver it goes.   Through the val - leys and o - ver the fields, the
be re - vived.   And those who lin - ger on this ri - ver's shore will
of the Lord.   A - long the banks of the ri - ver we run, we

Words and Music: Andy Park

84 Draw me closer

Draw me clo - ser, Lord;
Touch my eyes, Lord;

draw me clo - ser, dear Lord,
touch my eyes, dear Lord,

so that I might touch you,
so that I might see you,

so that I might touch you,
so that I might see you,

Lord, I want to touch you.
Lord, I want to see

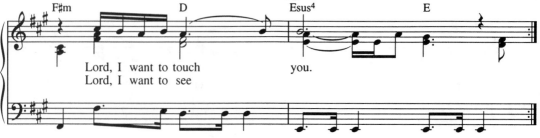

Words and Music: Stuart Devane and Glenn Gore

85 Earth lies spellbound

1. Earth lies spell-bound in dark-ness, sin's op-pres-sive night;
yet in Beth-le-hem hope is burn-ing bright.
My-ster-ies are un-fold-ing, but the on-ly sign
is a man-ger bed where a ba-by cries.

Chorus
Wake up, wake up, it's Christ-mas morn-ing,

2. Crowding stairways of starlight,
   choirs of angels sing:
   'Glory, glory to God
   in the highest heav'n.
   Peace is stilling the violence,
   hope is rising high,
   God is watching us now
   through a baby's eyes.

3. Weakness shatters the pow'rful,
   meekness shames the proud,
   vain imaginings
   come tumbling down.
   Ancient mercies remembered,
   hungry satisfied,
   lowly, humble hearts
   are lifted high.

Words and Music: Graham Kendrick

Great and marvellous are your deeds,
Lord God Almighty.
Just and true are your ways,
King of the ages.
Who will not fear you, O Lord,
and bring glory to your name?
For you alone are holy.
All nations will come
and worship before you,
for your righteous acts have been revealed.

Revelation 15:3-4

86 Every nation, power and tongue
(People just like us)

Ev-'ry na-tion, pow'r and tongue will bow down to your name;
ev-'ry eye will see, ev-'ry ear will hear your name pro-claimed. This is gon-na be
our cry un - til you come a-gain. Je - sus is the on - ly name by which man can be saved.

Words and Music: Russell Fragar

87 Exalt the Lord

Words and Music: Mike and Claire McIntosh

88 Faithful God

Words and Music: Chris Bowater

89 Faithful One

Faith-ful One, so un-chang-ing,
Age-less One, you're my rock of peace.
Lord of all, I de-pend on you,
I call out to you a-gain and a-gain,
I call out to you a-gain and a-

Words and Music: Brian Doerksen

90 Far and near
(Say it loud)

Verse

1. Far and near hear the call, wor - ship
   wide is the love hea - ven

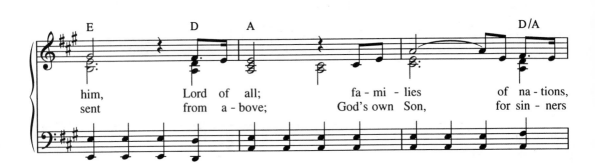

him, Lord of all; fa - mi - lies of na - tions,
sent from a - bove; God's own Son, for sin - ners

come, ce - le - brate what God has done. 2. Deep and
died, rose a - gain – he is a-

1.

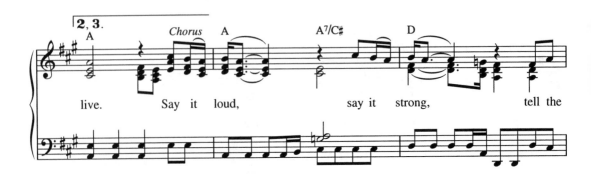

2, 3.

live. *Chorus* Say it loud, say it strong, tell the

world　　　what God has done;　　　say it

loud,　　　praise his name,　　　let the earth re-joice—

1.

for the Lord reigns.

2.

D.S.

3. At his reigns,　　　the Lord reigns.

3. At his name, let praise begin;
   oceans roar, nature sing,
   for he comes to judge the earth
   in righteousness and in his truth.

Words and Music: Graham Kendrick

91 Father God, I wonder
(I will sing your praises)

Words and Music: Ian Smale

92 Father God, we worship you

Worshipfully

1. Fa - ther God, we wor - ship you,
make us part of all you do.
As you move a - mong us now, we
wor - ship you.

2. Jesus King, we worship you,
   help us listen now to you.
   As you move among us now,
   we worship you.

3. Spirit pure, we worship you,
   with your fire our zeal renew.
   As you move among us now,
   we worship you.

Words and Music: Graham Kendrick

93 Father, hear our prayer

Meditatively

Fa - ther, hear our prayer, that our lives may be

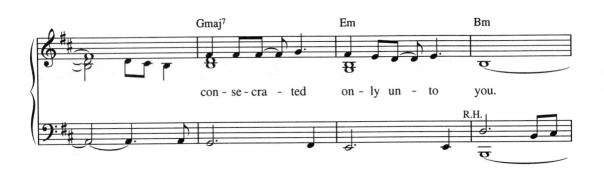

con - se - cra - ted on - ly un - to you.

Cleanse us with your fire,

fill us with your pow'r, that the world may

glo - ri - fy your name. Lord, have mer -

- cy on us. Christ, have mer -

- cy on us. Lord, have

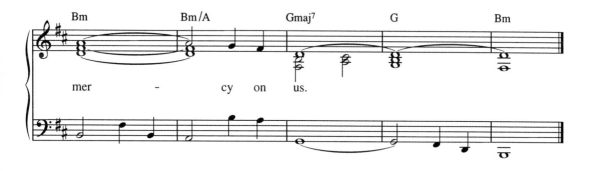

mer - cy on us.

Words and Music: Andy Piercy, arr. Alison Berry

Now the Lord is the Spirit,
and where the Spirit of the Lord is, there is freedom.
And we, who with unveiled faces all reflect the Lord's glory,
are being transformed into his likeness with ever-increasing glory,
which comes from the Lord, who is the Spirit.

2 Corinthians 3:17-18

94 Father, here I am
(Let forgiveness flow)

Words and Music: Danny Daniels

95 Father, I come to you
(Unending love)

1. Father, I come to you, lifting up my hands in the name of Jesus, by your grace I stand. Just because you love me and I love your Son, I know your favour, un-end-ing love.

2. I receive your favour, your unending love,
   not because I've earned it, not for what I've done,
   just because you love me and I love your Son,
   I know your favour, unending love.

3. It's the presence of your kingdom as your glory fills this place,
   and I see how much you love me as I look into your face.
   Nothing could be better, there's nothing I would trade
   for your favour, unending love.

Words and Music: John Barnett

96 Father in heaven, how we love you
(Blessed be the Lord God Almighty)

Majestically

Fa-ther in hea-ven, how we love you, we lift your name in all the earth. May your king-dom be es-tab-lished in our prai-ses as your peo-ple de-clare your migh-ty works. Bless-ed be the Lord God Al-migh-ty, who was and is and is to come. Bless-ed be the Lord God Al-migh-ty, who reigns for e-ver-more.

Words and Music: Bob Fitts

97 Father, I place into your hands

Gently

1. Fa-ther, I place in-to your hands the things I can-not do.

Fa-ther, I place in-to your hands the things that I've been through. Fa-ther, I place in-to your hands the way that I should go, for I know I al-ways can trust you.

2. Father, I place into your hands
my friends and family.
Father, I place into your hands
the things that trouble me.
Father, I place into your hands
the person I would be,
for I know I always can trust you.

3. Father, we love to see your face,
we love to hear your voice,
Father, we love to sing your praise
and in your name rejoice,
Father, we love to walk with you
and in your presence rest,
for we know we always can trust you.

4. Father, I want to be with you
and do the things you do.
Father, I want to speak the words
that you are speaking too.
Father, I want to love the ones
that you will draw to you,
for I know that I am one with you.

Words and Music: Jenny Hewer

98 Father, I want you to hold me

2. Father, I know you will hold me,
I know I am your child, your own.
Father, I know you will show me,
I feel your arms holding me,
I'm not alone.
I bring all my fears
and I lay them at your feet.
You are always here,
and you love me as I am,
yes, you love me as I am.

Words and Music: Brian Doerksen

99 Father of creation
(Let your glory fall)

2. Ruler of the nations,
   the world has yet to see
   the full release of your promise,
   the church in victory.

Turn to us, Lord, and touch us,
make us strong in your might.
Overcome our weakness,
that we could stand up and fight.

Words and Music: David Ruis

100 Father of life, draw me closer
(Let the peace of God reign)

Words and Music: Darlene Zschech

101 Father, we adore you
(Fountain of life)

Gently

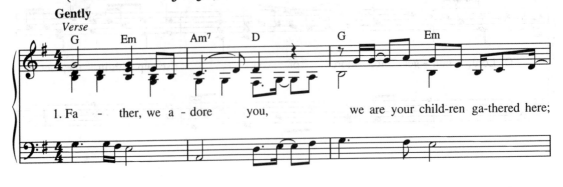

1. Fa - ther, we a - dore you, we are your child-ren ga-thered here;

to be with you is our de - light,

a feast be -yond com - pare. *to verse 2* *Chorus* You are the

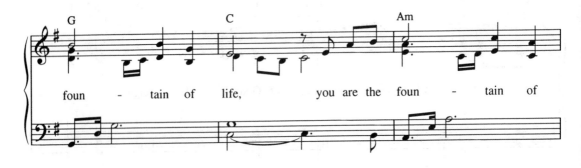

foun - tain of life, you are the foun - tain of

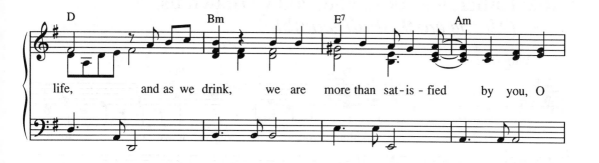

life,   and as we drink,   we are more than sat-is-fied   by you, O

Foun - tain of Life.

2. Father, in your presence
   there is such freedom to enjoy.
   We find in you a lasting peace
   that nothing can destroy.

Words and Music: Philip Lawson Johnston

102 Father, we adore you, you've drawn us
(All the earth shall worship)

With strength

1. Fa-ther, we a-dore you, you've drawn us to this place. We bow down be-fore you, hum-bly on our face.

Chorus

All the earth shall wor-ship at the throne of the King. Of his great and awe-some pow'r,

2. Jesus, we love you,
   because you first loved us,
   you reached out and healed us
   with your mighty touch.

3. Spirit, we need you,
   to lift us from this mire,
   consume and empower us
   with your holy fire.

Words and Music: Carl Tuttle

103 Father, we love you
(Glorify your name)

Worshipfully

1. Fa - ther, we love you, we wor - ship and a - dore you,

glo - ri - fy your name in all the earth.

Glo - ri - fy your name, glo - ri - fy your name,

glo - ri - fy your name in all the earth.

2. Jesus, we love you . . .

3. Spirit, we love you . . .

Words and Music: Donna Adkins

104 Father, you are my portion
(My delight)

Gently

1. Fa - ther, you are my por - tion in this life, and you are my hope and my de - light, and I love you, yes, I love you. Lord, I love you, my de - light.

last time

2. Jesus, you are my treasure in this life,
   and you are so pure and so kind,
   and I love you, yes I love you.
   Lord, I love you, my delight.

Words and Music: Andy Park

105 Filled with compassion
(For all the people who live on the earth)

Gently

1. Filled with com-pas-sion for all cre-a-tion,
Je-sus came in-to a world that was lost.
There was but one way that he could save us,
on-ly through suf-fer-ing death on a cross.

Chorus
God, you are wait-ing, your heart is break-ing

for all the peo - ple who live on the earth.

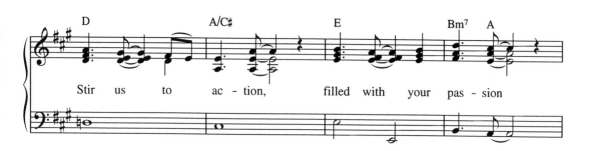

Stir us to ac - tion, filled with your pas - sion

for all the peo - ple who live on the earth.

last time

2. Great is your passion for all the people
   living and dying without knowing you.
   Having no saviour, they're lost for ever,
   if we don't speak out and lead them to you.

3. From ev'ry nation we shall be gathered,
   millions redeemed shall be Jesus' reward.
   Then he will turn and say to his Father:
   'Truly my suffering was worth it all.'

Words and Music: Noel and Tricia Richards

Shout for joy to the Lord, all the earth.
Worship the Lord with gladness;
come before him with joyful songs.
Know that the Lord is God.
It is he who made us, and we are his;
we are his people, the sheep of his pasture.

Enter his gates with thanksgiving
and his courts with praise;
give thanks to him and praise his name.
For the Lord is good and his love endures for ever;
his faithfulness continues through all generations.

Psalm 100

106 Fire

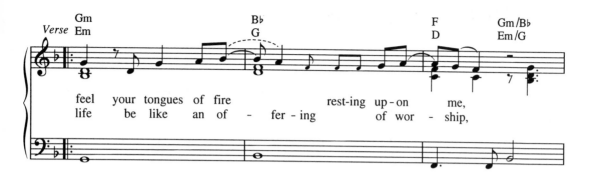

feel   your   tongues of fire   rest-ing up-on   me,
life   be   like   an of - fer - ing   of wor - ship,

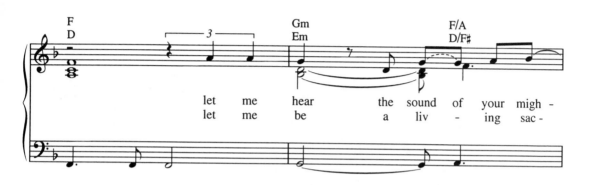

let   me   hear   the sound of your migh -
let   me   be   a   liv - ing sac -

- ty rush - ing wind.   4. Let my

- ri - fice   of praise.

Words and Music: Paul Oakley

107 5 0 0 0 + hungry folk

5 0 0 0 + hun - gry folk, 5 0 0 0 +
1 had 1 2 3 4 5, just 1 had 1 2

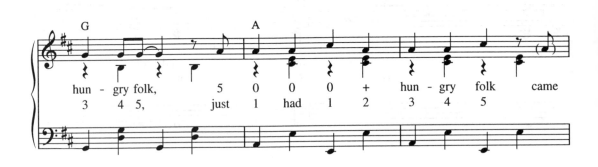

hun - gry folk, 5 0 0 0 + hun - gry folk came
3 4 5, just 1 had 1 2 3 4 5

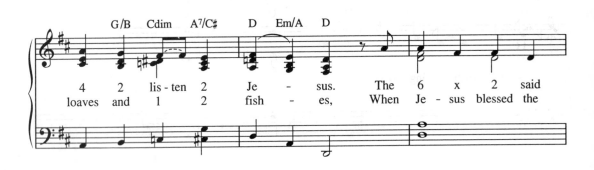

4 2 lis - ten 2 Je - sus. The 6 x 2 said
loaves and 1 2 fish - es, When Je - sus blessed the

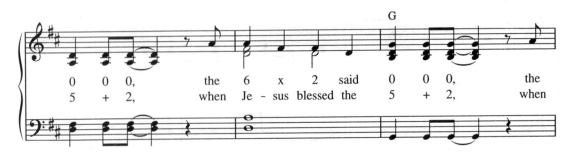

0 0 0, the 6 x 2 said 0 0 0, the
5 + 2, when Je - sus blessed the 5 + 2, when

Words and Music: Ian Smale

108 For all that you've done
(Thank you, Lord)

For all that you've done I will thank you. For all that you're go-ing to do. For all that you've pro-mised, and all that you are is all that has car-ried me through. Je-sus, I thank you. And I thank you, thank you, Lord. Thank you, thank you,

Words and Music: Dennis Jernigan

Therefore go and make disciples of all nations,
baptising them in the name of the Father
and of the Son and of the Holy Spirit,
and teaching them to obey
everything I have commanded you.
And surely I am with you always,
to the very end of the age.

Matthew 28:19-20

109 For I'm building a people of power

For I'm build-ing a peo-ple of pow-er and I'm mak-ing a peo-ple of praise, that will move through this land by my Spi-rit, and will glo-ri-fy my pre-cious name. Build your church, Lord, make us strong, Lord, join our hearts, Lord, through your Son. Make us one, Lord, in your bo-dy, in the King-dom of your Son.

Words and Music: Dave Richards

110 For the joys and for the sorrows
(For this I have Jesus)

2. For the tears that flow in secret,
   in the broken times,
   for the moments of elation,
   or the troubled mind;
   for all the disappointments,
   or the sting of old regrets,
   all my prayers and longings,
   that seem unanswered yet:

3. For the weakness of my body,
   the burdens of each day,
   for the nights of doubt and worry
   when sleep has fled away;
   needing reassurance
   and the will to start again,
   a steely-eyed endurance,
   the strength to fight and win:

Words and Music: Graham Kendrick

111 For this purpose

2. In the name of Jesus we stand,
by the power of his blood
we now claim this ground.
Satan has no authority here,
pow'rs of darkness must flee,
for Christ has the victory.

Words and Music: Graham Kendrick

Not to us, O Lord, not to us
but to your name be the glory,
because of your love and faithfulness.

Psalm 115:1

112 For thou, O Lord, art high
(I exalt thee)

Worshipfully with strength

Words and Music: Pete Sanchez Jnr.

113 For unto us a child is born

Words and Music: David Hadden

114 From heaven you came
(The Servant King)

him, to bring our lives as a dai-ly of-fer-ing of wor-ship

to next verse   *last time*

to   the Ser-vant King.   King.

2. There in the garden of tears,
   my heavy load he chose to bear;
   his heart with sorrow was torn.
   'Yet not my will but yours,' he said.

3. Come see his hands and his feet,
   the scars that speak of sacrifice,
   hands that flung stars into space,
   to cruel nails surrendered.

4. So let us learn how to serve,
   and in our lives enthrone him;
   each other's needs to prefer,
   for it is Christ we're serving.

Words and Music: Graham Kendrick

115 From the ends of the earth
(Lord most high)

Words and Music: Don Harris and Gary Sadler

Praise the Lord, you his angels,
you mighty ones who do his bidding,
who obey his word.
Praise the Lord, all his heavenly hosts,
you his servants who do his will.
Praise the Lord, all his works
everywhere in his dominion.

Psalm 103:20-22

116 From the sun's rising

Steadily

Verse

1. From the sun's ris-ing un-to the sun's set-ting, Je-sus our Lord shall be great in the earth; and all earth's king-doms shall be his do-min-ion, all of cre-a-tion shall sing of his worth.

Chorus

Let ev-'ry heart, ev-'ry voice, ev-'ry tongue join with spi-rits a-blaze; one in his love, we will

cir - cle the world with the song of his praise. O,

let all his peo-ple re - joice, and let all the earth hear his

1. 2. voice! **3.** voice! Let all his peo - ple re -

joice, and let all the earth hear his voice!

2. To ev'ry tongue, tribe
   and nation he sends us,
   to make disciples
   to teach and baptise.
   For all authority
   to him is given;
   now as his witnesses
   we shall arise.

3. Come, let us join with
   the church from all nations,
   cross ev'ry border,
   throw wide ev'ry door;
   workers with him
   as he gathers his harvest,
   till earth's far corners
   our Saviour adore.

Words and Music: Graham Kendrick

117 From where the sun rises

Chorus

E-ven in the night when the sun goes down, we're giv-ing you praise;

pass-ing it a-long as the world goes round, we're

giv-ing you praise.

2. We're lift-ing our

2. We're lifting our faces,
   looking at the One we all love –
   we're giving you praise,
   giving you praise.
   All colours and races
   joining with the angels above –
   we're giving you praise,
   giving you praise.

Words and Music: Graham Kendrick

118 Give thanks with a grateful heart

Words and Music: Henry Smith

The heavens declare the glory of God;
the skies proclaim the work of his hands.

Psalms 19:1

119 Gloria

Words: Traditional
Music: Jacques Berthier

120 Glory

Bright, joyful feel

Glo - ry, glo - ry in the high - est; glo - ry

to the Al - migh - ty; glo - ry to the Lamb of God, and

glo - ry to the liv - ing Word; glo - ry

Words and Music: Danny Daniels

121 Glory to the King of kings

2. Jesus, Lord, with eyes unveiled
   we will see your throne.
   Jesus, Prince of Peace,
   Son of God, Emmanuel.

Words and Music: Geoff Bullock

122 God, be gracious

Words and Music: Graham Kendrick

123 God forgave my sin
(Freely, freely)

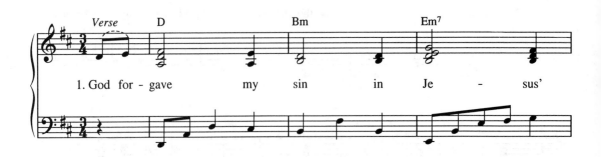

1. God for-gave my sin in Je - sus'

name, I've been born a - gain in Je - sus'

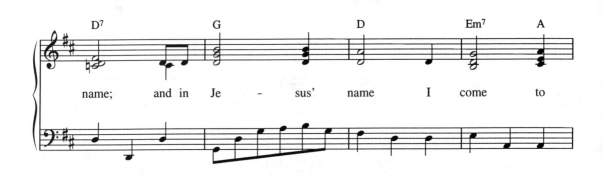

name; and in Je - sus' name I come to

you to share his love as he told me to.

2. All pow'r is given in Jesus' name,
   in earth and heav'n in Jesus' name;
   and in Jesus' name I come to you
   to share his pow'r as he told me to.

Words and Music: Carol Owens

124 God is good

Fast and rhythmic

God is good, we sing and shout it, God is good,

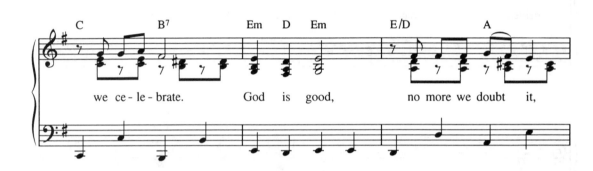

we ce - le - brate. God is good, no more we doubt it,

last time to Coda

God is good, we know it's true.

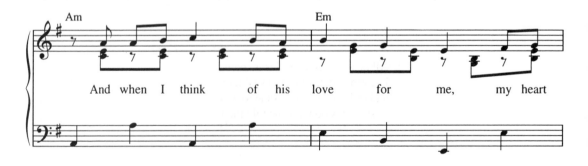

And when I think of his love for me, my heart

fills   with   praise   and I   feel   like   danc - ing.

For   in   his   heart   there is   room   for   me   and   I

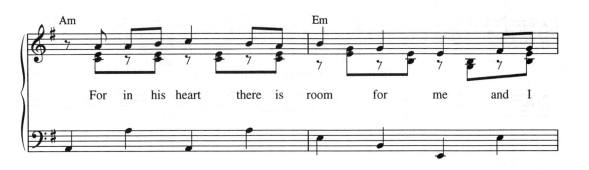

run   with   arms   op-en'd   wide.

D.C. al Coda

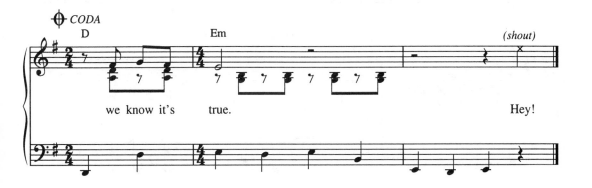

CODA

we   know   it's   true.   *(shout)*   Hey!

Words and Music: Graham Kendrick

125 God is good all the time

Words and Music: Don Moen and Paul Overstreet

126 God is great

God is great, a-maz-ing! Come, let his prai-ses ring, God is great, a-stound-ing! the whole cre-a-tion sings.

1. His clo-thing is splen-dour and

ma - jes - ty bright, for he wraps him-self in a gar-ment of light. He
spreads out the hea-vens, his pa - lace of stars, and rides on the wings of the
wind. sings.

2. What marvellous wisdom the Maker displays,
   the sea vast and spacious, the dolphins and whales.
   The earth full of creatures, the great and the small,
   he watches and cares for them all.

3. The rain forest canopies darken the skies,
   cathedrals of mist that resound with the choirs
   of creatures discordant, outrageous, ablaze
   in colourful pageants of praise.

4. Above his creation the Father presides.
   The pulse of the planets, the rhythm of tides.
   The moon marks the seasons, the day follows night,
   yet he knows ev'ry beat of my heart.

5. Let cannons of thunder salute their acclaim,
   the sunsets fly glorious banners of flame,
   the angels shout 'holy' again and again
   as they soar in the arch of the heavens.

Words and Music: Graham Kendrick and Steve Thompson

127 God is here, God is present

With awe

God is here, God is pre-sent, God is mov - ing by his

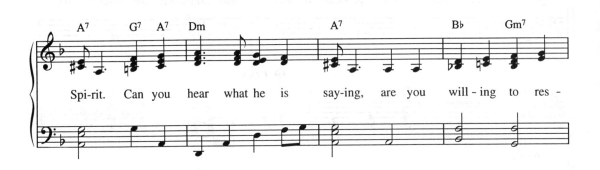

Spi-rit. Can you hear what he is say-ing, are you will - ing to res -

pond? God is here, God is pre-sent, God is mov - ing by his

Spi-rit. Lord, I o - pen up my life to you, please

Words and Music: Ian Smale

128 God is working his purpose out

glo - ry of God as the wa - ters co - ver the sea.

2. From the east to the utmost west
   wherever foot has trod,
   through the mouths of his messengers
   echoes forth the voice of God:
   'Listen to me, ye continents,
   ye islands, give ear to me,
   that the earth shall be filled with the glory of God
   as the waters cover the sea.'

3. March we forth in the strength of God,
   his banner is unfurled;
   let the light of the gospel shine
   in the darkness of the world:
   strengthen the weary, heal the sick
   and set ev'ry captive free,
   that the earth shall be filled with the glory of God
   as the waters cover the sea.

4. All our efforts are nothing worth
   unless God bless the deed;
   vain our hopes for the harvest tide
   till he brings to life the seed.
   Yet ever nearer draws the time,
   the time that shall surely be,
   when the earth shall be filled with the glory of God
   as the waters cover the sea.

Words: Arthur Campbell Ainger, adapted by Michael Forster
Music: Millicent Kingham

For where two or three come together in my name,
there am I with them.

Matthew 18:20

129 God of all comfort
(To seek your face)

Worshipfully

1. God of all com - fort,
cause you have called us, we're

God of all grace,
ga - thered in this place, oh,

we have come to seek you,

we have come to seek your face. 2. Be - face.

Words and Music: John Wimber

130 God of glory, we exalt your name

Brightly with strength and feeling

God of glo - ry, we ex - alt your name, you who reign in ma-jes - ty. We lift our hearts to you and we will wor - ship, praise and mag-ni-fy your ho - ly name. In pow'r res -

Words and Music: David Fellingham

131 God of glory
(Fire of God's glory)

God of glo - ry, you are wor - thy, you

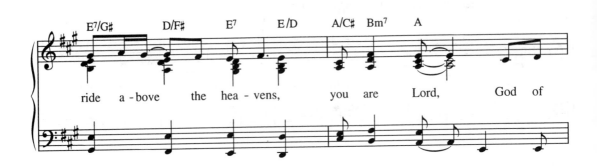

ride a - bove the hea - vens, you are Lord, God of

fi - re, my de - si - re is to

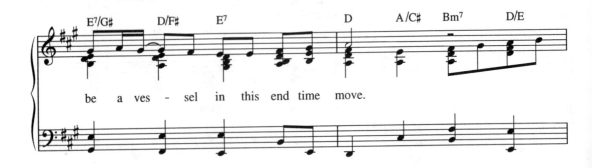

be a ves - sel in this end time move.

Words and Music: Simon and Tina Triffitt

132 God of grace
(I stand complete in you)

With feeling

God of grace, I turn my face to you, I can-not
Striv-ings and all an-guished dreams in rags lie at my

hide; my na-ked-ness, my shame, my guilt, are
feet; and on-ly grace pro-vides the way for

all be-fore your eyes.
me to stand com- plete. And your

grace clothes me in right — eous-

ness,   and your mer -   cy co-vers me   in

love.   Your life   a - dorns

and beau -   ti-fies,   I

stand   com-plete   in   you.

Words and Music: Chris Bowater

'Where, O death, is your victory?
Where, O death, is your sting?'
The sting of death is sin,
and the power of sin is the law.
But thanks be to God!
He gives us the victory through our Lord Jesus Christ.

1 Corinthians 15:55-57

133 God's not dead

God's not dead. No! He is a-live. God's not dead. No!
He is a-live. God's not dead. No! He is a-live.
Praise him with my mouth. Praise him with my feet. Praise him with my hands.
Love him in my life. Je-sus is a-live in me.

Words and Music: unknown arr. Stuart Townend

© Copyright 1991 Kingsway's Thankyou Music, P.O. Box 75, Eastbourne,
East Sussex, BN23 6NW, UK. Used by permission.

134 God will make a way

God will make a way where there seems to be no way.
He works in ways we can-not see. He will make a
way for me. He will be my guide, hold me
close-ly to his side, with love and strength for each new day.
He will make a way, he will make a way.

Words and Music: Don Moen

135 Great and mighty is he

Great and migh - ty is he,
great and migh - ty is he;
clothed in glo - ry, ar -
rayed in splen - dour,
great and migh - ty is he.
Let us lift his name up high,
ce - le - brate his grace;

last time to Coda

Words and Music: Todd Pettygrove

136 Great is the darkness
(Come, Lord Jesus)

Growing in strength

1. Great is the dark-ness that cov-ers the earth, op - pres-sion, in - jus - tice and pain.

Na - tions are slip - ping in hope-less des - pair, though many have come in your name.

Watch-ing while sa - ni - ty dies, touched by the mad - ness and lies.

Chorus

Come, Lord Je - sus, come, Lord Je - sus, pour out your Spi - rit, we pray.

Come, Lord Je - sus, come, Lord Je - sus, pour out your Spi - rit on us to - day.

to verses | *last time*

2. May now your church rise with power and love,
   this glorious gospel proclaim.
   In ev'ry nation salvation will come
   to those who believe in your name.
   Help us bring light to this world
   that we might speed your return.

3. Great celebrations on that final day
   when out of the heavens you come.
   Darkness will vanish, all sorrow will end,
   and rulers will bow at your throne.
   Our great commission complete,
   then face to face we shall meet.

Words and Music: Noel Richards and Gerald Coates

137 Great is the Lord and most worthy of praise

Great is the Lord and most wor-thy of praise, the
ci-ty of our God, the ho-ly place, the joy of the whole earth.
Great is the
Lord, in whom we have the vic - to - ry. He
aids us a - gainst the e - ne - my, we

Words and Music: Steve McEwan

138 Great is thy faithfulness

FAITHFULNESS (RUNYAN) 11 10 11 10 and Refrain

1. Great is thy faith - ful - ness, O God my Fa - ther,
there is no sha - dow of turn - ing with thee;
thou chang - est not, thy com - pas - sions, they fail not;
as thou hast been thou for e - ver wilt be.

Chorus

Great is thy faith - ful - ness! Great is thy faith - ful - ness!

Morn - ing by morn - ing new mer - cies I see;
all I have need - ed thy hand has pro - vi - ded,
great is thy faith - ful - ness, Lord, un - to me!

2. Summer and winter, and springtime and harvest,
   sun, moon and stars in their courses above,
   join with all nature in manifold witness
   to thy great faithfulness, mercy and love.

3. Pardon for sin and a peace that endureth,
   thine own dear presence to cheer and to guide;
   strength for today and bright hope for tomorrow,
   blessings all mine, with ten thousand beside!

Words: Thomas Obadiah Chisholm
Music: William Marion Runyan

139 Great is your name
(Only you deserve the glory)

1. Great is your name, great are your deeds, O

Lord. Day af - ter day your mer-cies dis-played

to all. There is none like

you, who loves the way you do, Je - ho - vah.

2. Faithful and true in all you do, O Lord.
   Saviour and King, my ev'rything, my all.
   There is none like you,
   who loves the way you do, Jehovah.

Words and Music: Jarrod Cooper

Therefore God exalted him to the highest place
and gave him the name that is above every name,
that at the name of Jesus every knee should bow,
in heaven and on earth and under the earth,
and every tongue confess that Jesus Christ is Lord,
to the glory of God the Father.

Philippians 2:9-11

140 Hail, Jesus, you're my King
(Victory chant)

Words and Music: Joseph Vogels

141 Hallelujah, hallelujah
(The Lord Almighty reigns)

Hal-le-lu - jah, hal-le-lu - jah, hal-le-lu - jah, the Lord reigns. Hal-le-lu - jah, hal-le-lu - jah, hal-le-lu - jah, the Lord Al-migh-ty reigns. He has showed his awe - some pow-

Words and Music: Terry Butler

142 Hallelujah! Jesus is alive

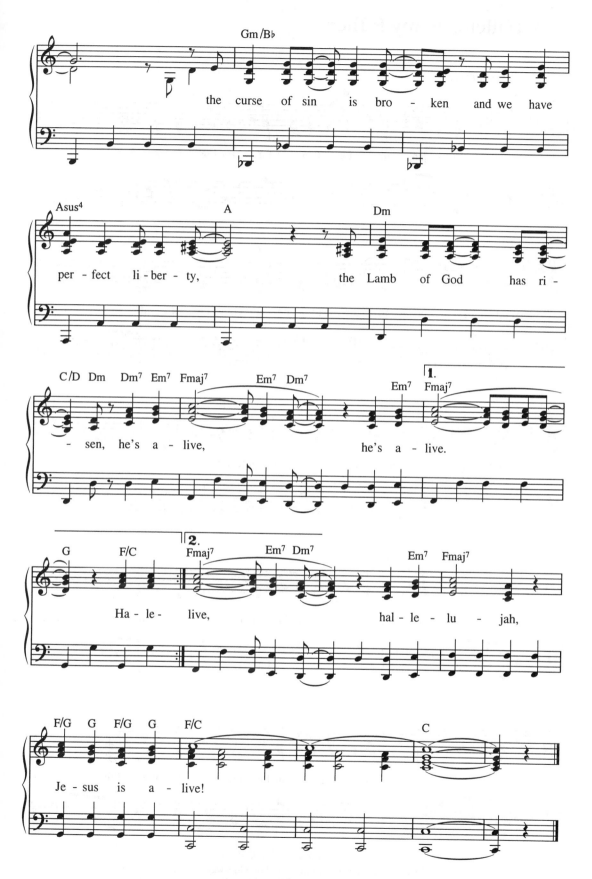

Words and Music: Ron Kenoly

143 Hallelujah, my Father

Worshipfully

Hal-le-lu - jah, my Fa - ther, for giv-ing us your Son;

send - ing him in - to the world to be gi-ven up for all.

Know - ing we would bruise him and smite him from the earth. Hal-le-

lu - jah, my Fa - ther, in his death is my birth; hal-le-

lu - jah, my Fa - ther, in his life is my life.

Words and Music: Tim Cullen

144 Hark, the herald-angels sing

MENDELSSOHN 77 77 D and Refrain

1. Hark, the he-rald-an-gels sing glo-ry to the new-born King; peace on earth and mer-cy mild, God and sin-ners re-con-ciled: joy-ful, all ye na-tions rise, join the tri-umph of the skies, with th'an-ge-lic host pro-claim,'Christ is born in Beth-le-hem.' Hark, the he-rald-an-gels sing glo-ry to the new-born King.

Chorus

Unison

2. Christ, by highest heav'n adored,
Christ, the everlasting Lord,
late in time behold him come,
offspring of a virgin's womb!
Veiled in flesh the Godhead see,
hail, th'incarnate Deity!
Pleased as man with us to dwell,
Jesus, our Emmanuel.

3. Hail, the heav'n-born Prince of Peace!
Hail, the Sun of Righteousness!
Light and life to all he brings,
ris'n with healing in his wings;
mild he lays his glory by,
born that we no more may die,
born to raise us from the earth,
born to give us second birth.

Words: Charles Wesley, George Whitefield, Martin Madan and others, alt.
Music: adapted from Felix Mendelssohn by William Hayman Cummings

145 Have you got an appetite?

1. Have you got an ap-pe-tite? Do you eat what is right? Are you feed-ing on the word of God? Are you fat or are you thin? Are you real-ly full with-in? Do you find your strength in him or are you starv-ing?

Chorus

You and me, all should be ex-er-cis-ing

2. If it's milk or meat you need,
   why not have a slap-up feed,
   and stop looking like a weed and start to grow?
   Take the full of fitness food,
   taste and see that God is good,
   come on, feed on what you should and be healthy.

Words and Music: Mick Gisbey

146 Have you heard the good news

Words and Music: Stuart Garrard

147 Have you not said
(Fill us up and send us out)

Rhythmically

1. Have you not said as we pass through wa - ter,

you will be with us? And you have said as we

walk through fire, we will not be burned.

We are not a - fraid, for you are with us; we will tes - ti - fy to the

hon - our of your name. We are wit - nes - ses,

2. Bring them from the west, sons and daughters,
   call them for your praise.
   Gather from the east all your children,
   coming home again.
   Bring them from afar, all the nations,
   from the north and south,
   drawing all the peoples in.
   Corners of the earth, come to see there's
   only one Saviour and King.

Words and Music: Matt Redman

Salvation is found in no one else,
for there is no other name under heaven given to men
by which we must be saved.

Acts 4:12

148 Hear, O Lord, our cry
(Revive us again)

With strength

Hear, O Lord, our cry: re - vive us, re - vive us a - gain.

For the sake of your glo - ry, re - vive us, re -

vive us a - gain. Lord, hear our cry.

Lord, hear our cry.

2. Hear, O Lord, our cry:
   revive us, revive us again.
   For the sake of the children,
   revive us, revive us again.
   Lord, hear our cry.
   Lord, hear our cry.

Words and Music: Graham Kendrick

149 Hear our cry

(Women) Hear our cry, O hear our cry: 'Je - sus, come!' Hear our cry, O
(Men) hear our cry: 'Je - sus, come!'

Verse

(Men) come!' 1. The tide of prayer is ris - ing, a deep - er
2. We lift our eyes with long - ing to see your

pas - sion burn - ing —
king - dom com - ing —
(Women) Hear our cry, O hear our cry: 'Je - sus,
(Men)

Chorus

(Women) come!' Hear our cry, O hear our cry: 'Je - sus, come!'
(Men)
(Women) Who - e - ver

is thirs - ty, come now and drink the wa - ters

(Men) Who - e - ver is thirs - ty, come now and drink the wa - ters

(Women) of life;

(Men) of life. 'Je - sus, come!' 'Je - sus, come!'

(Women) Hear our cry, O hear our cry: Hear our cry, O hear our cry: Come!'

3. The streets of teeming cities
   cry out for healing rivers –

4. Refresh them with your presence,
   give grace for deep repentance –

5. Tear back the shroud of shadows
   that covers all the peoples –

6. Revealing your salvation
   in ev'ry tribe and nation –

Words and Music: Graham Kendrick

150 Heaven invites you to a party

Joyful, with a strong rhythm

Hea-ven in-vites you to a par-ty, to ce-le-brate the birth of a

Son; an-gels re-joic-ing in the star-light, sing-ing

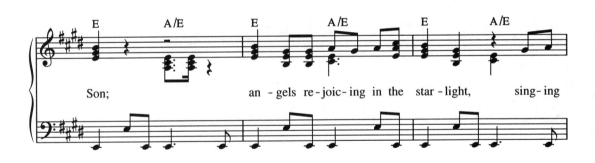

'Christ your Sa-viour has come'. come'. And it's for

Words and Music: Graham Kendrick

151 Heaven shall not wait

HEAVEN SHALL NOT WAIT Irregular

1. Heav'n shall not wait for the poor to lose their pa - tience, the scorned to smile, the des - pised to find a friend: Je - sus is Lord, he has cham-pioned the un - wan - ted; in him in - jus - tice con - fronts its time-ly

2. Heav'n shall not e - ver - more.

2. Heav'n shall not wait
   for the rich to share their fortunes,
   the proud to fall, the élite to tend the least:
   Jesus is Lord;
   he has shown his master's privilege –
   to kneel and wash servants' feet before they feast.

3. Heav'n shall not wait
   for the dawn of great ideas,
   thoughts of compassion divorced from cries of pain:
   Jesus is Lord;
   he has married word and action;
   his cross and company make his purpose plain.

4. Heav'n shall not wait
   for our legalised obedience,
   defined by statute, to strict conventions bound:
   Jesus is Lord;
   he has hallmarked true allegiance –
   goodness appears where his grace is sought and found.

5. Heav'n shall not wait
   for triumphant hallelujahs,
   when earth has passed and we reach another shore:
   Jesus is Lord
   in our present imperfection;
   his pow'r and love are for now and then for evermore.

Words and Music: John L. Bell and Graham Maule

152 He brought me to his banqueting table
(His banner over me is love)

Words and Music: Kevin Prosch

153 He has clothed us with his righteousness
(We rejoice in the grace of God)

1. He has clothed us with his right-eous-ness, cov - ered us with his great love. He has show - ered us with mer - cy, and we de - light to know the glo - rious fa - vour, won-drous fa - vour of God.

Chorus

We re-joice in the grace of God poured up-on our lives,
lov-ing kind-ness has come to us be-cause of Je - sus Christ.
We re-joice in the grace of God, our hearts o - ver-flow.
What a joy to know the grace of God.

2. He's brought us into his family,
   made us heirs with his own Son.
   All good things he freely gives us
   and we cannot conceive what God's preparing,
   God's preparing for us.

Words and Music: Steve Cook and Vicki Cook

154 He has fire in his eyes
(We will ride)

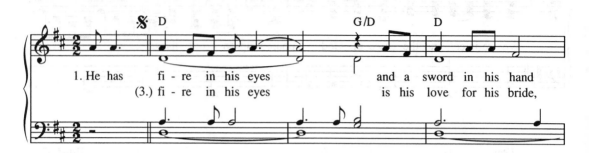

1. He has fi - re in his eyes and a sword in his hand
(3.) fi - re in his eyes is his love for his bride,

and he's rid - ing a white horse a - cross this land.
and he's long - ing that she be with him, right by his side.

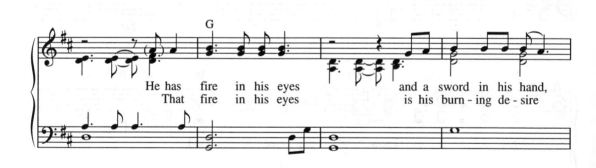

He has fire in his eyes and a sword in his hand,
That fire in his eyes is his burn - ing de - sire

he's rid - ing a white horse all a - cross this land.
that his bride be with him, right by his side,

Words and Music: Andy Park

155 He has risen

2. In the grave God did not leave him,
   for his body to decay;
   raised to life, the great awakening,
   Satan's pow'r he overcame.

3. If there were no resurrection,
   we ourselves could not be raised;
   but the Son of God is living,
   so our hope is not in vain.

4. When the Lord rides out of heaven,
   mighty angels at his side,
   they will sound the final trumpet,
   from the grave we shall arise.

5. He has given life immortal,
   we shall see him face to face;
   through eternity we'll praise him,
   Christ the champion of our faith.

Words and Music: Gerald Coates, Noel Richards and Tricia Richards

Praise God in his sanctuary;
praise him in his mighty heavens.
Praise him for his acts of power;
praise him for his surpassing greatness.

Psalm 150:1-2

156 He is exalted

Words and Music: Twila Paris

157 He is here

Words and Music: Graham Kendrick

It is written:
'As surely as I live,' says the Lord,
'Every knee will bow before me;
every tongue will confess to God.'

Romans 14:11

158 He is Lord

159 He is the Lord
(Show your power)

Strong and rhythmic

1. He is the Lord, and he reigns on high; he is the Lord. Spoke in-to the dark-ness, cre-a-ted the light. He is the Lord. Who is like un-to him, ne-ver end-ing in days; he is the Lord. And

Words and Music: Kevin Prosch

Shout for joy to the Lord, all the earth,
burst into jubilant song with music;
make music to the Lord with the harp,
with the harp and the sound of singing,
with trumpets and the blast of the ram's horn –
shout for joy before the Lord, the King.

Psalm 98:4-6

160 He is the mighty God

2. He is the One who gave
   his life for all the world,
   he is the Lord of lords,
   who rose up from the grave,
   defeated death and hell;
   he is the Lord of lords.

3. He's coming in the clouds
   and ev'ry eye shall see
   he is the Lord of lords;
   then ev'ry knee shall bow
   and ev'ry tongue proclaim
   he is the Lord of lords.

Words and Music: Carol Owen

161 Here I am

2. The time is right in the nation
   for works of power and authority;
   God's looking for a people who are willing
   to be counted in his glorious victory.

3. As salt are we ready to savour,
   in darkness are we ready to be light?
   God's seeking out a very special people
   to manifest his truth and his might.

Words and Music: Chris Bowater

162 Here in your presence

1. Here in your pre - sence,

be-hold-ing your glo - ry, bow-ing in

rev - 'rence we wor-ship you on - ly.

Stand-ing be - fore you, we love and a -

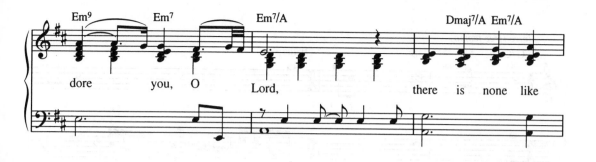

dore   you,   O   Lord,   there is none like

you.

2. Name above all names,
   beholding your glory,
   to Jesus, our Saviour,
   our lives we surrender.

3. Worthy of glory
   worthy of honour,
   we give you blessing,
   glory and power.

Words and Music: Don Moen

163 Here is bread

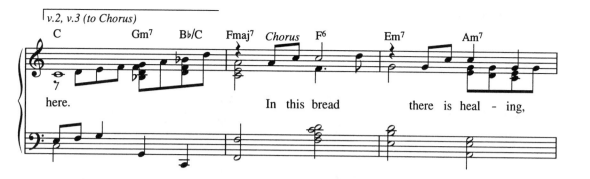

here.   In this bread   there is heal - ing,

in this cup   is   life   for   e - ver.   In this mo - ment,

by the Spi - rit,   Christ is with   us   here.

2. Here is grace, here is peace,
   Christ is with us, he is with us;
   know his grace, find his peace,
   feast on Jesus here.

3. Here we are, joined in one,
   Christ is with us, he is with us;
   we'll proclaim till he comes
   Jesus crucified.

Words and Music: Graham Kendrick

164 Here is love

DIM OND IESU

1. Here is love vast as the o-cean, lov-ing kind-ness as the flood. When the
Prince of Life, our ran-som, shed for us his pre-cious blood. Who his
love will not re-mem-ber? Who can cease to sing his praise? He can
ne-ver be for-got-ten, through-out heav'n's e-ter-nal days.

2. On the mount of crucifixion
fountains opened deep and wide;
through the floodgates of God's mercy
flowed a vast and gracious tide.
Grace and love, like mighty rivers,
poured incessant from above,
and heaven's peace and perfect justice
kissed a guilty world in love.

Words: William Rees
Music: Robert Lowry

165 Here we stand in total surrender

Words and Music: C. Groves and A. Piercy

166 He's given me a garment of praise

He's gi-ven me a gar-ment of praise in-stead of a spi-rit of des-pair. He's gi-ven me a gar-ment of praise in-stead of a spi-rit of des-pair.

Words and Music: David Hadden

167 He that is in us

He that is in us is great - er than he that is

in the world. He that is

in us is great - er than he that is in

the world. 1. There - fore I will sing and

I will re-joice for his Spi - rit lives in me.

Christ the liv - ing one has o - ver -

come and we share in his vic - to - ry.

2. All the powers of death and hell and sin
lie crushed beneath his feet.
Jesus owns the name above all names,
crowned with honour and majesty.

Words and Music: Graham Kendrick

168 He walked where I walk
(God with us)

Quite quick, with a steady rhythm

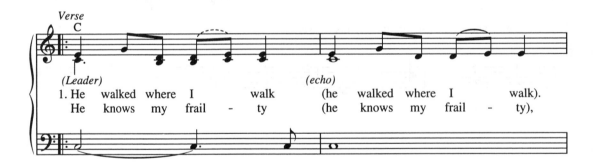

Verse

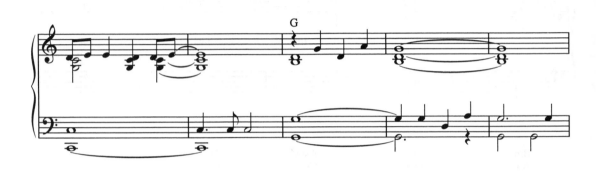

(Leader)

(echo)

1. He walked where I walk (he walked where I walk).
He knows my frail - ty (he knows my frail - ty),

He stood where I stand (he stood where I stand). He felt what I feel
shared my hu - ma - ni - ty (shared my hu - ma - ni - ty), tempt - ed in ev - 'ry way

(he felt what I feel). He un-der-stands (he un-der-stands).
(tempt-ed in ev-'ry way), yet with-out sin (yet with-out

sin).

Chorus

God with us, so close to us,

God with us, Im-ma - nu - el!

(Leader) (All)
2. One of a hated race, (echo)
stung by the prejudice, (echo)
suff'ring injustice, (echo)
yet he forgives. (echo)
Wept for my wasted years, (echo)
paid for my wickedness, (echo)
he died in my place, (echo)
that I might live. (echo)

Words and Music: Graham Kendrick

169 He was pierced
(Like a lamb)

Thoughtful

1. He was pierced for our trans - gres-sions,
led like a lamb to the slaugh-ter, and
al -

bruised for our in - i - qui - ties;
though he was in - no-cent of crime; and to
and cut

bring us peace he was pun-ished,
off from the land of the liv - ing; and
he

by his stripes we are healed.
paid for the guilt that was mine.

2. He was

to next verse

Words and Music: Maggi Dawn

170 Higher, higher
(Cast your burdens)

Words and Music: Unknown, arr. Stuart Townend

171 His love

it reach-es to

me.

2. His love is stronger than the angels and demons.
His love, it keeps me in my life's darkest hour.
His love secures me on the pathway to heaven,
and his love is my strength and pow'r.

3. His love is sweeter than the sweetest of honey.
His love is better than the choicest of wine.
His love, it satisfies the deepest of hunger,
and his love, in Jesus it's mine.

4. Your love . . .

Words and Music: David Ruis

172 Hold me closer to you
(May I never lose sight of you)

Hold me clos-er to you each day; may my love for you ne- -ver fade. Keep my fo-cus on all that's true; may I ne-ver lose sight of you. of you.

1. In my fail-ure, in my suc - cess,

if in sad-ness or hap - pi - ness, be the hope I am cling-

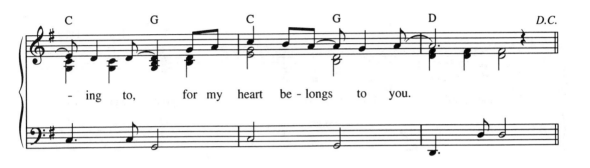

- ing to, for my heart be - longs to you.

2. You are only a breath away,
   watching over me ev'ry day;
   in my heart I am filled with peace
   when I hear you speak to me.

3. No one loves me in the way you do,
   no one cares for me like you do.
   Feels like heaven has broken through;
   God, you know how I love you.

Words and Music: Noel and Tricia Richards

173 Hold me, Lord

Words and Music: Danny Daniels

174 Holiness is your life in me
(Only the blood)

Expressively

Verse

Ho-li-ness is your life in me, mak-ing me clean through your blood.

Ho-li-ness is your fire in me,

purg-ing my heart like a flood. I know

you are per-fect in ho-li-ness.

Your life in me, set-ting me free, mak-ing me ho-ly.

Words and Music: Brian Doerksen

175 Holiness unto the Lord

Quite slow, with strength

Verse

Ho - li - ness un-to the Lord, un-to the King.

Ho - li - ness un-to your name I will

sing.

Chorus

Ho - li - ness un - to Je - sus,

ho-li-ness un-to you, Lord. Ho-li-ness un-to

Je - sus, ho - li - ness un - to you, Lord.

2. I love you, I love your ways,
   I love your name.
   I love you, and all my days
   I'll proclaim:

Words and Music: Danny Daniels

176 Holy, holy, holy! Lord God Almighty

NICAEA 11 12 12 10

1. Ho-ly, ho-ly, ho-ly! Lord God Al-migh-ty! Ear-ly in the
morn-ing our song shall rise to thee; ho-ly, ho-ly, ho-ly!
mer-ci-ful and migh-ty! God in three per-sons, bless-ed Tri-ni-ty!

2. Holy, holy, holy! all the saints adore thee,
    casting down their golden crowns around the glassy sea;
    cherubim and seraphim falling down before thee,
    which wert, and art, and evermore shalt be.

3. Holy, holy, holy! though the darkness hide thee,
    though the eye made blind by sin thy glory may not see,
    only thou art holy, there is none beside thee,
    perfect in pow'r, in love, and purity.

4. Holy, holy, holy! Lord God Almighty!
    All thy works shall praise thy name, in earth, and sky, and sea;
    holy, holy, holy! merciful and mighty!
    God in three persons, blessèd Trinity!

Words: Reginald Heber, alt.
Music: John Bacchus Dykes

177 Holy, holy, Lord God Almighty

Words and Music: Richard Lewis

Sing to the Lord a new song;
sing to the Lord, all the earth.
Sing to the Lord, praise his name;
proclaim his salvation day after day.
Declare his glory among the nations,
his marvellous deeds among all peoples.

Psalm 96:1-3

178 Holy, holy, Lord, you're worthy
(Hallowed be your name)

Ho-ly, ho-ly, Lord, you're wor-thy and I'm ho-noured to sing your praise. King of glo-ry, God Al-migh-ty, hal-low-ed be your name. All cre-a-tion, ev-'ry na-tion, has its be-ing by your word; as your will is

Words and Music: Ron Kenoly and Louis Smith

179 Holy One of God

Words and Music: Geoff Bullock

In a loud voice they sang:
'Worthy is the Lamb, who was slain,
to receive power and wealth and
wisdom and strength
and honour and glory and praise!'

Revelation 5:12

180 Holy Spirit, come

Ho - ly Spi - rit, come,

Ho - ly Spi - rit, come.

Heal our hearts, our lives,

cleanse our thoughts, our minds.

Ho - ly   Spi - rit,   come,

O come to   us.

2. Holy Spirit, fall,
   Holy Spirit, fall.
   Drench us with your love,
   fill our lives with peace.
   Holy Spirit, fall,
   O fall on us.

3. Holy Spirit, flow,
   Holy Spirit, flow.
   Lead us in your will,
   empowered to proclaim.
   Holy Spirit, flow,
   O flow through us.

Words and Music: Geoff Bullock

181 Holy Spirit, we welcome you

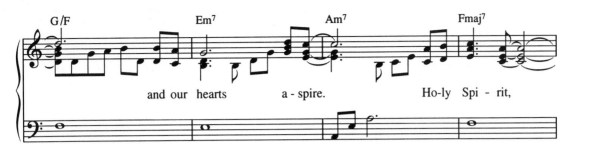

and our hearts a-spire. Ho-ly Spi - rit,

Ho-ly Spi - rit, Ho-ly Spi - rit,

we wel-come you. you.

2. Holy Spirit, we welcome you.
   Holy Spirit, we welcome you.
   Let the breeze of your presence blow,
   that your children here might truly know
   how to move in the Spirit's flow.
   Holy Spirit, Holy Spirit,
   Holy Spirit, we welcome you.

3. Holy Spirit, we welcome you.
   Holy Spirit, we welcome you.
   Please accomplish in me today
   some new work of loving grace, I pray;
   unreservedly have your way.
   Holy Spirit, Holy Spirit,
   Holy Spirit, we welcome you.

Words and Music: Chris Bowater

Clap your hands, all you nations;
shout to God with cries of joy.
How awesome is the Lord Most High,
the great King over all the earth!

Psalm 47:1-2

182 Hosanna

Words and Music: Carl Tuttle

183 How can I be free from sin?
(Lead me to the cross)

Moderately

1. How can I be free from sin? Lead me to the cross of

Je - sus, from the guilt, the pow'r, the pain,

lead me to the cross of Je - sus.

There's no o - ther way, no price that I could pay,

simp-ly to the cross I cling.

This is all I need, this is all I plead,

that his blood was shed for me.

2. How can I know peace within?
   Lead me to the cross of Jesus,
   sing a song of joy again,
   lead me to the cross of Jesus.

   Flowing from above,
   all-forgiving love,
   from the Father's heart to me.
   What a gift of grace,
   his own righteousness,
   clothing me in purity.

3. How can I live day by day?
   Lead me to the cross of Jesus,
   following his narrow way,
   lead me to the cross of Jesus.

Words and Music: Graham Kendrick and Steve Thompson

Love the Lord your God with all your heart
and with all your soul
and with all your strength.

Deuteronomy 6:5

184 How can I not love you

1. How can I not love you, when I see all that you've gi-ven me? How can I not love you, Je-sus, my Lord? I love you, first and last, in your love I've come to rest. I will dwell be-fore your throne, you are my e-ter-nal home.

2. How can I not serve you,
when I see all that you've done for me?
How can I not serve you,
Jesus, my Lord?

I draw near by your grace,
I desire to seek your face.
In your presence there is light,
you are my eternal life.

Words and Music: Wes Sutton

185 How deep the Father's love for us

many sons to glo - ry.

2. Behold the man upon a cross,
   my sin upon his shoulders;
   ashamed, I hear my mocking voice
   call out among the scoffers.
   It was my sin that held him there
   until it was accomplished;
   his dying breath has brought me life –
   I know that it is finished.

3. I will not boast in anything,
   no gifts, no pow'r, no wisdom;
   but I will boast in Jesus Christ,
   his death and resurrection.
   Why should I gain from his reward?
   I cannot give an answer,
   but this I know with all my heart,
   his wounds have paid my ransom.

Words and Music: Stuart Townend

186 How firm a foundation

MONTGOMERY 11 11 11 11

1. How firm a foun - da - tion, you saints of the Lord, is laid for your faith in his ex - cel - lent word; what more can he say than to you he has said, you who un - to Je - sus for re - fuge have fled?

2. Fear not, I am with you, O be not dismayed;
   for I am your God, and will still give you aid;
   I'll strengthen you, help you, and cause you to stand,
   upheld by my righteous, omnipotent hand.

3. In ev'ry condition, in sickness, in health,
   in poverty's vale, or abounding in wealth;
   at home and abroad, on the land, on the sea,
   as your days may demand shall your strength ever be.

4. When through the deep waters I call you to go,
   the rivers of grief shall not you overflow;
   for I will be with you in trouble to bless,
   and sanctify to you your deepest distress.

5. When through fiery trials your pathway shall lie,
   my grace all-sufficient shall be your supply;
   the flame shall not hurt you, my only design
   your dross to consume and your gold to refine.

6. The soul that on Jesus has leaned for repose
   I will not, I cannot, desert to its foes;
   that soul, though all hell should endeavour to shake,
   I never will leave, I will never forsake.

Words: Richard Keen
Music: *Magdalen Hospital Hymns*

187 How good and how pleasant

2. How deep are the rivers that run
   when we are one in Jesus
   and share with the Father and Son
   the blessings of his everlasting life.

Words and Music: Graham Kendrick

188 How lovely is your dwelling-place
(Better is one day)

1. How love-ly is your dwell-ing-place, O Lord Al-migh-ty. My soul longs and e-ven faints for you. For here my heart is sat-is-fied, with-in your pre-sence. I sing be-neath the sha-dow of your wings. Bet-ter is

Words and Music: Matt Redman

189 How lovely on the mountains
(Our God reigns)

Triumphantly, with pace

1. How love-ly on the moun-tains are the feet of him who brings good news, good news, pro-claim-ing peace, an-nounc-ing news of hap-pi - ness: our God reigns, our God reigns, our God reigns, our God reigns, our God reigns, our God reigns!

2. You watchmen, lift your voices joyfully as one,
shout for your King, your King.
See eye to eye the Lord restoring Zion:
your God reigns, your God reigns!

3. Waste places of Jerusalem, break forth with joy,
we are redeemed, redeemed.
The Lord has saved and comforted his people:
your God reigns, your God reigns!

4. Ends of the earth, see the salvation of your God,
Jesus is Lord, is Lord.
Before the nations he has bared his holy arm:
your God reigns, your God reigns!

Words and Music: Leonard E. Smith Jnr.

I will proclaim the name of the Lord.
Oh, praise the greatness of our God!
He is the Rock, his works are perfect,
and all his ways are just.
A faithful God who does no wrong,
upright and just is he.

Deuteronomy 32:3-4

190 How sweet the name of Jesus sounds

SAINT PETER CM

1. How sweet the name of Je - sus sounds in a be - liev - er's ear! It soothes our sor - rows, heals our wounds, and drives a - way our fear.

2. It makes the wounded spirit whole,
   and calms the troubled breast;
   'tis manna to the hungry soul,
   and to the weary rest.

3. Dear name! the rock on which I build,
   my shield and hiding-place,
   my never-failing treas'ry filled
   with boundless stores of grace.

4. Jesus! my Shepherd, Saviour, Friend,
   my Prophet, Priest, and King,
   my Lord, my life, my way, my end,
   accept the praise I bring.

5. Weak is the effort of my heart,
   and cold my warmest thought;
   but when I see thee as thou art,
   I'll praise thee as I ought.

6. Till then I would thy love proclaim
   with ev'ry fleeting breath;
   and may the music of thy name
   refresh my soul in death.

Words: John Newton, alt.
Music: Alexander Robert Reinagle

191 I am a new creation

Words and Music: Dave Bilbrough

192 I am so thankful

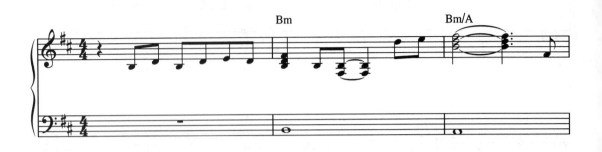

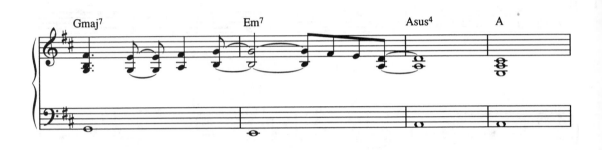

I am so thank - ful

for the full - ness of your love. I am so thank -

-ful for the shed-ding of your blood.

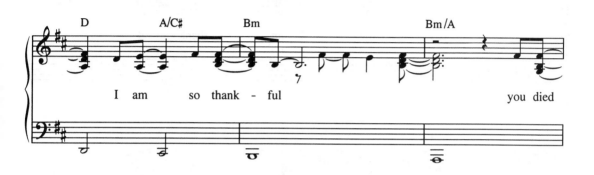

I am so thank - ful you died

in my place. Oh, Lord, I'm

1, 2. *3rd time instrumental*

thank - ful for your love. I am so

love.   I am so thank - ful for your

love.   Oh, Lord, I'm

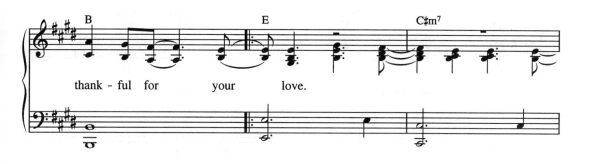

thank - ful for your love.

I'm thank - ful for your love.

Words and Music: Loren Bieg

193 I am standing beneath your wings
(Blessed be the name)

1. I am stand-ing be-neath your wings,
I am rest-ing in your shel-ter,
your great faith-ful-ness has been my shield
and it makes me want to sing.

2. I sing praises to your name, O Lord,
   for you daily bear my burdens.
   Your great faithfulness is my reward
   and it makes me want to sing.

Words and Music: Andy Park

Will you not revive us again,
that your people may rejoice in you?
Show us your unfailing love, O Lord,
and grant us your salvation.

Psalm 85:6-7

194 I am the God that healeth thee

2. You are the God that healeth me,
   you are the Lord, my healer;
   you sent your word and healed my disease,
   you are the Lord, my healer.

Words and Music: Don Moen

© Copyright 1986 Integrity's Hosanna! Music. Administered by Kingsway's
Thankyou Music, P.O. Box 75, Eastbourne, East Sussex, BN23 6NW, Used by permission.

195 I believe in Jesus

Words and Music: Marc Nelson

196 I believe the promise

Words and Music: Russell Fragar

197 I bow my knee before your throne

Words and Music: Bonnie Deuschle

198 I bow my knee
(I'll love you more)

Words and Music: Rob and Debbie Eastwood

199 I cannot tell

LONDONDERRY AIR 11 10 11 10 11 10 11 12

Words © Copyright Control (revived 1996).
This arrangement © Copyright 1996 Kevin Mayhew Ltd.

home, and that he lived at Na - za - reth and

la - boured, and so the Sa-viour, Sa-viour of the world, is come.

2. I cannot tell how silently he suffered,
   as with his peace he graced this place of tears,
   or how his heart upon the cross was broken,
   the crown of pain to three and thirty years.
   But this I know, he heals the broken-hearted,
   and stays our sin, and calms our lurking fear,
   and lifts the burden from the heavy laden,
   for yet the Saviour, Saviour of the world, is here.

3. I cannot tell how he will win the nations,
   how he will claim his earthly heritage,
   how satisfy the needs and aspirations
   of east and west, of sinner and of sage.
   But this I know, all flesh shall see his glory,
   and he shall reap the harvest he has sown,
   and some glad day his sun shall shine in splendour
   when he the Saviour, Saviour of the world, is known.

4. I cannot tell how all the lands shall worship,
   when, at his bidding, ev'ry storm is stilled,
   or who can say how great the jubilation
   when ev'ry heart with perfect love is filled.
   But this I know, the skies will thrill with rapture,
   and myriad, myriad human voices sing,
   and earth to heav'n, and heav'n to earth will answer:
   'At last the Saviour, Saviour of the world, is King!'

Words: William Young Fullerton, alt.
Music: traditional Irish melody arr. Noel Rawsthorne

200 I could sing unending songs
(The happy song)

O, I could sing un - end - ing songs of how you saved my
soul. Well, I could dance a thou - sand miles be -
cause of your great love.
My heart is burst - ing, Lord, to tell of all you've done.
Of how you changed my life and wiped a - way the past.

Words and Music: Martin Smith

In that day you will say:
'Give thanks to the Lord, call on his name;
make known among the nations what he has done,
and proclaim that his name is exalted.
Sing to the Lord, for he has done glorious things;
let this be known to all the world.'

Isaiah 12:4-5

201 I cry out for your hand
(Good to me)

I cry out for your hand of mer-cy to heal me. I am weak, I need your love to free me. Oh, Lord, my rock, my strength in weak-ness, come res - cue me, oh, Lord.

1. 2. You are my hope, your pro - mise ne - ver

Words and Music: Craig Musseau

202 If you are encouraged

2. Be sure you do nothing
   out of selfishness or pride,
   never seeing past your own concerns;
   but humbly keep the int'rests
   of each other in your hearts,
   seeing them as better than yourselves:

Words and Music: Graham Kendrick

203 I give you all the honour
(I worship you)

Majestically

1. I give you all the hon-our and praise that's due your name, for you are the King of Glo-ry, the Cre-a-tor of all things.

Chorus And I wor-ship you, I give my life to you, I fall down on my

2. As your Spirit moves upon me now,
   you meet my deepest need,
   and I lift my hands up to your throne,
   your mercy I've received.

3. You have broken chains that bound me,
   you've set this captive free,
   I will lift my voice to praise your name
   for all eternity.

Words and Music: Carl Tuttle

204 I have come to love you

1. I have come to love you, I have come to

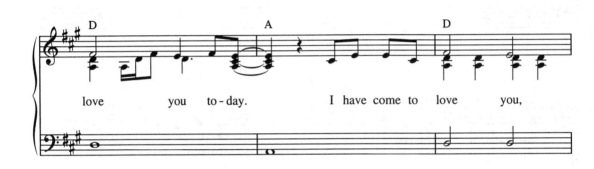

love you to-day. I have come to love you,

I have come to love you to-day. *Chorus* And to-day

and for e-ver-more I'll love your name.

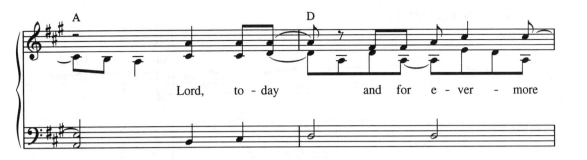

Lord, to - day and for e - ver - more

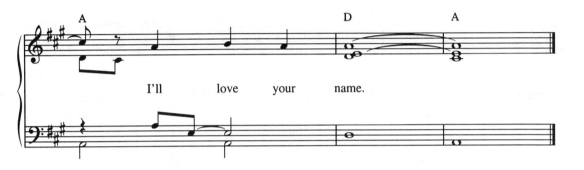

I'll love your name.

2. I have come to worship,
   I have come to worship today.
   I have come to worship,
   I have come to worship today.

3. I have come to thank you,
   I have come to thank you today.
   I have come to thank you,
   I have come to thank you today.

Words and Music: Matt Redman

205 I have made you too small
(Be magnified)

Lord, be mag - ni - fied, O Lord, be mag - ni - fied.

Chorus
Be mag - ni - fied, O Lord,

you are high-ly ex - al - ted; and there is no-thing you

can't do, O Lord, my eyes are on you. Be

mag - ni - fied, O Lord, be mag - ni - fied.

2. I have leaned on the wisdom of men,
   O Lord, forgive me;
   and I have responded to them
   instead of your light and your mercy.
   But now, O Lord . . .

Words and Music: Lynn DeShazo

206 I heard the voice of Jesus say (Tune 1)

KINGSFOLD DCM

1. I heard the voice of Je-sus say, 'Come un-to me and rest; lay down, thou wea-ry one, lay down thy head up-on my breast.' I came to Je-sus as I was, so wea-ry, worn and sad; I found in him a rest-ing-place, and he has made me glad.

206a I heard the voice of Jesus say (Tune 2)

VOX DILECTI DCM

2. I heard the voice of Jesus say,
   'Behold, I freely give
   the living water, thirsty one;
   stoop down and drink and live.'
   I came to Jesus, and I drank
   of that life-giving stream;
   my thirst was quenched, my soul revived,
   and now I live in him.

3. I heard the voice of Jesus say,
   'I am this dark world's light;
   look unto me, thy morn shall rise,
   and all thy day be bright.'
   I looked to Jesus, and I found
   in him my star, my sun;
   and in that light of life I'll walk
   till trav'lling days are done.

Words: Horatius Bonar
Music – Tune 1: traditional English melody collected by Lucy Broadwater,
adapted and arr. Ralph Vaughan Williams
Tune 2: John Bacchus Dykes

207 I just want to be where you are

I just want to be where you are,
dwell-ing dai – ly in your pre – sence; I don't want to
wor – ship from a – far: draw me near to where you are.
I just want to be where you are,

Words and Music: Don Moen

Hear my voice when I call to you.
May my prayer be set before you like incense.

Psalm 141:1b-2a

208 I just want to praise you

Words and Music: Arthur Tannous

209 I know a place
(At the cross)

I know a place, a won-der-ful place, where ac-cused and con-demned find mer-cy and grace, where the wrongs we have done and the

Words and Music: Randy and Terry Butler

210 I know it

I know it, I know it, his blood has set me free, I've been de-
li-vered, for-gi-ven, fear has got no hold on me.
I'm set a-part, not liv-ing life my own way,
not hold-ing back till I see him face to face be-cause I
know it, oh yes, I

Words and Music: Darlene Zschech

The Spirit of the Sovereign Lord is on me,
because the Lord has anointed me
to preach good news to the poor.
He has sent me to bind up the broken-hearted,
to proclaim freedom for the captives
and release from darkness for the prisoners . . .

Isaiah 61:1

211 I lift my eyes up to the mountains
(Psalm 121)

Steadily

I lift my eyes up to the moun - tains, where does my help come from? My help comes from you, ma-ker of hea - ven, cre - a - tor of the earth.

last time / *Fine* — O how I need you, Lord, you are my on - ly hope; you're my on - ly prayer.

So I will wait for you to come and res - cue me, come and give me life.

D.C al Fine

Words and Music: Brian Doerksen

212 I lift my hands
(I will serve no foreign god)

Gently flowing

I lift my hands to the com-ing King, to the great 'I AM', to you I sing, for you're the One who reigns with-in my heart.

And I will serve no for-eign god, or a-ny o-ther trea - sure; you are my heart's de-sire, Spi-rit with-out mea - sure. Un-to your name I would bring my sac - ri - fice.

Words and Music: Andre Kempen

213 I love to be in your presence

I love to be in your pre - sence with your peo-ple sing-ing prai - ses; I love to stand and re - joice, lift my hands and raise my voice. I

Words and Music: Paul Baloche and Ed Kerr

Praise the Lord.
How good it is to sing praises to our God,
how pleasant and fitting to praise him!

Psalm 147:1

214 I love you, Lord, and I lift my voice

Words and Music: Laurie Klein

215 I love you, Lord
(Holy is your name)

1. I love you, Lord,   with all of my heart.
2. I love you, Lord,   with all of my mind.

I love you, Lord,
I love you, Lord,

with all of my soul.
with all of my strength.   Let all that is with-in

me   cry, 'Ho - ly is   your name.'   Let

Words and Music: Mike Day and Dave Bell

Oh, the depth of the riches
of the wisdom and knowledge of God!
How unsearchable his judgements,
and his paths beyond tracing out!

For from him and through him
and to him are all things.
To him be the glory for ever! Amen.

Romans 11:33, 36

216 I love your presence

2. Your Holy Spirit's here, mighty Counsellor;
   yes, your Spirit's here, with releasing pow'r.
   Your Holy Spirit's here, poured out from above;
   yes, your Spirit's here, showing Father's love.

Words and Music: Fabienne Pons, trans. Judith Robertson

217 I'm accepted, I'm forgiven

Words and Music: Rob Hayward

© Copyright 1985 Kingsway's Thankyou Music, P.O. Box 75, Eastbourne,
East Sussex, BN23 6NW, UK. Used by permission.

218 I'm gonna click

2. I'm gonna zoom, zoom, zoom,
   around the room, room, room,
   I'm gonna zoom around the room and praise the Lord!
   Because of all he's done, I'm gonna make him 'number one',
   I'm gonna zoom around the room and praise the Lord!

3. I'm gonna sing, sing, sing,
   I'm gonna shout, shout, shout,
   I'm gonna sing, I'm gonna shout and praise the Lord!
   Because of all he's done, I'm gonna make him 'number one',
   I'm gonna sing, I'm gonna shout and praise the Lord!

4. I'm gonna click, click, click,
   I'm gonna clap, clap, clap,
   I'm gonna zoom around the room and praise the Lord!
   Because of all he's done, I'm gonna make him 'number one',
   I'm gonna sing, I'm gonna shout and praise the Lord!

Words and Music: adapted Capt. Alan J. Price arr. B. Chesser

219 Immanuel, O Immanuel

Words and Music: Graham Kendrick

220 Immortal, invisible, God only wise

SAINT DENIO 11 11 11 11

1. Im - mor - tal, in - vi - si - ble, God on - ly wise, in light in - ac - ces - si - ble hid from our eyes, most bless - ed, most glo - rious, the An-cient of Days, al - migh - ty, vic - to - rious, thy great name we praise.

2. Unresting, unhasting, and silent as light,
   nor wanting, nor wasting, thou rulest in might;
   thy justice like mountains high soaring above
   thy clouds which are fountains of goodness and love.

3. To all life thou givest, to both great and small;
   in all life thou livest, the true life of all;
   we blossom and flourish as leaves on the tree,
   and wither and perish; but naught changeth thee.

4. Great Father of glory, pure Father of light,
   thine angels adore thee, all veiling their sight;
   all laud we would render, O help us to see
   'tis only the splendour of light hideth thee.

5. *repeat 1st verse*

Words: Walter Chalmers Smith
Music: traditional Welsh hymn melody

221 I'm so secure
(In your hands)

1. I'm so se-cure, you're here with me;
2. You gave your life in your end - less love,

you stay the same, your
you set me free and

love re - mains here in my heart.
showed the way: now I am found.

So close I be-lieve
you're hold-ing me now, in your hands I be-long.

You'll ne - ver let me go. So close I be - lieve

Words and Music: Reuben Morgan

222 I'm special

With feeling

I'm spe-cial be-cause God has loved me, for he

gave the best thing that he had to save me;

his own Son, Je - sus, cru - ci - fied to take the

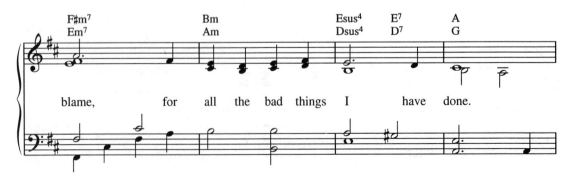

blame, for all the bad things I have done.

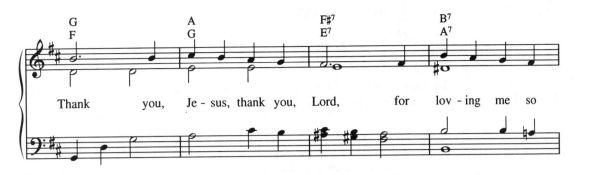

Thank you, Je - sus, thank you, Lord, for lov - ing me so

much. I know I don't de - serve a - ny - thing;

help me feel your love right now to know deep in my

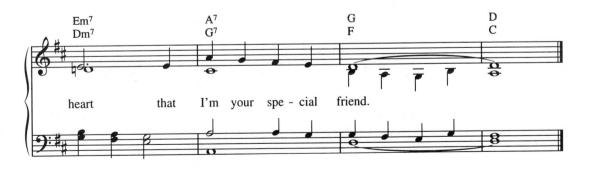

heart that I'm your spe - cial friend.

Words and Music: Graham Kendrick

223 I'm standing here to testify
(Come to the light)

With a steady rhythm

(Leader)
I'm stand-ing here to tes - ti - fy,
did not think I could have peace,
(All) O, the Lord is good. *(Leader)* to

sing of how he changed my heart.
trapped in - side by fear and shame.
(All) O, the Lord is good. *(Leader)* He

I was bound by hate and pride,
wiped a - way all of my grief,
(All) O, the Lord is good. *(Leader)* when

1st and 3rd times
ne - ver know - ing of his light.
I be - lieved up - on his name.
(All) O, the Lord is good. I

2nd and 4th times
Chorus
Come to the light,

come as you are; you can be a friend of God.

Words and Music: Kevin Prosch

224 I'm your child

1. I'm your child and you are my God. I thank you, Fa - ther, for your lov-ing care. I'm your child and you are my God. You've made me spe - cial and you're al - ways there.

2. I'm your child and you are my God.
   I love you Jesus, you're close to me.
   I'm your child and you are my God.
   I give you worship, I bow the knee.

3. I'm your child and you are my God.
   Holy Spirit, flow out to me.
   I'm your child and you are my God.
   You give me power and authority.

Words and Music: Richard Hubbard

225 In Christ alone

In Christ a - lone I place my trust, and find my glo - ry in the pow – er of the cross; in ev - 'ry vic - to - ry let it be said of me my source of strength, my source of hope is Christ a - lone.

Words and Music: Shawn Craig and Don Koch

226 I need you more

I need you more, more than yes-ter-day,

I need you more, more than words can say.

I need you more than e-ver be-fore,

I need you, Lord, I need you, Lord.

F#m7
Em7   E/G#
                                       D/F#

'cause I ne - ver want to go back to

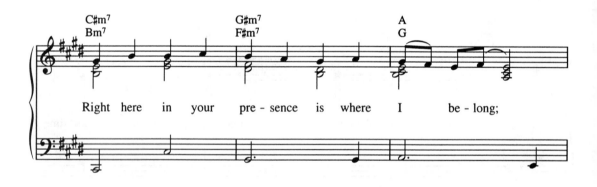

A   A/B   CODA
G   G/A   (D.C.)   E   G#m7
                                        D   F#m7

my old life.   I need you, Lord.

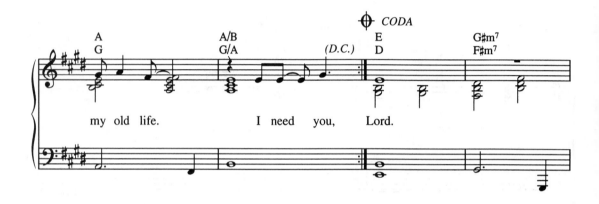

C#m7   G#m7   A
Bm7   F#m7   G

Right here in your pre - sence is where I be - long;

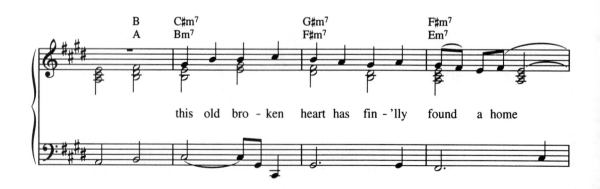

B   C#m7   G#m7   F#m7
A   Bm7   F#m7   Em7

this old bro - ken heart has fin - 'lly found a home

Words and Music: Lindell Cooley and Bruce Haynes

227 In every circumstance

With a 12/8 feel

In ev-'ry cir - cum-stance of life you are
with me, glo - rious Fa - ther. And I have put
my trust in you, that I may
know the glo - ri-ous hope to which I'm called.
And by the pow'r

Words and Music: David Fellingham

228 In heavenly armour
(The battle belongs to the Lord)

With strength

1. In hea-ven-ly ar - mour we'll en- ter the land, the bat - tle be - longs to the Lord.

No wea-pon that's fash - ion'd a - gainst us will stand, the bat - tle be - longs to the Lord.

And we sing glo - ry, hon - our,

pow - er and strength to the Lord. We sing glo - ry,

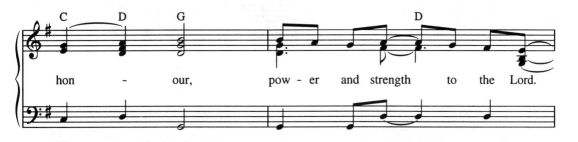

hon - our, pow - er and strength to the Lord.

2. When the power of darkness comes in like a flood,
   the battle belongs to the Lord.
   He'll raise up a standard, the power of his blood,
   the battle belongs to the Lord.

3. When your enemy presses in hard, do not fear,
   the battle belongs to the Lord.
   Take courage, my friend, your redemption is near,
   the battle belongs to the Lord.

Words and Music: Jamie Owens-Collins

229 In moments like these

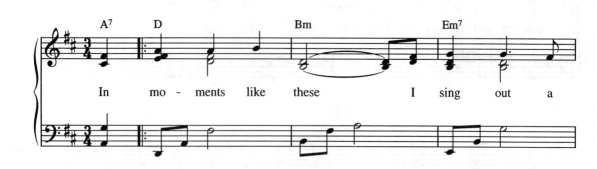

In mo - ments like these I sing out a

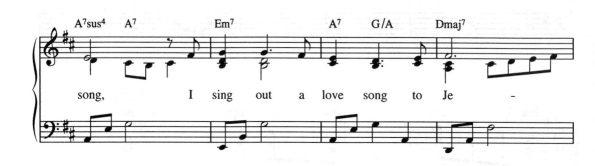

song, I sing out a love song to Je -

sus. In mo - ments like these I lift up my

hands, I lift up my hands to the Lord.

Words and Music: David Graham

Praise the Lord.
How good it is to sing praises to our God,
how pleasant and fitting to praise him!

Psalm 147:1

230 In my life, Lord
(Lord, be glorified)

Prayerfully

1. In my life, Lord, be glo-ri-fied,

be glo-ri-fied. In my life, Lord,

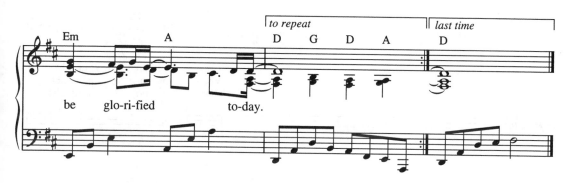

to repeat | *last time*

be glo-ri-fied to-day.

2. In your church, Lord,
be glorified, be glorified.
In your church, Lord,
be glorified today.

Words and Music: Bob Kilpatrick

© Copyright 1978 Bob Kilpatrick Music. Administered by CopyCare,
P.O. Box 77, Hailsham, East Sussex, BN27 3EF, UK. Used by permission.

231 In the morning when I rise
(All I want)

1. In the morn-ing when I rise ex-pec-tant-ly, I lift
2. Earth-ly cares and pas-sions pale when you take a-way the
3. No-thing in the world com-pares to the love that I can

my eyes and I see you (and
veil and I see you (and
share a-lone with you (a-

I see you).
I see you). Gaz-ing on your heav'n-
lone with you). When you o-pen hea-
There is no-thing else

- ly throne, in your pre-sence I'm at home,
- ven's door, all I want is to have more,
so real as the things that you re-veal when

Words and Music: Andy Park

The Lord is my rock, my fortress and my deliverer;
my God is my rock, in whom I take refuge.
He is my shield and the horn of my salvation, my stronghold.

The Lord lives! Praise be to my Rock!
Exalted be God my Saviour!

Psalm 18:2, 46

232 In the presence of a holy God

233 In the secret

1. In the se – cret, in the qui – et place, in the still – ness you are there. In the se – cret, in the qui – et hour I wait on – ly for you 'cause I want to know you more.

2. I am reaching for the highest goal,
   that I might receive the prize.
   Pressing onward, pushing ev'ry hindrance aside,
   out of my way, 'cause I want to know you more.

Words and Music: Andy Park

234 In the tomb so cold
(Christ is risen!)

Triumphantly

1. In the tomb so cold they laid him, death its vic-tim

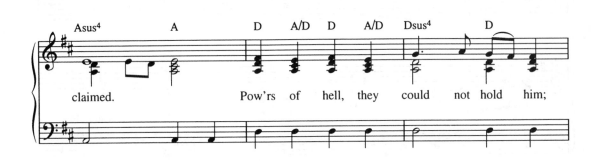

claimed. Pow'rs of hell, they could not hold him;

Chorus

(Men)

back to life he came! Christ is ri-sen!

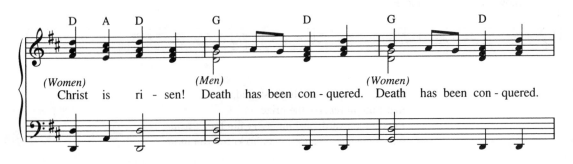

(Women) Christ is ri-sen! *(Men)* Death has been con-quered. *(Women)* Death has been con-quered.

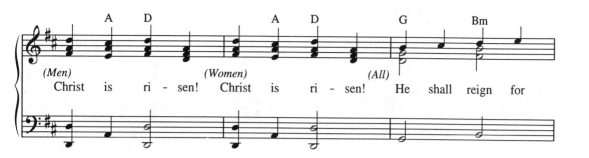

(Men) (Women) (All)
Christ is ri - sen! Christ is ri - sen! He shall reign for

e - ver.

2. Hell had spent its fury on him,
   left him crucified.
   Yet, by blood, he boldly conquered,
   sin and death defied.

3. Now the fear of death is broken,
   love has won the crown.
   Pris'ners of the darkness listen,
   walls are tumbling down.

4. Raised from death to heav'n ascending,
   love's exalted King.
   Let his song of joy, unending,
   through the nations ring!

   (Chorus twice to end)

Words and Music: Graham Kendrick

235 I reach up high

2. May my whole life be a song of praise
   to worship God in ev'ry way.
   In this song the actions praise his name,
   I want my actions ev'ry day to do the same.

Words and Music: Judy Bailey

236 I receive your love

Gently

1. I re-ceive your love, I re-ceive your love, in my heart I re-ceive your love, O Lord. I re-ceive your love by your Spi-rit with-in me, I re-ceive, I re-ceive your love.

2. I confess your love,
   I confess your love,
   from my heart I confess your love, O Lord.
   I confess your love
   by your Spirit within me,
   I confess, I confess your love.

Words and Music: Paul Armstrong

237 Is anyone thirsty?

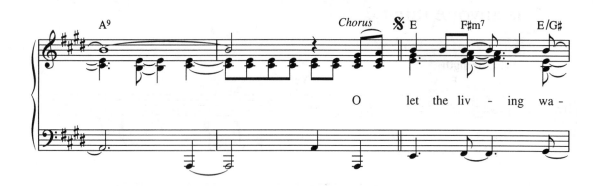

O let the liv - ing wa -

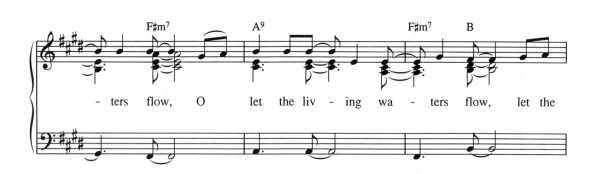

- ters flow, O let the liv - ing wa - ters flow, let the

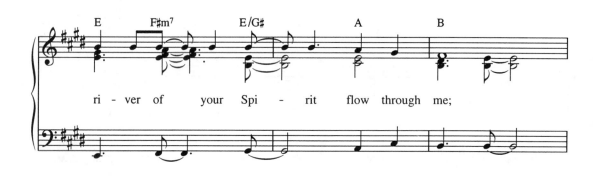

ri - ver of your Spi - rit flow through me;

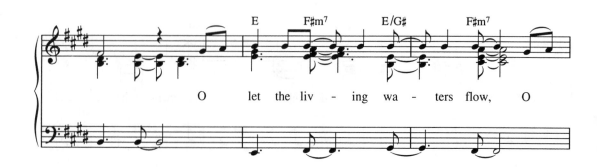

O let the liv - ing wa - ters flow, O

let the liv – ing wa – ters flow, let the ri – ver of your Spi –

– rit flow through me. Flow through

me. Let the liv – ing wa – ters flow,

1. let the liv – ing wa – ters flow, **2.** – ters flow, O

Words and Music: Graham Kendrick

238 I see the Lord

Words and Music: Chris Falson

239 I sing a simple song of love
(Arms of love)

Gently, with feeling

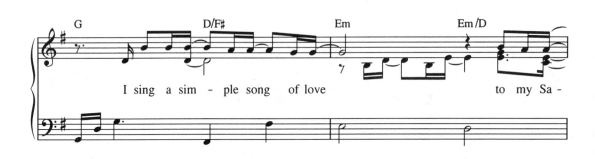

I sing a sim - ple song of love to my Sa -

- viour, to my Je - sus.

Words and Music: Craig Musseau

240 I sing praises

2. I give glory to your name, O Lord,
   glory to your name, O Lord,
   for your name is great and greatly to be praised. *(twice)*

Words and Music: Terry MacAlmon

241 Is it true today
(History maker)

Is it true to-day
to-day
that when peo-
that when peo-

- ple pray
- ple pray
cloud-less skies will break,
we'll see dead men rise

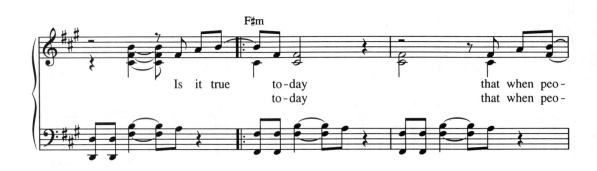

kings and queens will shake?
and the blind set free.
Yes, it's true

Words and Music: Martin Smith

242 Isn't he beautiful

2. Yes, you are beautiful,
   beautiful, yes, you are . . .

Words and Music: John Wimber

243 I stand amazed in the presence

2. For me it was in the garden
   he prayed – 'Not my will, but thine';
   he had no tears for his own griefs,
   but sweat drops of blood for mine,

3. In pity angels beheld him,
   and came from the world of light,
   to comfort him in the sorrows
   he bore for my soul that night.

4. He took my sins and my sorrows,
   he made them his very own;
   he bore the burden to Calvary,
   and suffered, and died alone.

5. When with the ransomed in glory
   his face I at last shall see,
   'twill be my joy through the ages
   to sing of his love for me.

Words and Music: Charles H. Gabriel

This righteousness from God
comes through faith in Jesus Christ
to all who believe.
There is no difference,
for all have sinned
and fall short of the glory of God,
and are justified freely by his grace
through the redemption that came by Christ Jesus.

Romans 3:22-24

244 I stand before the presence

Words and Music: Mavis Ford

245 I stand before your throne

Words and Music: Matthew Ling

246 I, the Lord of sea and sky
(Here I am, Lord)

1. I, the Lord of sea and sky, I have heard my peo-ple cry.
All who dwell in dark and sin my hand will save.
I who made the stars of night, I will make their
dark-ness bright. Who will bear my light to them? Whom shall I
send?

Chorus
Here I am, Lord. Is it

2. I, the Lord of snow and rain,
   I have borne my people's pain.
   I have wept for love of them.
   They turn away.
   I will break their hearts of stone,
   give them hearts for love alone.
   I will speak my word to them.
   Whom shall I send?

3. I, the Lord of wind and flame,
   I will tend the poor and lame.
   I will set a feast for them.
   My hand will save.
   Finest bread I will provide
   till their hearts be satisfied.
   I will give my life to them.
   Whom shall I send?

Words and Music: Dan Schutte

'Father, glorify your name!'
Then a voice came from heaven,
'I have glorified it, and will glorify it again.'

John 12:28

247 It is to you

Words and Music: Duke Kerr

© Copyright Duke Kerr and Remission Music UK, 50 Parkview Crescent, Bentley, Walsall, WS5 8TY.
Used by permission from the album *Melody of the Heart*.

248 It's our confession, Lord
(Sweet mercies)

It's our con-fes-sion, Lord, that we are weak, so ve - ry weak, but you are strong. And though we've no-thing, Lord, to lay at your feet, we come to your feet and say, 'Help us a - long'. A bro-ken heart and a con - trite spi - rit you have yet to de - ny.

Words and Music: David Ruis

249 It's rising up

With expectation

1. It's ris-ing up from coast to coast,
   for-mer things have ta-ken place. Can

north to south, and east to west; the cry of hearts that
this be the new day of praise? A heav'n-ly song that

love your name, which with one voice we will pro-claim.
comes to birth, and reach-es out to all

the earth. O let the cry to na-tions ring, that

2. The

3. And we have heard the lion's roar,
  that speaks of heaven's love and pow'r.
  Is this the time, is this the call
  that ushers in your kingdom rule?
  O let the cry to nations ring,
  that all may come and all may sing:
   'Jesus is alive!' (Ev'ry heart sing:)
   'Jesus is alive!' (With one voice sing:)
   'Jesus is alive!' (All the earth sing:)
   'Jesus is alive!'

Words and Music: Matt Redman and Martin Smith

250 It's your blood

Words and Music: Michael Christ

251 I've found a friend
(Joy in the Holy Ghost)

1. I've found a friend, O such a friend, he made my heart his home.
   Ho - ly Spi - rit fills me up and I need him ev - 'ry day

God him - self is with me and I
for fire, faith and con - fi - dence and

know I'm ne - ver a - lone.
know - ing what to say.

I know all my to - mor -
I gave my heart and all

- rows will be bet - ter than all my hopes ;
I am to the one who loves me most;

we've got

We've got pow – er o – ver fear and death and hearts

filled up with joy.

2. The

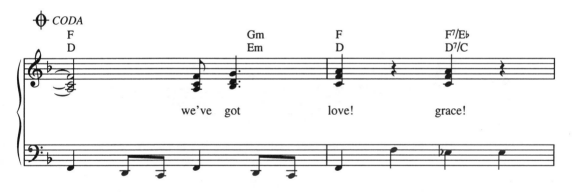

CODA

we've got love! grace!

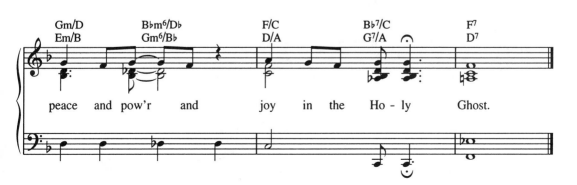

peace and pow'r and joy in the Ho – ly Ghost.

Words and Music: Russell Fragar

252 I've got a love song

Gently, building with each verse

1. I've got a love song in my heart (I've got a love song in my heart).
2. I've got a pas - sion in my heart (I've got a pas - sion in my heart).
5. I've ne - ver known a love like this (I've ne - ver known a love like this).

last time to Coda

1. / 2. It is for you, Lord, my God (It is for you, Lord, my God).
5. I've ne - ver known a love like this (I've ne - ver known a love like this).

Chorus

La la la, la la, la la, la la la, la la, la la,

2nd time to v. 3
4th time to v. 5

la la la, la la, la la.

Double time *Verse*

3. I've got re - joic - ing in my heart
4. And there is danc - ing in my heart

(I've got re - joic - ing in my heart).
(And there is danc - ing in my heart).

It is for you, Lord, my God

after v.4 D.S. CODA

(It is for you, Lord, my God).

Words and Music: Matt Redman

253 I walk by faith

I walk by faith, each

step by faith, to live by

faith, I put my trust in you. I

Ev - 'ry step I take

Words and Music: Chris Falson

254 I want to be a tree that's bearing fruit
(I want to be a blooming tree)

I want to be a tree that's bear-ing fruit, that God has pruned and caused to

shoot, O, up in the sky, so ve-ry, ve-ry high. I want to be, I want to be a

bloom-ing tree, God has pro-mised his Ho-ly Spi-rit will wa-ter our roots and

help us grow. Lis-ten and o-bey, and be-fore you know it your

fruit will start to grow, grow, grow, grow, grow.

Words and Music: Doug Horley

255 I want to be out of my depth in your love

you lead, put-ting all trust in you;
so tight, made my se-cu - ri-ty;

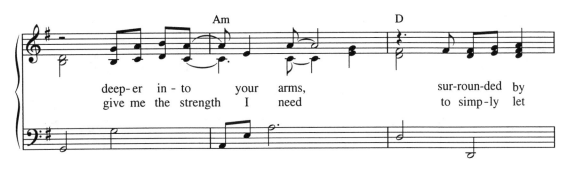

deep-er in-to your arms, sur-roun-ded by
give me the strength I need to simp-ly let

1. you. **2.** go. *D.S. al Fine*
I want to be

Words and Music: Doug Horley and Noel Richards

256 I want to serve the purpose of God
(In my generation)

Driving

1. I want to serve the pur-pose of God in my ge- ne- ra- tion. I want to serve the pur-pose of God while I am a- live. I want to give my life for some-thing that'll last for e - ver, oh, I de-light, I de-light to do your will.

2. I want to build with silver and gold in my generation.
I want to build with silver and gold while I am alive.
I want to give my life . . .

3. I want to see the kingdom of God in my generation.
I want to see the kingdom of God while I am alive.
I want to give my life . . .

4. I want to see the Lord come again in my generation.
I want to see the Lord come again while I am alive.
I want to give my life . . .

Words and Music: Mark Altrogge

257 I went to the enemy's camp
(Enemy's camp)

I went to the e-ne-my's camp and I
took back what he stole from me,
I took back what he stole from me,
I took back what he
stole from me. I went to the e-ne-my's camp and I

This song may be sung in conjunction with 'Look what the Lord has done'. (No. 326)

took back what he stole from me. He's un-der my feet, he's

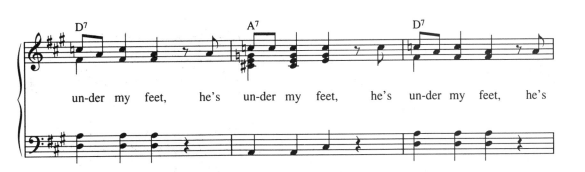

un-der my feet, he's un-der my feet, he's un-der my feet, he's

un-der my feet, he's un-der my feet, Sa-tan is un-der my

feet. I Sa-tan is un-der my feet.

Words and Music: Richard Black

258 I will be yours
(Eternity)

Gently flowing

I will be yours, you will be mine, to-ge-ther in e-ter-ni-ty. Our hearts of love will be en-twined, to-ge-ther in e-ter-ni-ty,

repeat intro if desired

Words and Music: Brian Doerksen

259 I will build my church

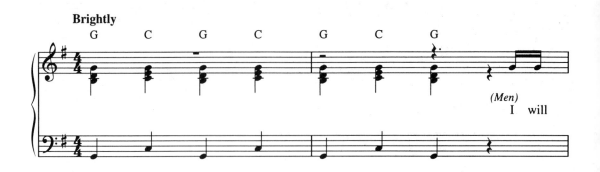

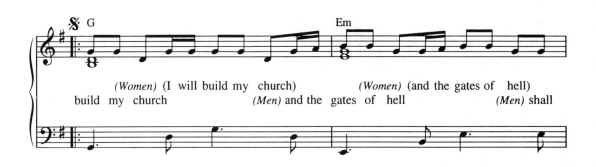

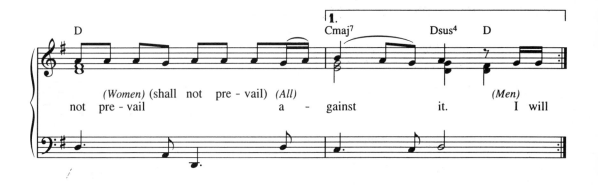

bow down! And you pow'rs on the earth be - low,

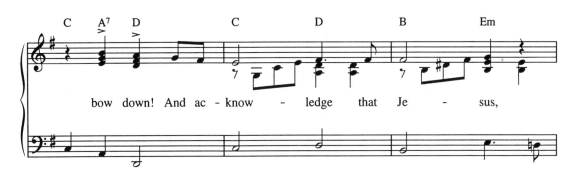

bow down! And ac - know - ledge that Je - sus,

Je - sus, Je - sus is Lord,

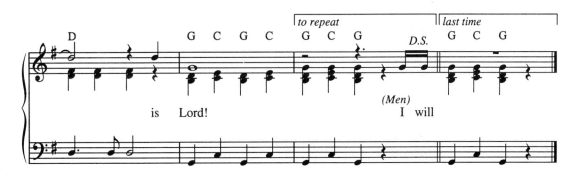

to repeat   *last time*

D.S.

is Lord!   *(Men)* I will

Words and Music: Graham Kendrick

260 I will change your name

I will change your name,
you shall no long-er be called
your new name shall be
wound - ed out - cast,
con - fi - dence, joy - ful - ness,
lone - ly or a - fraid.
o - ver - com - ing one.

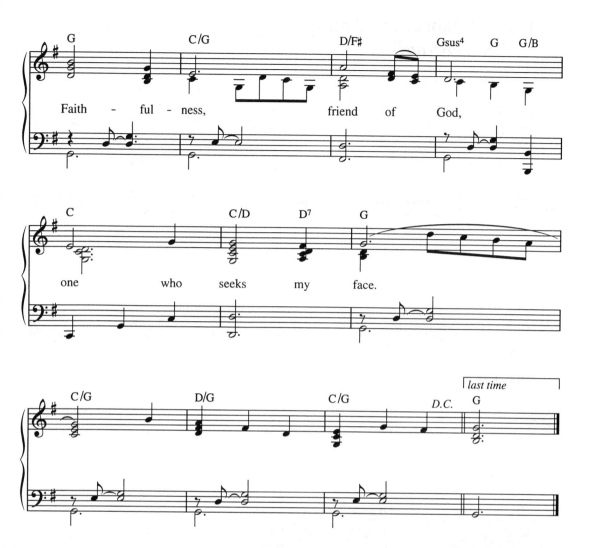

Faith - ful - ness, friend of God, one who seeks my face.

Words and Music: D.J. Butler

261 I will dance, I will sing
(Undignified)

With life and energy

I will dance, I will sing, to be mad for my King.

No-thing, Lord, is hin-der-ing the pas-sion in my soul.

pas-sion in my soul. And I'll be-come

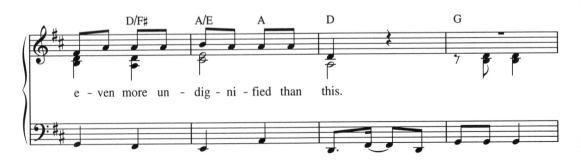

e-ven more un-dig-ni-fied than this.

Words and Music: Matt Redman

262 I will enter his gates
(He has made me glad)

Words and Music: Leona von Brethorst

263 I will lift my voice

2. I will lift my hands to the Lord of lords
   as an offering to him.
   I will lift my life to the Lord of lords
   as an offering to him.

Words and Music: Geoff Bullock

264 I will never be the same again

Words and Music: Geoff Bullock

265 I will offer up my life
(This thankful heart)

1. I will of-fer up my life in spi-rit and truth, pour-ing out the oil of love as my wor-ship to you. In sur-ren-der I must give my ev-'ry part; Lord, re-ceive the sac-ri-fice of a bro-ken heart.

Je-sus, what can I give, what can I bring to so faith-ful a friend,

2. You deserve my ev'ry breath
for you've paid the great cost;
giving up your life to death,
even death on a cross.
You took all my shame away,
there defeated my sin,
opened up the gates of heav'n,
and have beckoned me in.

Words and Music: Matt Redman

266 I will praise you all my life
(O faithful God)

With strength

I will praise you all my life; I will sing to you with my whole heart. I will trust in you, my hope and my help, my Ma-ker and my faith-ful God. O faith-ful God, O faith-ful God, you lift me up and you up-hold my cause; you give me life, you dry my eyes, you're al-ways near, you're a faith-ful God.

Words and Music: Mark Altrogge

© Copyright 1987 PDI Music/Word Music. Administered by CopyCare,
P.O. Box 77, Hailsham, East Sussex, BN27 3EF, UK. Used by permission.

267 I will seek you

Words and Music: Matthew Lockwood

268 I will seek your face, O Lord

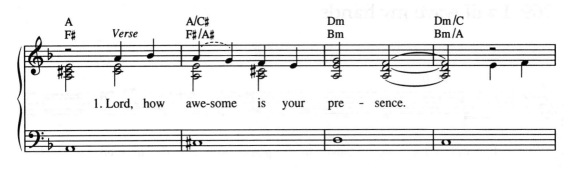

1. Lord, how awe-some is your pre - sence.

Who can stand in your light?

Those who by your grace and mer - cy

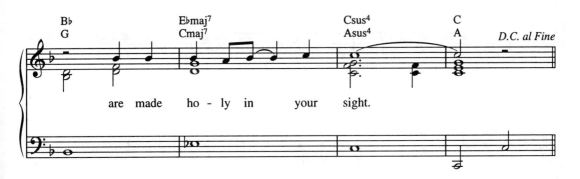

D.C. al Fine

are made ho - ly in your sight.

2. I will dwell in your presence
   all the days of my life;
   there to gaze upon your glory,
   and to worship only you.

Words and Music: Noel and Tricia Richards

269 I will wave my hands

I will wave my hands in praise and a - do - ra - tion, I will
wave my hands in praise and a - do - ra - tion, I will wave my hands in
praise and a - do - ra - tion, praise and a - do - ra - tion to the liv - ing God. For he's
gi - ven me hands that just love clap - ping: one, two,

Words and Music: Ian Smale

270 I will worship
(You alone are worthy of my praise)

Worshipfully, with strength

1. I will worship (I will worship) with
   I will seek you (I will seek you)

all of my heart (with all of my heart).
all of my days (all of my days).

I will praise you (I will praise you) with
I will fol-low (I will fol-low)

all of my strength (all my strength).
all of your ways (all your ways).

2. I will bow down (I will bow down),
   hail you as King (hail you as King).
   I will serve you (I will serve you),
   give you ev'rything (give you ev'rything).
   I will lift up (I will lift up)
   my eyes to your throne (my eyes to your throne).
   I will trust you (I will trust you),
   I will trust you alone (trust in you alone).

Words and Music: David Ruis

271 I worship you, Almighty God

Words and Music: Sondra Corbett

272 I worship you, O Lamb of God

2. I kneel before (I kneel before)
the Lamb of God,
who takes away (who takes away)
the sin of the world.
Alleluia.

Words and Music: Graham Kendrick

Therefore God exalted him to the highest place
and gave him the name that is above every name,
that at the name of Jesus every knee should bow,
in heaven and on earth and under the earth,
and every tongue confess that Jesus Christ is Lord,
to the glory of God the Father.

Philippians 2:9-11

273 Jesus, at your name
(You are the Christ)

Je - sus, at your name we bow the knee.

Je-sus, at your name we bow the knee. Je - sus, at your name we

bow the knee, and ac - know-ledge you as Lord.

You are the Christ, you are the Lord.

Through your Spi-rit in our lives we know who you are.

Words and Music: Chris Bowater

274 Jesus Christ
(Once again)

2. Now you are exalted to the highest place,
   King of the heavens, where one day I'll bow.
   But for now I marvel at this saving grace,
   and I'm full of praise once again,
   I'm full of praise once again.

Words and Music: Matt Redman

275 Jesus Christ is Lord of all
(Jesus is our battle cry)

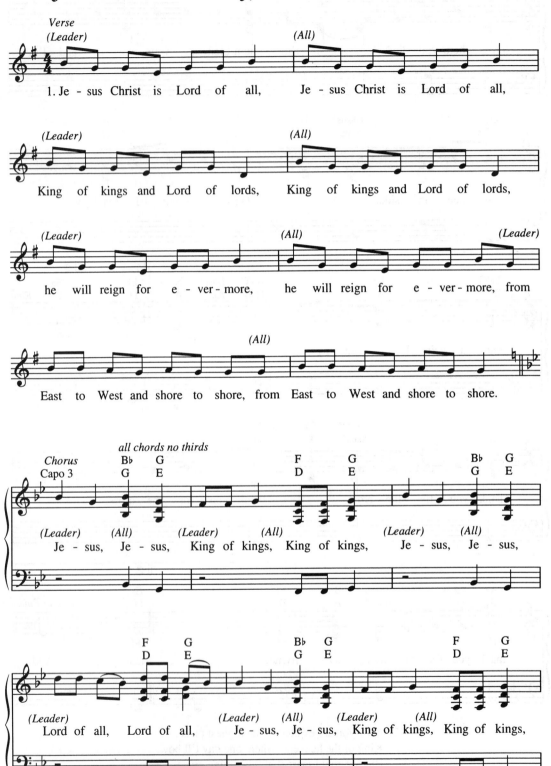

Verse
(Leader) ... *(All)*

1. Je - sus Christ is Lord of all, Je - sus Christ is Lord of all,

(Leader) ... *(All)*

King of kings and Lord of lords, King of kings and Lord of lords,

(Leader) ... *(All)* ... *(Leader)*

he will reign for e - ver - more, he will reign for e - ver - more, from

(All)

East to West and shore to shore, from East to West and shore to shore.

Chorus
Capo 3

all chords no thirds

(Leader) *(All)* *(Leader)* *(All)* *(Leader)* *(All)*

Je - sus, Je - sus, King of kings, King of kings, Je - sus, Je - sus,

(Leader) *(Leader)* *(All)* *(Leader)* *(All)*

Lord of all, Lord of all, Je - sus, Je - sus, King of kings, King of kings,

(Leader) (All)   (Leader)   (All)
Je - sus, Je - sus, Lord of all, Lord of all, Lord of

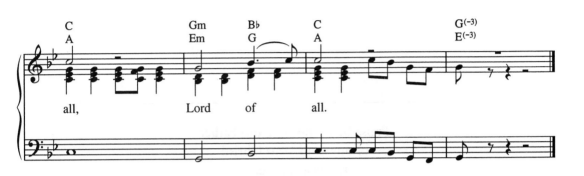

all,   Lord   of   all.

2. *(Leader)*   Jesus is our battle cry,
   (All)   Jesus is our battle cry,
   (Leader)   King of justice, peace and joy.
   (All)   King of justice, peace and joy.
   (Leader)   We want Jesus more and more,
   (All)   we want Jesus more and more,
   (Leader)   he's the one we're marching for,
   (All)   he's the one we're marching for.

Words and Music: Graham Kendrick

Praise be to the God and Father
of our Lord Jesus Christ!
In his great mercy
he has given us new birth into a living hope
through the resurrection of Jesus Christ from the dead.

1 Peter 1:3

276 Jesus Christ is risen today

EASTER HYMN 77 77 and Alleluias

1. Jesus Christ is ris'n to-day, al - le - lu - ia!
our tri-um-phant ho-ly day, al - le - lu - ia!
who did once, up - on the cross, al - le - lu - ia!
suf - fer to re - deem our loss, al - le - lu - ia!

2. Hymns of praise then let us sing, alleluia!
unto Christ, our heav'nly King, alleluia!
who endured the cross and grave, alleluia!
sinners to redeem and save, alleluia!

3. But the pains that he endured, alleluia!
our salvation have procured; alleluia!
now above the sky he's King, alleluia!
where the angels ever sing, alleluia!

Words and Music: from *Lyra Davidica*

277 Jesus Christ is the Lord of all

Words and Music: Steve Israel and Gerrit Gustafson

278 Jesus, God's righteousness revealed
(This kingdom)

2. Jesus, the expression of God's love,
   the grace of God, the word of God, revealed to us;
   Jesus, God's holiness displayed,
   now glorified, now justified, his kingdom comes.

Words and Music: Geoff Bullock

279 Jesus, how lovely you are

Je - sus, how love-ly you are,

you are so gen - tle, so pure and kind.

You shine as the morn - ing star,

Je - sus, how love-ly you are. love-ly you are.

1. Hal - le - lu - jah, Je-sus is my Lord and King;

hal - le - lu - jah, Je-sus is my ev - 'ry - thing.

2. Hallelujah, Jesus died and rose again;
   hallelujah, Jesus forgave all my sin.

3. Hallelujah, Jesus is meek and lowly;
   hallelujah, Jesus is pure and holy.

4. Hallelujah, Jesus is the Bridegroom;
   hallelujah, Jesus will take his bride soon.

Words and Music: Dave Bolton

280 Jesus! I am resting, resting

TRANQUILLITY 87 85 D

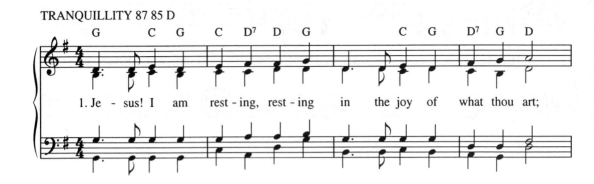

1. Je - sus! I am rest - ing, rest - ing in the joy of what thou art;

I am find - ing out the great - ness of thy lov - ing heart.

Thou hast bid me gaze up - on thee, and thy beau - ty fills my soul,

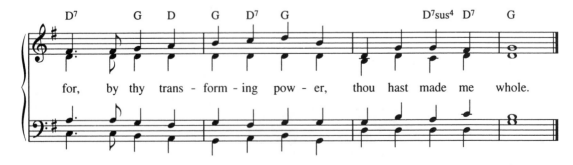

for, by thy trans - form - ing pow - er, thou hast made me whole.

2. O how great thy loving kindness,
   vaster, broader than the sea!
   O how marvellous thy goodness,
   lavished all on me!
   Yes, I rest in thee, beloved,
   know what wealth of grace is thine,
   know thy certainty of promise,
   and have made it mine.

3. Simply trusting thee, Lord Jesus,
   I behold thee as thou art,
   and thy love so pure, so changeless,
   satisfies my heart,
   satisfies its deepest longings,
   meets, supplies its ev'ry need,
   compasses me round with blessings;
   thine is love indeed!

4. Ever lift thy face upon me,
   as I work and wait for thee;
   resting 'neath thy smile, Lord Jesus,
   earth's dark shadows flee.
   Brightness of my Father's glory,
   sunshine of my Father's face,
   keep me ever trusting, resting,
   fill me with thy grace.

Words: Jean Sophia Pigott
Music: James Mountain

281 Jesus, I am thirsty
(More of you)

Je - sus, I am thirs - ty, won't you come and fill me? Earth - ly things have left me dry, on - ly you can sa - tis - fy, all I want is more of you. All I want is

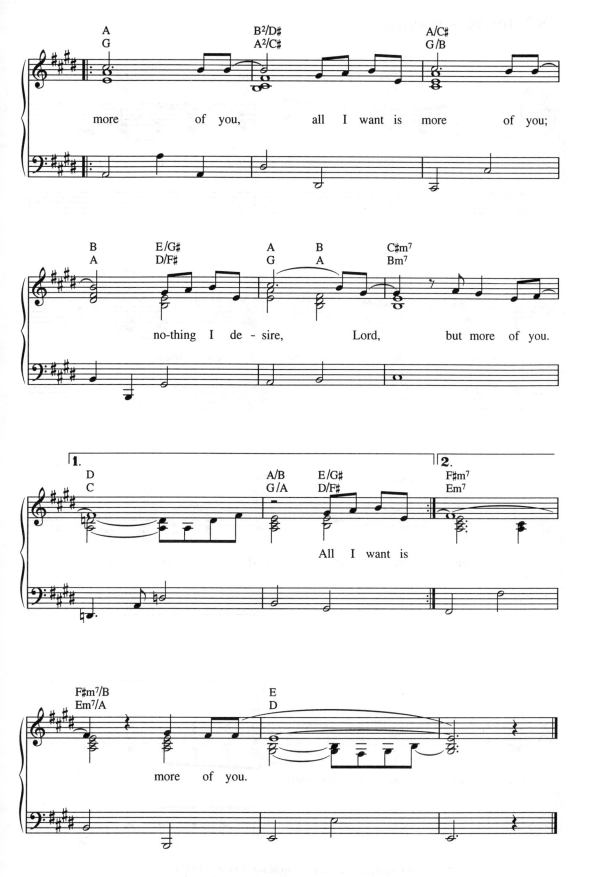

Words and Music: Don Harris and Martin J. Nystrom

282 Jesus is greater

Words and Music: Gill Hutchinson

283 Jesus is King

1. Je - sus is King and I will ex-tol him,
give him the glo - ry and hon - our his name.
He reigns on high, en - throned in the hea - vens,
Word of the Fa - ther, ex - al - ted for us.

2. We have a hope that is steadfast and certain,
gone through the curtain and touching the throne.
We have a Priest who is there interceding,
pouring his grace on our lives day by day.

3. We come to him, our Priest and Apostle,
clothed in his glory and bearing his name,
laying our lives with gladness before him;
filled with his Spirit we worship the King.

4. O holy One, our hearts do adore you;
thrilled with your goodness we give you our praise.
Angels in light with worship surround him,
Jesus, our Saviour, for ever the same.

Words and Music: Wendy Churchill

284 Jesus is Lord!

With majesty

1. Jesus is Lord! creation's voice proclaims it, for by his pow'r each tree and flow'r was planned and made. Jesus is Lord! the universe declares it, sun, moon and stars in heaven cry,

Chorus

'Jesus is Lord!' Jesus is Lord! Jesus is Lord! Praise him with hallelujahs for Jesus is Lord.

2. Jesus is Lord! yet from his throne eternal
in flesh he came to die in pain
on Calv'ry's tree.
Jesus is Lord! from him all life proceeding,
yet gave his life a ransom
thus setting us free.

3. Jesus is Lord! o'er sin the mighty conqu'ror,
from death he rose, and all his foes
shall own his name.
Jesus is Lord! God sent his Holy Spirit
to show by works of power
that Jesus is Lord.

Words and Music: David Mansell

© Copyright 1982 Springtide/Word Music. Administered by CopyCare,
P.O. Box 77, Hailsham, East Sussex, BN27 3EF, UK. Used by permission.

285 Jesus is the name we honour
(Jesus is our God)

Brightly

1. Jesus is the name we honour; Jesus is the name we praise. Majestic Name above all other names, the highest heav'n and earth proclaim that Jesus is our God. We will

glo - ri - fy, we will lift him high, we will give him hon - our and praise. We will glo - ri - fy, we will lift him high, we will give him hon - our and praise.

2. Jesus is the name we worship;
   Jesus is the name we trust.
   He is the King above all other kings,
   let all creation stand and sing
   that Jesus is our God.

3. Jesus is the Father's splendour;
   Jesus is the Father's joy.
   He will return to reign in majesty,
   and ev'ry eye at last will see
   that Jesus is our God.

Words and Music: Philip Lawson Johnston

286 Jesus, Jesus
(Holy and anointed One)

Je - sus, Je - sus,
ho - ly and a - noin - ted One,
ri - sen and ex - al - ted One, Je - sus.

sus. Your name is like ho - ney on my lips, your Spi - rit like wa-

- ter to my soul. Your word is a lamp un - to my feet.

Je - sus, I love you, I love you.

Words and Music: John Barnett

287 Jesus, Jesus, Jesus

Words and Music: Chris Bowater

288 Jesus, Jesus, you have the name
(Hearts on fire)

Je - sus (Je - sus), Je - sus (Je - sus).

You have the name that's high - er than all o - ther names.

Je - sus (Je - sus), Je - sus (Je - sus).

You are the King, the migh - ty God, the one who reigns.

Glo - rious in splen - dour and ma - jes - ty,

Words and Music: David Hadden arr. Christopher Tambling

289 Jesus' love has got under our skin
(Under our skin)

Je-sus' love has got un-der our skin,

Je-sus' love has got un-der our skin.

Deep-er than col-our oh; rich-er than

cul-ture oh; strong-er than e-mo-tion oh;

wi-der than the o-cean oh. Don't you want to

Words and Music: Graham Kendrick

When Jesus spoke again to the people,
he said, 'I am the light of the world.
Whoever follows me will never walk in darkness,
but will have the light of life.'

John 8:12

290 Jesus, lover of my soul

I love you, I need you, though my world will fall, I'll

ne - ver let you go. My Sa - viour,

my clos - est friend, I will wor-ship you un -

1. til the ve - ry end. **2.** til the ve - ry end.

Words and Music: John Ezzy, Daniel Grul and Stephen McPherson

291 Jesus, name above all names

Gently

Je - sus, name a - bove all names, beau - ti - ful Sa - viour, glo - ri - ous Lord; Em - ma - nu - el, God is with us, bless - ed Re - deem - er, Liv - ing Word.

Words and Music: Naida Hearn

292 Jesus put this song into our hearts

'Hebrew' style, getting faster
(verse 5 instrumental)

1. Jesus put this song into our hearts,
Jesus put this song into our hearts,
it's a song of joy no one can take away,
Jesus put this song into our hearts.

2. Jesus taught us how to live in harmony,
Jesus taught us how to live in harmony,
diff'rent faces, diff'rent races, he made us one,
Jesus taught us how to live in harmony.

3. Jesus taught us how to be a family,
Jesus taught us how to be a family,
loving one another with the love that he gives,
Jesus taught us how to be a family.

4. Jesus turned our sorrow into dancing,
Jesus turned our sorrow into dancing,
changed our tears of sadness into rivers of joy,
Jesus turned our sorrow into a dance.

Words and Music: Graham Kendrick

293 Jesus reigns

sin; gen - tle, hum - ble Lamb of God with a

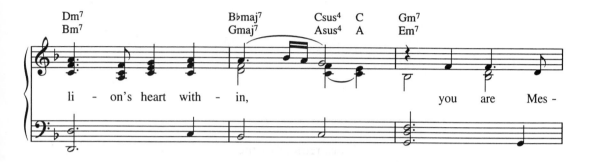

li - on's heart with - in, you are Mes -

si - ah and you're com - ing back a - gain. Je - sus

2. Jesus, mighty living Lord,
   whose face shines like the sun;
   awesome in your majesty,
   you are God's Holy One,
   you are Messiah
   and you're coming back again.

3. Jesus, Name above all names,
   the most exalted One,
   you are the Way, the Truth, the Life,
   God's precious living Son,
   you are Messiah
   and you're coming back again.

Words and Music: Colin Owen

'Jesus, remember me
when you come into your kingdom.'
Jesus answered him,
'I tell you the truth,
today you will be with me in paradise.'

Luke 23:42-43

294 Jesus, remember me

Je - sus, re - mem-ber me when you come in - to your king - dom.

Je - sus, re - mem-ber me when you come in - to your king - dom.

Words: from Scripture
Music: Jacques Berthier

295 Jesus, restore to us again

1. Jesus, restore to us again the gospel of your holy name, that comes with pow'r, not words alone, owned, signed and sealed from heaven's throne. Spirit and word in one agree; the promise to the power wed.

The word is near, here in our mouths and in our hearts, the

word of faith; pro - claim it on the Spi - rit's breath:

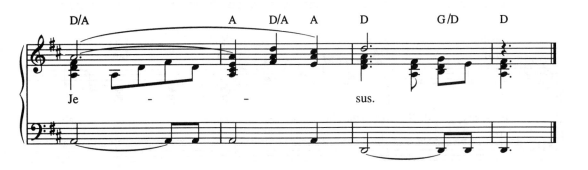

Je - - sus.

2. Your word, O Lord, eternal stands,
   fixed and unchanging in the heav'ns.
   The Word made flesh, to earth came down
   to heal our world with nail-pierced hands.
   Among us here you lived and breathed,
   you are the message we received.

3. Spirit of truth, lead us, we pray,
   into all truth as we obey.
   And as God's will we gladly choose,
   your ancient pow'r again will prove
   Christ's teaching truly comes from God,
   he is indeed the living Word.

4. Upon the heights of this dark land
   with Moses and Elijah stand.
   Reveal your glory once again,
   show us your face, declare your name.
   Prophets and law, in you, complete
   where promises and power meet.

5. Grant us in this decisive hour
   to know the Scriptures and the pow'r;
   the knowledge in experience proved,
   the pow'r that moves and works by love.
   May words and works join hands as one,
   the word go forth, the Spirit come.

Words and Music: Graham Kendrick

296 Jesus shall take the highest honour

Words and Music: Chris Bowater

297 Jesus, take me as I am

Tenderly

Je-sus, take me as I am, I can come no o-ther way. Take me deep-er in-to you, make my flesh life die a-way. Make me like a pre-cious stone, crys-tal clear and fine-ly honed. Life of Je-sus shin-ing through, giv-ing glo-ry back to you.

Words and Music: Dave Bryant

© Copyright 1978 Kingsway's Thankyou Music, P.O. Box 75, Eastbourne,
East Sussex, BN23 6NW, UK. Used by permission.

298 Jesus, the name high over all

LYDIA CM extended

1. Je - sus, the name high o - ver all, in hell, or earth, or sky: an - gels and mor-tals pros-trate fall, and de - vils fear and fly, and de - vils fear and fly.

2. Jesus, the name to sinners dear,
   the name to sinners giv'n;
   it scatters all their guilty fear,
   it turns their hell to heav'n.

3. Jesus, the pris'ner's fetters breaks,
   and bruises Satan's head;
   pow'r into strengthless souls he speaks,
   and life into the dead.

4. O, that the world might taste and see
   the riches of his grace!
   The arms of love that compass me,
   hold all the human race.

5. His only righteousness I show,
   his saving grace proclaim:
   'tis all my business here below
   to cry: 'Behold the Lamb!'

6. Happy, if with my latest breath
   I may but gasp his name:
   preach him to all, and cry in death:
   'Behold, behold the Lamb!'

Words: Charles Wesley
Music: Thomas Phillips

299 Jesus, we celebrate your victory

2. His Spirit in us releases us from fear,
   the way to him is open, with boldness we draw near.
   And in his presence our problems disappear;
   our hearts responding to his love.

Words and Music: John Gibson

300 Jesus, we enthrone you

With reverence

Je - sus, we en - throne you,

we pro - claim you our King,

stand - ing here in the midst of us,

we raise you up with our praise.

And as we wor - ship, build a throne,

and as we wor - ship, build a throne,

and as we wor - ship, build a throne; come, Lord

Je - sus, and take your place.

Words and Music: Paul Kyle

301 Jesus, what a beautiful name

Words and Music: Tanya Riches

302 Jesus, you're my firm foundation
(Firm foundation)

Je - sus, you're my firm foun - da - tion,
I know I can stand se - cure;
Je - sus, you're my firm foun - da - tion,
I put my hope in your ho - ly word,
I put my hope in your ho - ly word.

(Men)   2. Your word is faithful,
(Women)   your word is faithful,
(Men)   mighty in power,
(Women)   mighty in power;
(Men)   God will deliver me,
(Women)   God will deliver me,
(Men)   of this I'm sure,
(All)   of this I'm sure.

Words and Music: Nancy Gordon and Jamie Harvill

303 Jesus, your loving kindness
(Your love)

Je - sus, your lov - ing kind-ness, I'm so

blessed by all that you've done, this life that you give.

Je - sus, your lov - ing kind-ness

is life that's chang-ing my heart, draw-ing me

near to you. Your love is bet -

Words and Music: Reuben Morgan

304 Jesus, your name is power

2. Jesus, your name is healing,
   Jesus, your name gives sight.
   Jesus, your name will free ev'ry captive,
   Jesus, your name is life.

3. Jesus, your name is holy,
   Jesus, your name brings light.
   Jesus, your name above ev'ry other,
   Jesus, your name is life.

4. *repeat verse 1*

Words: Claire Cloninger
Music: Morris Chapman, arr. H. Rogers

305 Joy to the world

ANTIOCH CM

1. Joy to the world! The Lord is come; let earth re-ceive her King; let ev-'ry heart pre-pare him room and heav'n and na-ture sing, and heav'n and na-ture sing, and and heav'n and na-ture sing, and heav'n and na-ture heav'n, and heav'n and na-ture sing! sing,

2. Joy to the earth! The Saviour reigns;
   let us our songs employ;
   while fields and floods, rocks, hills and plains
   repeat the sounding joy,
   repeat the sounding joy,
   repeat, repeat the sounding joy.

3. He rules the world with truth and grace,
   and makes the nations prove
   the glories of his righteousness,
   and wonders of his love,
   and wonders of his love,
   and wonders, wonders of his love.

Words: Isaac Watts, alt.
Music: George Frideric Handel

306 Just as I am, without one plea (Tune 1)

MISERICORDIA 88 86

1. Just as I am, with-out one plea but that thy
blood was shed for me, and that thou bid'st me
come to thee, O Lamb of God, I come.

306a Just as I am, without one plea (Tune 2)

SAFFRON WALDEN 88 86

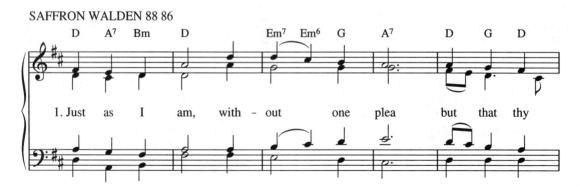

1. Just as I am, with-out one plea but that thy

blood was shed for me, and that thou bid'st me

come to thee, O Lamb of God, I come.

2. Just as I am, though tossed about
   with many a conflict, many a doubt,
   fightings and fears within, without,
   O Lamb of God, I come.

3. Just as I am, poor, wretched, blind;
   sight, riches, healing of the mind,
   yea, all I need, in thee to find,
   O Lamb of God, I come.

4. Just as I am, thou wilt receive,
   wilt welcome, pardon, cleanse, relieve:
   because thy promise I believe,
   O Lamb of God, I come.

5. Just as I am, thy love unknown
   has broken ev'ry barrier down,
   now to be thine, yea, thine alone,
   O Lamb of God, I come.

6. Just as I am, of that free love
   the breadth, length, depth and height to prove,
   here for a season, then above,
   O Lamb of God, I come.

Words: Charlotte Elliott
Music – Tune 1: Henry Smart
Tune2: Arthur Henry Brown

Praise him with the sounding of the trumpet,
praise him with the harp and lyre,
praise him with tambourine and dancing,
praise him with the strings and flute,
praise him with the clash of cymbals,
praise him with resounding cymbals.

Psalm 150:3-5

307 King of kings and Lord of lords

May be sung as a 2-part round, the second voices beginning when the first voices reach ⊕

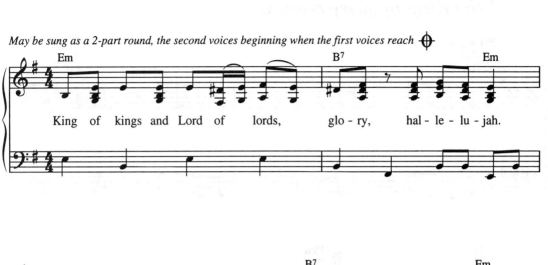

King of kings and Lord of lords, glo - ry, hal - le - lu - jah.

King of kings and Lord of lords, glo - ry, hal - le - lu - jah.

Je - sus, Prince of Peace, glo - ry, hal - le - lu - jah.

optional ending

Je - sus, Prince of Peace, glo - ry, hal - le - lu - jah.

Words and Music: Naomi Batya and Sophie Conty

308 King of kings
(The King of glory comes)

(last time: cheers, shouts of victory, etc.)

SHOUT:

Almighty God, you are the Rock;
all your works are perfect,
and all your ways are just.
You are a faithful God who does no wrong.
Yet we your people,
both church and nation,
are covered with shame
because of our unfaithfulness to you.
We have sinned so seriously against you,
and against one another –
therefore the foundations of our society crumble.
Have mercy, Lord,
forgive us, Lord,
restore us, Lord,
revive your church again;
let justice flow
like rivers,
and righteousness like a never-failing stream.

Words and Music: Graham Kendrick

309 King of kings, majesty

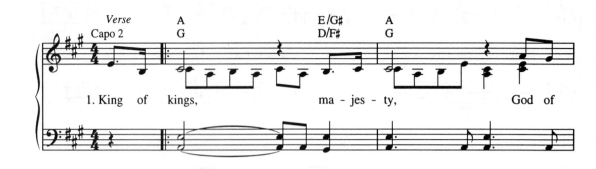

2. Earth and heav'n worship you,
   love eternal, faithful and true,
   who bought the nations, ransomed souls,
   brought this sinner near to your throne;
   all within me cries out in praise.

Words and Music: Jarrod Cooper

310 Lamb of God

Words and Music: Chris Bowater

He said, 'If you listen carefully
to the voice of the Lord your God
and do what is right in his eyes,
if you pay attention to his commands
and keep all his decrees,
I will not bring on you any of the diseases
I brought on the Egyptians,
for I am the Lord, who heals you.'

Exodus 15:26

311 Lead us, heavenly Father, lead us

MANNHEIM 87 87 87

1. Lead us, heav'n-ly Fa-ther, lead us o'er the world's tem-pes-tuous sea; guard us, guide us, keep us, feed us, for we have no help but thee; yet pos-ses-sing ev-'ry bless-ing if our God our Fa-ther be.

2. Saviour, breathe forgiveness o'er us:
all our weakness thou dost know;
thou didst tread this earth before us,
thou didst feel its keenest woe;
lone and dreary, faint and weary,
through the desert thou didst go.

3. Spirit of our God, descending,
fill our hearts with heav'nly joy,
love with ev'ry passion blending,
pleasure that can never cloy:
thus provided, pardoned, guided,
nothing can our peace destroy.

Words: James Edmeston
Music: Friedrich Filitz

312 Led like a lamb
(You're alive)

1. Led like a lamb to the slaugh – ter in si – lence and shame, there on your back you car – ried a world of vio – lence and pain. Bleed-ing, dy – ing, bleed-ing,

Optional antiphonal alleluias: the congregation divides into three parts.

2. At break of dawn, poor Mary,
   still weeping she came,
   when through her grief she heard your voice
   now speaking her name.
   (Men) (Women) (Men) (Women)
   Mary, Master, Mary, Master.

3. At the right hand of the Father
   now seated on high
   you have begun your eternal reign
   of justice and joy.
   Glory, glory, glory, glory.

Words and Music: Graham Kendrick

313 Let it be to me

Let it be to me ac-cord-ing to your word. Let it be to me ac-cord-ing to your word. I am your ser-vant, no rights shall I de-mand. Let it be to me, let it be to me, let it be to me ac-cord-ing to your word.

Words and Music: Graham Kendrick

314 Let it rain

for the fire,   now is the time   to   see

your   pow – er.   Take our prayers   as a - bun -

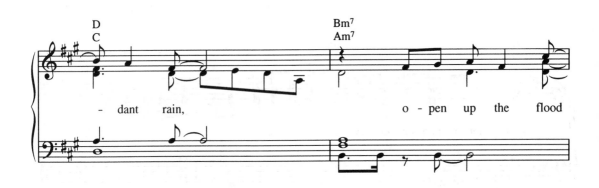

– dant rain,   o – pen up the flood

– gates of hea – ven.   Let the trum - pet   sound

Words and Music: Joel Pott

I will praise you, O Lord, among the nations;
I will sing of you among the peoples.
For great is your love, reaching to the heavens;
your faithfulness reaches to the skies.
Be exalted, O God, above the heavens;
let your glory be over all the earth.

Psalm 57:9-11

315 Let me be a sacrifice

Let me be a sac-ri-fice, ho-ly and ac-cep-ta-ble, let me be a sac-ri-fice, con-sumed in your praise; let me be a sac-ri-fice, ho-ly and ac-cep-ta-ble, let me be a sac-ri-fice, wor-ship-ping your name.

Words and Music: Daniel Gardner

316 Let the righteous sing

Bright and rhythmic

Let the right - eous sing, come, let the right - eous dance, re -
Shout for joy to God who rides up - on the clouds; how

joice be - fore your God, be hap - py and joy - ful.
awe-some are his deeds, so great is his pow - er.

Give him your praise. We give you our praise.

last time to Coda

He gives the de - so - late a

Words and Music: Bryn Haworth

But the fruit of the Spirit is love, joy, peace,
patience, kindness, goodness, faithfulness,
gentleness and self-control.
Against such things there is no law.

Galatians 5:22-23

317 Let there be love

Words and Music: Dave Bilbrough

318 Let your living water flow
(Living water)

With a strong beat

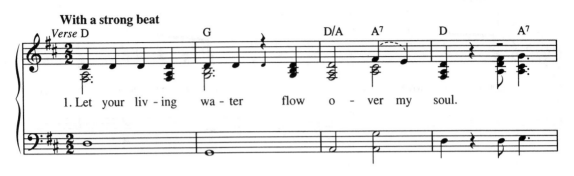

1. Let your liv-ing wa-ter flow o-ver my soul.

Let your Ho-ly Spi-rit come and take con - trol of

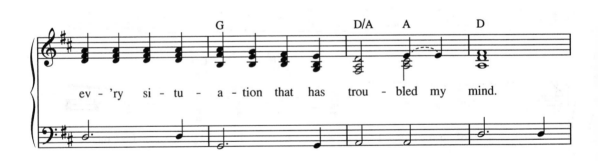

ev-'ry si-tu - a-tion that has trou - bled my mind.

All my cares and bur-dens on to you I roll. roll.

2. Come now, Holy Spirit, and take control.
   Hold me in your loving arms and make me whole.
   Wipe away all doubt and fear and take my pride.
   Draw me to your love and keep me by your side.

3. Give your life to Jesus, let him fill your soul.
   Let him take you in his arms and make you whole.
   As you give your life to him, he'll set you free.
   You will live and reign with him eternally.

4. Let your living water flow over my soul.
   Let your Holy Spirit come and take control
   of ev'ry situation that has troubled my mind.
   All my cares and burdens on to you I roll.

Words and Music: John Watson

319 Let your love come down

2. There is power in your love,
   bringing laughter out of tears.
   It can heal the wounded soul.
   In the streets where anger reigns,
   love will wash away the pain.
   We are calling, heaven's love come down.

Words and Music: Noel and Tricia Richards

320 Let your word go forth

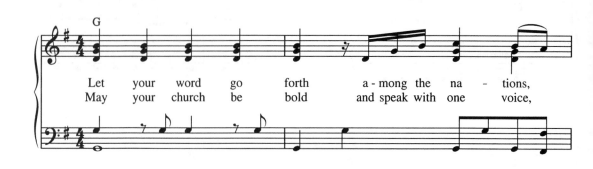

Let your word go forth a-mong the na - tions,
May your church be bold and speak with one voice,

let your voice be heard a-mong the peo - ple. May they know our
may our hearts be strong and ne - ver fail - ing. May we know no

1.
God, the on-ly true God, reigns on earth as you reign in hea - ven.

2.
fear ex-cept a ho - ly fear of you, my King.

This song may be sung in conjunction with 'Not by might'. (No. 376)

Words and Music: Robin Mark

321 Lift up your heads
(O you gates)

2. Up from the dead he ascends,
through ev'ry rank of heav'nly power.
Let heaven prepare the highest place,
throw wide the everlasting doors.

3. With trumpet blast and shouts of joy,
all heaven greets the risen King.
With angel choirs come line the way,
throw wide the gates and welcome him.

Words and Music: Graham Kendrick

322 Like a candle flame
(The candle song)

Softly, with awe

Verse

1. Like a can - dle flame, flick - 'ring small in our dark - ness,
un - cre - a - ted light shines through in - fant eyes.

Chorus

(Women) God is with us, al - le -
(Men) God is with us, al - le - lu - ia,

lu - ia, come to save us, al - le - lu -

Am   Em   F   Am   Em   F   G

come to save us, al - le - lu - ia, al - le - lu -

1, 2.   Dm⁷ G *D.C.* **3.**   *last time*

C   C   *D.S.* C

(All)

ia!   ia!   ia!

2. Stars and angels sing,
   yet the earth
   sleeps in shadows;
   can this tiny spark
   set a world on fire?

3. Yet his light shall shine
   from our lives,
   spirit blazing,
   as we touch the flame
   of his holy fire.

Words and Music: Graham Kendrick

In him the whole building is joined together
and rises to become a holy temple in the Lord.
And in him you too are being built together
to become a dwelling in which God lives by his Spirit.

Ephesians 2:21-22

323 Living under the shadow of his wing

With strength

1. Liv-ing un-der the sha-dow of his wing
we find se-cu-ri-ty.
Stand-ing in his pre-sence we will bring our
wor - ship, wor - ship,
wor - ship to the King.

2. Bowed in adoration at his feet
we dwell in harmony.
Voices joined together that repeat,
worthy, worthy, worthy is the Lamb.

3. Heart to heart embracing in his love
reveals his purity.
Soaring in my spirit like a dove,
holy, holy, holy is the Lord.

Words and Music: David Hadden and Bob Silvester

324 Lo, he comes with clouds descending

HELMSLEY 87 87 47

1. Lo, he comes with clouds des - cend - ing,
once for mor - tal sin - ners slain; thou - sand
thou - sand saints at - tend - ing swell the
tri - umph of his train. Al - le -

lu - ia! Al - le - lu - ia, Al - le -

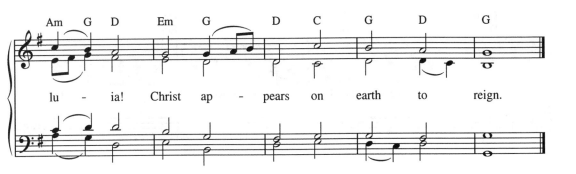

lu - ia! Christ ap - pears on earth to reign.

2. Ev'ry eye shall now behold him
robed in glorious majesty;
we who set at naught and sold him,
pierced and nailed him to the tree,
deeply wailing, deeply wailing, deeply wailing,
shall the true Messiah see.

3. Those dear tokens of his passion
still his dazzling body bears,
cause of endless exultation
to his ransomed worshippers:
with what rapture, with what rapture, with what rapture
gaze we on those glorious scars!

4. Yea, amen, let all adore thee,
high on thine eternal throne;
Saviour, take the pow'r and glory,
claim the kingdom for thine own.
Alleluia! Alleluia! Alleluia!
Thou shalt reign, and thou alone.

Words: Charles Wesley, John Cennick and Martin Madan, alt.
Music: from John Wesley's *Select Hymns with Tunes Annext*.

325 Look what God has done
(And his love goes on and on)

2. Look at all we've shared in him,
   joy and laughter, tears and pain,
   grace to carry on when days were dark
   and all our strength was gone.
   Look at all the prayers he's heard,
   all the times he's proved his word;
   blessing on our homes,
   children that have grown,
   look what God has done.

3. Freely we have all received,
   freely we must also give,
   thinking of the price he paid
   that we might be his very own.
   Born for such a time as this,
   chosen for the harvest years,
   we have just begun,
   the best is yet to come,
   look what God has done.

Words and Music: Graham Kendrick

326 Look what the Lord has done

This song may be sung in conjunction with 'I went to the enemy's camp'. (No. 257)

Words and Music: Mark David Hanby

327 Lord, for the years
(Lord of the years)

LORD OF THE YEARS 11 10 11 10

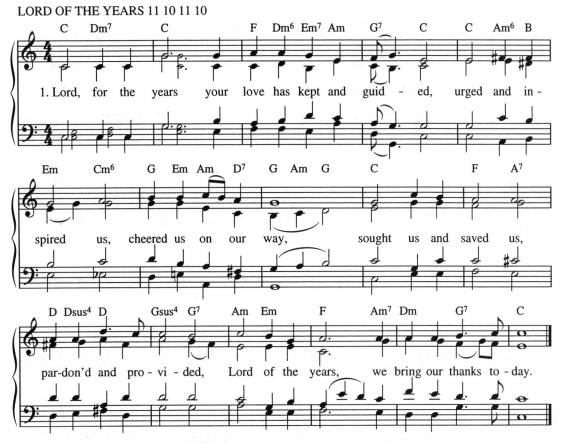

1. Lord, for the years your love has kept and guid-ed, urged and in-spired us, cheered us on our way, sought us and saved us, par-don'd and pro-vi-ded, Lord of the years, we bring our thanks to-day.

2. Lord, for that word, the word of life which fires us,
   speaks to our hearts and sets our souls ablaze,
   teaches and trains, rebukes us and inspires us:
   Lord of the word, receive your people's praise.

3. Lord, for our land, in this our generation,
   spirits oppressed by pleasure, wealth and care;
   for young and old, for commonwealth and nation,
   Lord of our land, be pleased to hear our prayer.

4. Lord, for our world; when we disown and doubt you,
   loveless in strength, and comfortless in pain,
   hungry and helpless, lost indeed without you:
   Lord of the world, we pray that Christ may reign.

5. Lord, for ourselves; in living pow'r remake us —
   self on the cross and Christ upon the throne,
   past put behind us, for the future take us,
   Lord of our lives, to live for Christ alone.

Words: Timothy Dudley-Smith
Music: Michael Baughen arr. David Iliff

328 Lord, have mercy
(Prayer song)

Lord, have mer-cy on us, come and heal our land.

Cleanse with your fire, heal with your touch. Hum - bly we bow and call up-on you now. O Lord, have mer - cy on us. O

329 Lord, I come to you
(Power of your love)

1. Lord, I come to you, let my heart be
2. Lord, un-veil my eyes, let me see you

changed, re-newed, flow-ing from the
face to face, the know-ledge of your

grace that I found in you.
love as you live in me.

And, Lord, I've come to know
Lord, re-new my mind

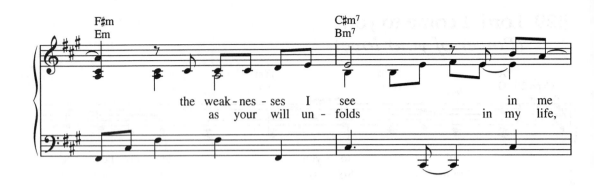

the weak - nes - ses   I   see   in   me
as   your   will   un - folds   in   my   life,

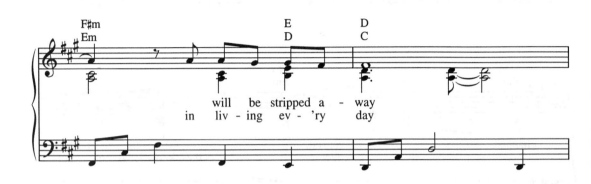

will   be   stripped   a - way
in   liv - ing   ev - 'ry   day

by   the   pow'r   of   your   love.
in   the   pow'r   of   your   love.

Chorus

Hold   me   close,   let   your   love   sur - round

Words and Music: Geoff Bullock

330 Lord, I lift your name on high
(You came from heaven to earth)

Steadily

Lord, I lift your name on high;

Lord, I love to sing your prai - ses.

I'm so glad you're in my life;

I'm so glad you came to save us.

You came from hea - ven to earth to show the way,

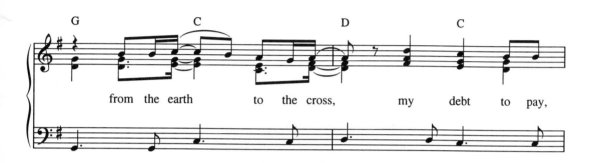

from the earth to the cross, my debt to pay,

from the cross to the grave, from the grave to the sky,

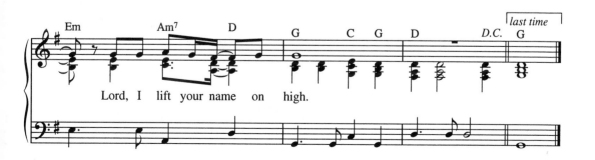

Lord, I lift your name on high.

Words and Music: Rick Founds

Give thanks to the Lord, call on his name;
make known among the nations what he has done,
and proclaim that his name is exalted.
Sing to the Lord, for he has done glorious things;
let this be known to all the world.

Isaiah 12:4-5

331 Lord my heart cries out
(Glory to the King)

Lord, my heart cries out, glo-ry to the King, my great-est love in life. I hand you ev-'ry-thing. Glo-ry, glo-ry, I hear the an-gels sing. O-pen my ears, let me hear your voice to know that sweet sound. O, my soul, re-joice. Glo-ry,

Words and Music: Darlene Zschech

332 Lord of lords

1. Lord of lords, King of kings, ma-ker of hea – ven and earth
2. Lord, you're right-teous in all your ways. We bless your ho – ly name

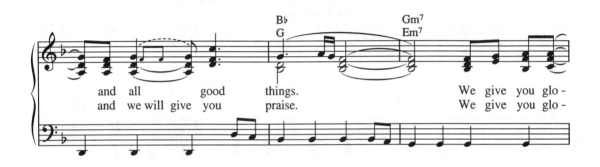

and all good things. We give you glo-
and we will give you praise. We give you glo-

– ry. Lord Je – ho – vah,
– ry. You reign for e – ver in

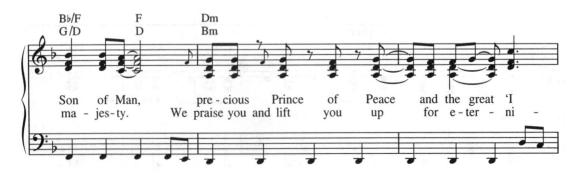

Son of Man, pre – cious Prince of Peace and the great 'I
ma – jes-ty. We praise you and lift you up for e – ter – ni –

Words and Music: Jessy Dixon, Randy Scruggs and John Thompson

333 Lord of the heavens

Lord of the hea - vens and the earth,
my Sa - viour, Re - deem - er, ri - sen Lord,
all hon-our and glo - ry, pow'r and strength
to him up - on the throne.

Ho - ly, ho - ly, you are wor - thy,
Glo - ry, glo - ry, hal - le - lu - jah,

Words and Music: Lucy Fisher

The Lord will surely comfort Zion
and will look with compassion on all her ruins;
he will make her deserts like Eden,
her wastelands like the garden of the Lord.
Joy and gladness will be found in her,
thanksgiving and the sound of singing.

Isaiah 51:3

334 Lord, prepare me
(Sanctuary)

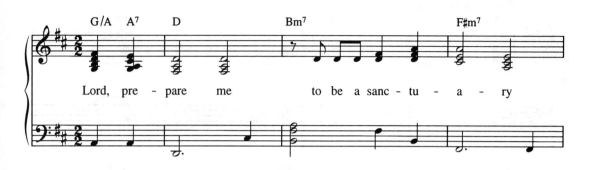

Lord, pre-pare me to be a sanc-tu-a-ry

pure and ho-ly, tried and true,

with thanks-giv-ing. I'll be a liv-ing

sanc-tu-a-ry for you.

335 Lord, the light of your love
(Shine, Jesus, shine)

1. Lord, the light of your love is shin - ing,
in the midst of the dark - ness, shin - ing; Je - sus, Light of the
World, shine up - on us, set us free by the truth you now bring us.
Shine on me, shine on me.

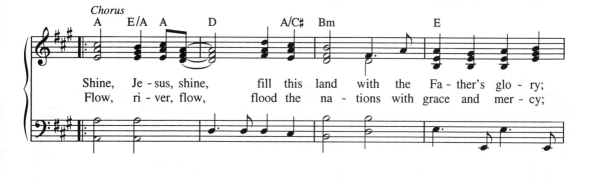

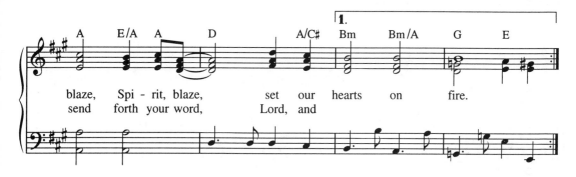

2. Lord, I come to your awesome presence,
   from the shadows into your radiance;
   by the blood I may enter your brightness,
   search me, try me, consume all my darkness.
   Shine on me, shine on me.

3. As we gaze on your kingly brightness,
   so our faces display your likeness,
   ever changing from glory to glory;
   mirrored here may our lives tell your story.
   Shine on me, shine on me.

   (Chorus twice to end)

Words and Music: Graham Kendrick

336 Lord, we lift you high

Words and Music: Judy Bailey

337 Lord, we long for you
(Heal our nation)

Heal our na - tion! Heal our na - tion! Pour out your Spi - rit on this land!

2. Lord, we hear your Spirit coming closer,
   a mighty wave to break upon our land,
   bringing justice and forgiveness.
   God, we cry to you, 'Revive us!'

Words and Music: Trish Morgan, Ray Goudie, Ian Townend and Dave Bankhead

338 Lord, we long to see your glory

Words and Music: Richard Lewis

339 Lord, you are more precious

Words and Music: Lynn DeShazo

340 Lord, you are so precious to me

Lord, you are so gracious to me . . .
Lord, you are a father to me . . .
Lord, you are so faithful to me . . .
Lord, you are so loving to me . . .

Words and Music: Graham Kendrick

© Copyright 1986 Kingsway's Thankyou Music, P.O. Box 75, Eastbourne,
East Sussex, BN23 6NW, UK. Used by permission.

341 Lord, you have my heart

Tenderly

Lord, you have my heart, and I will search for yours;

Je - sus, take my life and lead me on.

Lord, you have my heart, and I will search for yours;

let me be to you a sac - ri - fice.

(Men) And

Words and Music: Martin Smith

342 Lord, you put a tongue in my mouth

With pace

1. Lord, you put a tongue in my mouth and I want to
sing to you.
Lord, you put a tongue in my mouth and I want to
sing to you.
Lord, you put a tongue in my mouth and I want to

sing on - ly to you. Lord Je - sus,

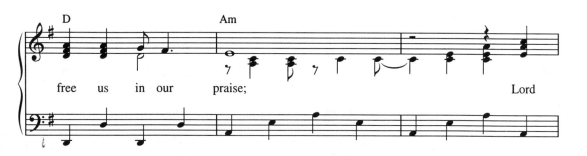

free us in our praise; Lord

Je - sus, free us in our

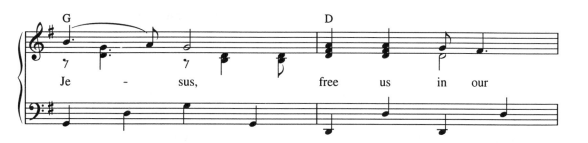

1st and 2nd times   *last time*

praise.

2. Lord, you put some hands on my arms
   which I want to raise to you . . . *etc.*

3. Lord, you put some feet on my legs
   and I want to dance to you . . . *etc.*

Words and Music: Ian Smale

343 Love divine, all loves excelling (Tune 1)

LOVE DIVINE 87 87

1. Love di - vine, all loves ex - cel - ling, joy of heav'n, to earth come down, fix in us thy hum - ble dwell - ing, all thy faith - ful mer - cies crown.

2. Jesu, thou art all compassion,
   pure unbounded love thou art;
   visit us with thy salvation,
   enter ev'ry trembling heart.

3. Breathe, O breathe thy loving Spirit
   into ev'ry troubled breast;
   let us all in thee inherit,
   let us find thy promised rest.

4. Take away the love of sinning,
   Alpha and Omega be;
   end of faith, as its beginning,
   set our hearts at liberty.

5. Come, almighty to deliver,
   let us all thy grace receive;
   suddenly return, and never,
   never more thy temples leave.

6. Thee we would be always blessing,
   serve thee as thy hosts above;
   pray, and praise thee without ceasing,
   glory in thy perfect love.

7. Finish then thy new creation,
   pure and spotless let us be;
   let us see thy great salvation
   perfectly restored in thee.

8. Changed from glory into glory,
   till in heav'n we take our place,
   till we cast our crowns before thee,
   lost in wonder, love, and praise.

343a Love divine, all loves excelling (Tune 2)

BLAENWERN 87 87

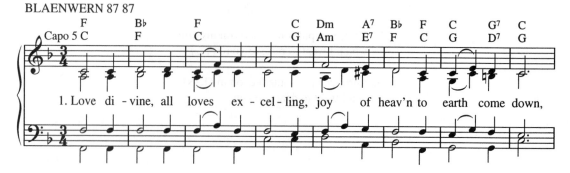

1. Love di - vine, all loves ex - cel - ling, joy of heav'n to earth come down,

fix in us thy hum-ble dwell-ing, all thy faith-ful mer-cies crown.

Je-su, thou art all com-pas-sion, pure un-bound-ed love thou art;

vi-sit us with thy sal-va-tion, en-ter ev-'ry trem-bling heart.

2. Breathe, O breathe thy loving Spirit
   into ev'ry troubled breast;
   let us all in thee inherit,
   let us find thy promised rest.
   Take away the love of sinning,
   Alpha and Omega be;
   end of faith, as its beginning,
   set our hearts at liberty.

3. Come, almighty to deliver,
   let us all thy grace receive;
   suddenly return, and never,
   never more thy temples leave.
   Thee we would be always blessing,
   serve thee as thy hosts above;
   pray, and praise thee without ceasing,
   glory in thy perfect love.

4. Finish then thy new creation,
   pure and spotless let us be;
   let us see thy great salvation
   perfectly restored in thee.
   Changed from glory into glory,
   till in heav'n we take our place,
   till we cast our crowns before thee,
   lost in wonder, love, and praise.

Words: Charles Wesley, alt.
Music – Tune 1: John Stainer
Tune 2: William Penfro Rowlands
Music © Copyright control (revived 1996).

344 Love of Christ, come now

Words and Music: Graham Kendrick

345 Low in the grave he lay

CHRIST AROSE 65 64 and Refrain

lives for e - ver with his saints to reign. He a - rose! He a - rose! Hal - le - lu - jah! Christ a - rose!

2. Vainly they watch his bed,
   Jesus, my Saviour;
   vainly they seal the dead,
   Jesus, my Lord.

3. Death cannot keep its prey,
   Jesus, my Saviour;
   he tore the bars away,
   Jesus, my Lord.

Words and Music: Robert Lowry

346 Majesty

Triumphantly

Ma - jes - ty, wor - ship his ma - jes - ty,

un - to Je - sus be glo - ry, hon - our and praise.

Ma - jes - ty, king-dom au -

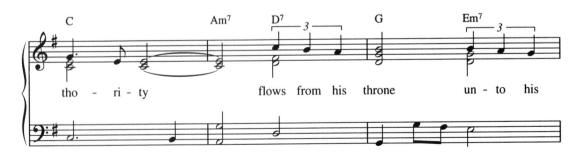

tho - ri - ty flows from his throne un - to his

Words and Music: Jack W. Hayford

347 Make a joyful noise, all ye people
(Worship the Lord)

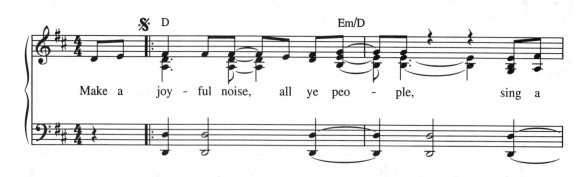

Make a joy-ful noise, all ye peo-ple, sing a

song to the Lord of his good-ness and his mer-

-cy, of his faith-ful-ness and love. Make a

Wor-ship the Lord, let's praise

his ho — ly name. Wor - ship the Lord,

1.

let's mag — ni – fy his name.

2.

— ni – fy his name.

to repeat *to end*

D.S.

Words and Music: Edwin Hawkins

348 Make me a channel of your peace

2. Make me a channel of your peace.
   Where there's despair in life, let me bring hope.
   Where there is darkness, only light,
   and where there's sadness, ever joy.

3. Make me a channel of your peace.
   It is in pardoning that we are pardoned,
   in giving of ourselves that we receive,
   and in dying that we're born to eternal life.

Dedicated to Mrs Frances Tracy

Words and Music: Sebastian Temple, based on the Prayer of St Francis

349 Make way, make way

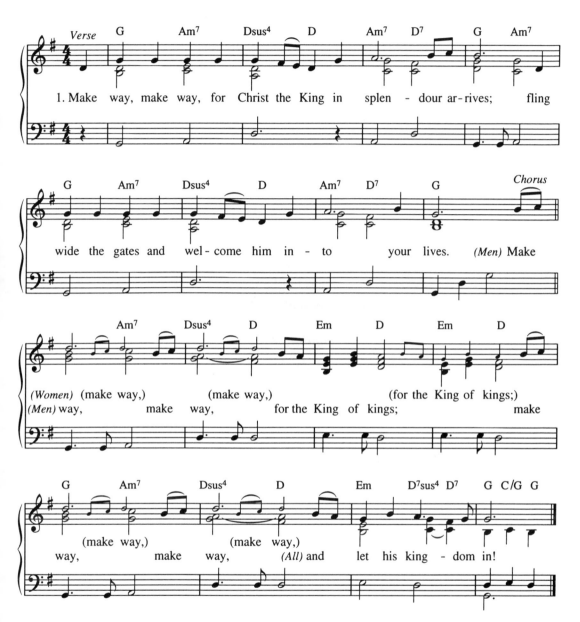

1. Make way, make way, for Christ the King in splen-dour ar-rives; fling wide the gates and wel-come him in-to your lives. *(Men)* Make

(Women) (make way,) (make way,) (for the King of kings;)
(Men) way, make way, for the King of kings; make

(make way,) (make way,)
way, make way, *(All)* and let his king-dom in!

2. He comes the broken hearts to heal,
   the pris'ners to free;
   the deaf shall hear, the lame shall dance,
   the blind shall see.

3. And those who mourn with heavy hearts,
   who weep and sigh,
   with laughter, joy and royal crown
   he'll beautify.

4. We call you now to worship him
   as Lord of all,
   to have no gods before him,
   their thrones must fall.

Words and Music: Graham Kendrick
© Copyright 1986 Kingsway's Thankyou Music, P.O. Box 75, Eastbourne,
East Sussex, BN23 6NW, UK. Used by permission.

He is not here;
he has risen, just as he said.

Matthew 28:6a

350 Man of sorrows

GETHSEMANE 777 8

1. Man of sor-rows! What a name for the Son of God who came
ru-ined sin-ners to re-claim! Al-le-lu-ia! What a Sa-viour!

2. Bearing shame and scoffing rude,
   in my place condemned he stood;
   sealed my pardon with his blood:
   Alleluia! What a Saviour!

3. Guilty, vile and helpless we;
   spotless Lamb of God was he:
   full atonement – can it be?
   Alleluia! What a Saviour!

4. Lifted up was he to die:
   'It is finished!' was his cry;
   now in heav'n exalted high:
   Alleluia! What a Saviour!

5. When he comes, our glorious King,
   all his ransomned home to bring,
   then anew this song we'll sing:
   Alleluia! What a Saviour!

Words and Music: Philipp Bliss, alt.

351 May our worship be as fragrance
(A living sacrifice)

May our wor - ship be as fra - grance, may our

wor - ship be as in - cense poured forth, may our

wor - ship be ac - cep - ta - ble as a liv - ing

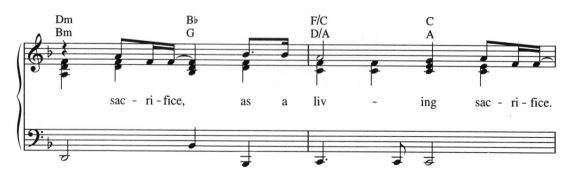

sac - ri - fice, as a liv - ing sac - ri - fice.

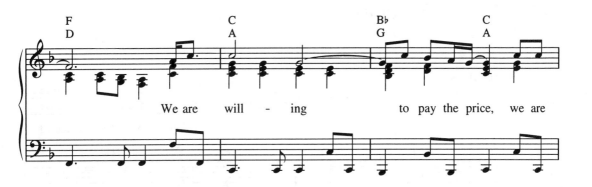

We are will – ing to pay the price, we are

will – ing to lay down our lives as an

off – 'ring of o – be – di – ence, as a liv – ing

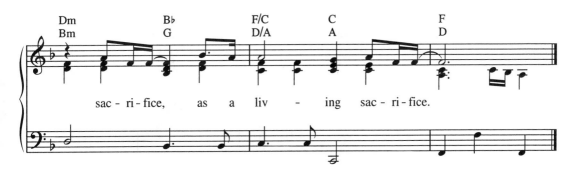

sac – ri – fice, as a liv – ing sac – ri – fice.

Words and Music: Chris Bowater

352 May the fragrance

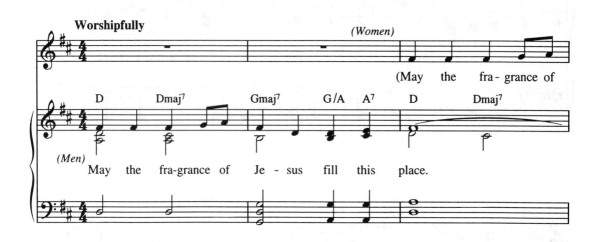

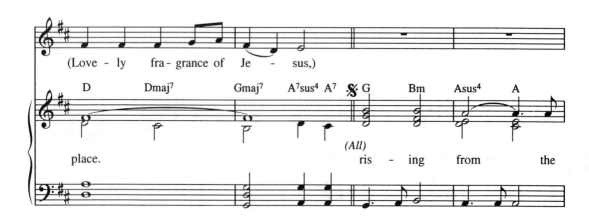

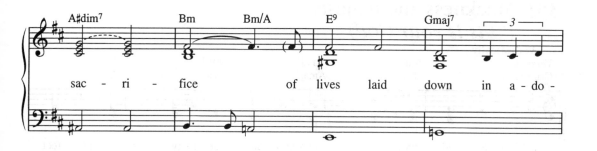

sac - ri - fice   of lives laid down in a - do -

verse 3 D.S. ⌐last time

ra - tion.

2. *(Men)*   May the glory of Jesus fill his church.
   (Women)   May the glory of Jesus fill his church.
   (Men)   May the glory of Jesus fill his church.
   (Women)   Radiant glory of Jesus,
   (All)   shining from our faces
                as we gaze in adoration.

3. *(Men)*   May the beauty of Jesus fill my life.
   (Women)   May the beauty of Jesus fill my life.
   (Men)   May the beauty of Jesus fill my life.
   (Women)   Perfect beauty of Jesus,
   (All)   fill my thoughts, my words, my deeds;
                may I give in adoration.
                Fill my thoughts, my words, my deeds;
                may I give in adoration.

Words and Music: Graham Kendrick

353 Meekness and majesty
(This is your God)

Majestically

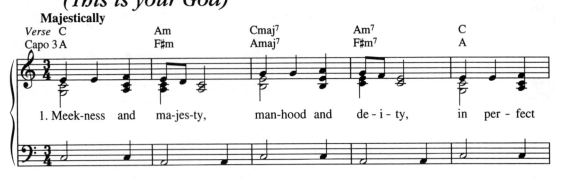

Verse C   Am   Cmaj7   Am7   C
Capo 3 A   F#m   Amaj7   F#m7   A

1. Meek-ness and ma-jes-ty, man-hood and de-i-ty, in per-fect

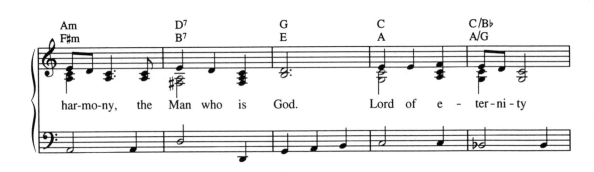

Am   D7   G   C   C/B♭
F#m   B7   E   A   A/G

har-mo-ny, the Man who is God. Lord of e - ter-ni-ty

F   F#dim   Em   Am   F   C/G   G
D   D#dim   C#m   F#m   D   A/E   E

dwells in hu - ma-ni-ty, kneels in hu - mi-li-ty and wash-es our

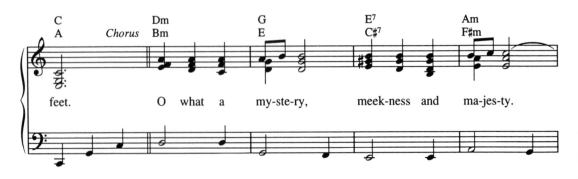

C   Dm   G   E7   Am
A   *Chorus* Bm   E   C#7   F#m

feet. O what a my-ste-ry, meek-ness and ma-jes-ty.

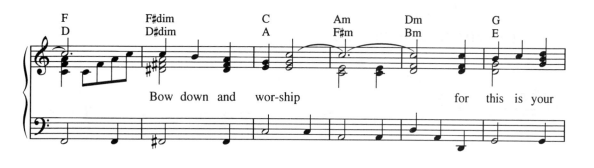

Bow down and wor-ship for this is your

God, this is your God.

1st and 2nd times

last time

God,

this is your God.

2. Father's pure radiance,
   perfect in innocence,
   yet learns obedience
   to death on a cross.
   Suffering to give us life,
   conquering through sacrifice,
   and as they crucify
   prays: 'Father forgive.'

3. Wisdom unsearchable,
   God the invisible,
   love indestructible
   in frailty appears.
   Lord of infinity,
   stooping so tenderly,
   lifts our humanity
   to the heights of his throne.

Words and Music: Graham Kendrick

354 Men of faith
(Shout to the North)

1. Men of faith, rise up and sing of the great and glo-rious King. You are strong when you feel weak, in your bro-ken-ness com-plete.

Chorus
Shout to the north and the south, sing to the east and the west. Je-sus is Sa-viour to all, Lord of hea-ven and earth.

last time to Coda

1st and 3rd times
2. Rise up,
3. Rise up,

2nd time

We've been through fire, we've been through rain,
we've been re-fined by the pow'r of his name. We've fall-en deep-er
in love with you, you've burned the truth on our lips.
earth, Lord of hea-ven and earth,
Lord of hea-ven and earth, Lord of hea-ven and earth.

2. Rise up, women of the truth,
   stand and sing to broken hearts.
   Who can know the healing pow'r
   of our awesome King of love?

3. Rise up, church with broken wings,
   fill this place with songs again
   of our God who reigns on high,
   by his grace again we'll fly.

Words and Music: Martin Smith

Who is a God like you,
who pardons sin
and forgives the transgression
of the remnant of his inheritance?
You do not stay angry for ever
but delight to show mercy.

Micah 7:18

355 Mercy is falling

Mer-cy is fall - ing, is fall - ing, is fall - ing, mer-cy it falls like the sweet spring rain. Mer-cy is fall - ing, is fall - ing all o - ver me. Hey O, I re - ceive your mer - cy. Hey O, I re - ceive your grace. Hey O, I will dance for e - ver - more.

Words and Music: David Ruis

356 Mighty God

2. A light to those in darkness,
   and a guide to paths of peace;
   love and mercy dawns,
   grace, forgiveness and salvation.
   Light for revelation,
   glory to your people;
   Son of the Most High,
   God's love-gift to all.

Words and Music: Mark Johnson, Helen Johnson and Chris Bowater

357 Mighty is our God

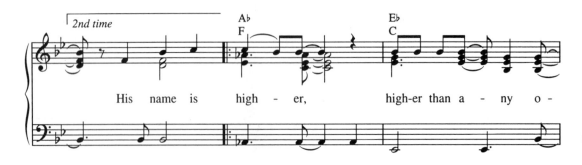

Words and Music: Eugene Greco, Gerrit Gustafson and Don Moen

358 More about Jesus

MORE ABOUT JESUS LM and Refrain

1. More a-bout Je - sus would I know, more of his grace to
o - thers show; more of his sav - ing full - ness see,
more of his love who died for me.

Chorus
More, more a-bout Je - sus, more, more a-bout Je - sus;
More, more a-bout Je - sus, more, more a - bout Je - sus;

more of his sav - ing full - ness see, more of his love who died for me.

2. More about Jesus let me learn,
   more of his holy will discern;
   Spirit of God my teacher be,
   showing the things of Christ to me.

3. More about Jesus; in his word,
   holding communion with my Lord;
   hearing his voice in ev'ry line,
   making each faithful saying mine.

4. More about Jesus; on his throne,
   riches in glory all his own;
   more of his kingdom's sure increase;
   more of his coming, Prince of Peace.

Words: E.E. Hewitt
Music: J.R. Sweney

359 More love, more power

Words and Music: Jude del Hierro

360 More of your glory

Words and Music: Lindell Cooley and Bruce Haynes

361 More than oxygen

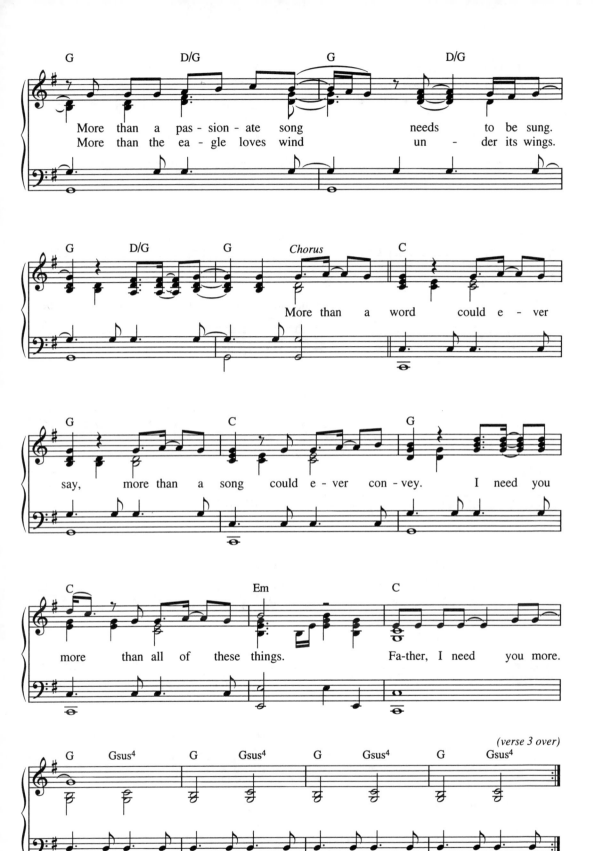

More than a word could e - ver say, more than a

song could e - ver con - vey. I need you more than all of these

things. Fa-ther, I need you more.

Words and Music: Brian Doerksen

362 My first love
(Like a child)

As a jig

1. My first love is a blaz-ing fire, I feel his pow'r-ful love in me; for he has kin-dled a flame of pas-sion, and I will let it grow in me. And in the night I will sing your praise, my love.

And in the morn-ing I'll seek your face, my love.

Chorus

And like a child I will dance in your pre-sence.

2. My first love is a rushing river,
   a waterfall that will never cease;
   and in the torrent of tears and laughter,
   I feel a healing power released.
   And I will draw from your well of life, my love.
   And in your grace I'll be satisfied, my love.

3. Restore the years of the church's slumber,
   revive the fire that has grown so dim;
   renew the love of those first encounters,
   that we may come alive again.
   And we will rise like the dawn throughout the earth,
   until the trumpet announces your return.

Words and Music: Stuart Townend

363 My heart is full
(All the glory)

1. My heart is full of ad-mi-ra-tion for you, my Lord, my God and King. Your ex-cel-lence, my in-spi-ra-tion, your words of grace have made my spi-rit sing.

All the glo-ry, hon-our and

pow'r be - long to you, be - long to you.

Je - sus, Sa - viour, a - noint - ed

One, I wor - ship you, I wor - ship you.

2. *(Men)*   You love what's right and hate what's evil,
            therefore your God sets you on high,
(Women) and on your head pours oil of gladness,
            while fragrance fills your royal palaces.

3. *(All)*   Your throne, O God, will last for ever,
            justice will be your royal decree.
            In majesty, ride out victorious,
            for righteousness, truth and humility.

Words and Music: Graham Kendrick

364 My heart will sing to you
(Great love)

1. My heart will sing to you be - cause of your great love, a love so rich, so pure, a love be-yond com - pare; the wil - der - ness, the bar-ren place, be-come a bless-ing in the warmth of your em - brace. 2. When earth-ly face. May my

2. When earthly wisdom dims the light of knowing you,
   or if my search for understanding clouds your way,
   to you I fly, my hiding-place,
   where revelation is beholding face to face.

Words and Music: Robin Mark

365 My hope is built (Tune 1)
(The solid Rock)

1. My hope is built on no-thing less than Je-sus' blood and right-eous-ness. I dare not trust the sweet-est frame, but whol-ly lean on Je-sus' name. On Christ the so-lid Rock I stand; all o-ther ground is sink-ing sand, all o-ther ground is sink-ing sand.

365a My hope is built (Tune 2)
(The solid Rock)

1. My hope is built on no-thing less than Je-sus' blood and right-eous-

2. When darkness veils his lovely face,
   I rest on his unchanging grace;
   in ev'ry high and stormy gale
   my anchor holds within the veil.

3. His oath, his covenant, his blood
   support me in the 'whelming flood;
   when all around my soul gives way,
   he then is all my hope and stay.

4. When he shall come with trumpet sound,
   O may I then in him be found;
   dressed in his righteousness alone,
   faultless to stand before the throne.

Words: Edward Mote
Music – Tune 1: W.B. Bradbury
Tune 2: Traditional

366 My Jesus, I love thee

1. My Je - sus, I love thee, I know thou art mine. For thee all the fol - lies of sin I re - sign. My gra - cious Re - deem - er, my Sa - viour art

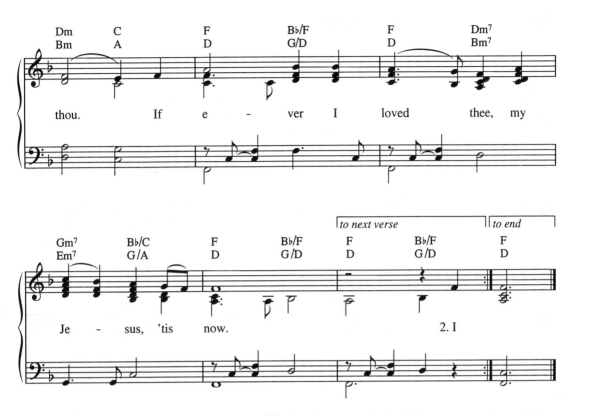

2. I love thee because thou has first lovèd me,
   and purchased my pardon on Calvary's tree.
   I love thee for wearing the thorns on thy brow.
   If ever I loved thee, my Jesus, 'tis now.

3. In mansions of glory and endless delight,
   I'll ever adore thee in heaven so bright.
   I'll sing with a glittering crown on my brow.
   If ever I loved thee, my Jesus, 'tis now.

Words and Music: William R. Featherston and Adoniram J. Gordon

367 My Jesus, my Saviour
(Shout to the Lord)

let us sing
of your hands.
For
pow - er and ma - jes - ty, praise
e - ver I'll love you, for e -
to the King.

to the King.
- ver I'll stand.
Moun-tains bow down and the seas
No - thing com - pares to the pro -

1.
will roar at the sound of your name.

2.
- mise I have in you.

Words and Music: Darlene Zschech

368 My life is in you, Lord

My life is in you, Lord, my strength is in you, Lord, my

hope is in you, Lord, in you, it's in you. My

life is in you, Lord, my strength is in you, Lord, my

last time to Coda

hope is in you, Lord, in you, it's in you. I will

Words and Music: Daniel Gardner

369 My lips shall praise you
(Restorer of my soul)

With energy

Chorus

My lips shall praise you, my great Re - deem - er; my heart will wor - ship, Al - might - y Sa - viour. Sa - viour.

1. You take all my guilt a - way, turn the dark - est

night   to   bright - est   day;   you   are   the   re -

sto - rer   of   my   soul.

2. Love that conquers ev'ry fear,
   in the midst of trouble you draw near;
   you are the restorer of my soul.

3. You're the source of happiness,
   bringing peace when I am in distress;
   you are the restorer of my soul.

Words and Music: Noel and Tricia Richards

370 My Lord, what love is this
(Amazing love)

With strength

1. My Lord, what love is this, that pays so dear-ly, that I, the guil-ty one, may go free!

A-maz-ing love, O what sac-ri-fice, the

2. And so they watched him die,
   despised, rejected;
   but O, the blood he shed
   flowed for me!

3. And now this love of Christ
   shall flow like rivers;
   come, wash your guilt away,
   live again!

Words and Music: Graham Kendrick

371 My Spirit rests in you
(Shadow of your wings)

1. My spi - rit rests in you a - lone, you're all I know.

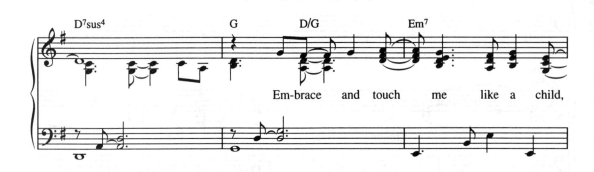

Em-brace and touch me like a child,

Chorus

I'm safe in you. You're my shel - ter through it all,

you're my ref - uge and my strength. Lord, I hide

2. My Lord, you're faithful,
you supply all good things,
you know completely
all my thoughts,
my deepest needs.

Words and Music: Reuben Morgan

372 Nearer, my God, to thee

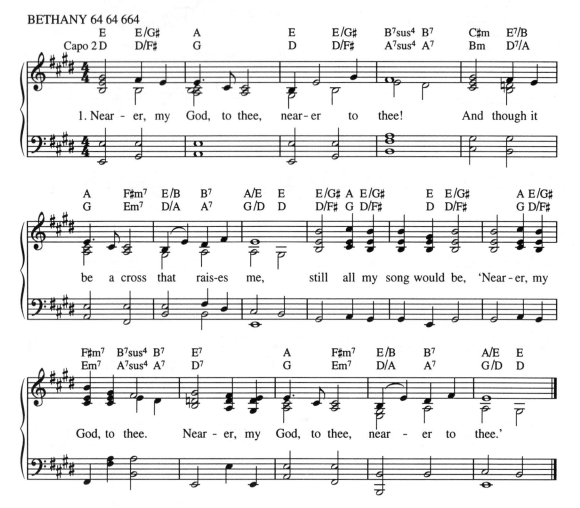

BETHANY 64 64 664

1. Near - er, my God, to thee, near-er to thee! And though it
be a cross that rais-es me, still all my song would be, 'Near - er, my
God, to thee. Near - er, my God, to thee, near - er to thee.'

2. Though, like the wanderer,
   the sun gone down,
   darkness be over me,
   my rest a stone;
   yet in my dreams I'd be
   nearer, my God, to thee.
   Nearer, my God, to thee,
   nearer to thee!

3. There let the way appear,
   steps unto heav'n;
   all that thou sendest me
   in mercy giv'n:
   angels to beckon me
   nearer, my God to thee.
   Nearer, my God, to thee,
   nearer to thee!

4. Then, with my waking thoughts
   bright with thy praise,
   out of my stony griefs
   Bethel I'll raise;
   so by my woes to be
   nearer, my God, to thee.
   Nearer, my God, to thee,
   nearer to thee!

5. Or if on joyful wing
   cleaving the sky,
   sun, moon and stars forgot,
   upwards I fly,
   still all my song shall be,
   'Nearer, my God, to thee.
   Nearer, my God, to thee,
   nearer to thee.'

Words: Sarah Flower Adams
Music: Lowell Mason

373 No one but you, Lord
(Only you)

Slowly, with strength

2. Father, I love you,
   come satisfy the longing in my heart.
   Fill me, overwhelm me,
   until I know your love deep in my heart.

Words and Music: Andy Park

374 No other name

No o-ther name but the name of Je-sus, no o-ther
name but the name of the Lord; no o-ther
name but the name of Je - sus is wor - thy of glo-ry, and
wor - thy of hon-our, and wor - thy of pow-er and all

last time to Coda

Words and Music: Robert Gay

375 No scenes of stately majesty

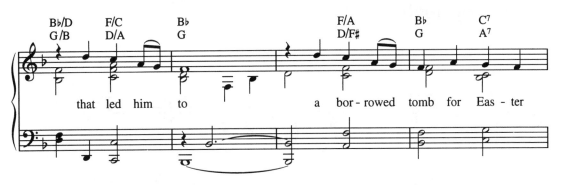

that led him to a bor-rowed tomb for Eas-ter

day.

2. No wreaths upon the ground were laid
   for the King of kings.
   only a crown of thorns remained
   where he gave his love.
   A message scrawled in irony –
   King of the Jews –
   lay trampled where they turned away,
   and no-one knew
   that it was the first Easter Day.

3. Yet nature's finest colours blaze
   for the King of kings.
   And stars in jewelled clusters say,
   'Worship heaven's King.'
   Two thousand springtimes more have bloomed –
   is that enough?
   Oh, how can I be satisfied
   until he hears
   the whole world sing of Easter love.

4. My prayers shall be a fragrance sweet
   for the King of kings.
   My love the flowers at his feet
   for the King of love.
   My vigil is to watch and pray
   until he comes.
   My highest tribute to obey
   and live to know
   the power of that first Easter Day.

5. I long for scenes of majesty
   for the risen King.
   or nights aglow with candle flame
   for the King of love.
   A nation hushed upon its knees
   at Calvary,
   where all our sins and griefs were nailed
   and hope was born
   of everlasting Easter Day.

Words and Music: Graham Kendrick

376 Not by might

No, not by might, nor e - ven

pow'r, but by your Spi - rit, O

Lord. Heal - er of

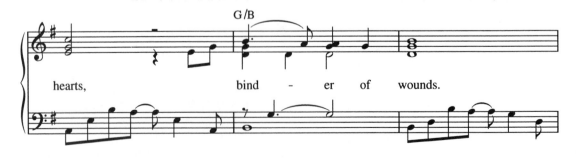

hearts, bind - er of wounds.

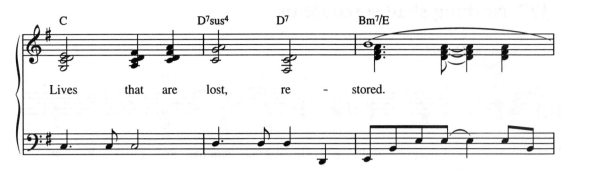

Lives that are lost, re - stored.

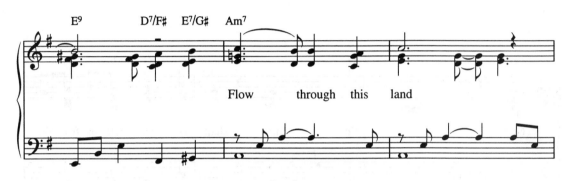

Flow through this land

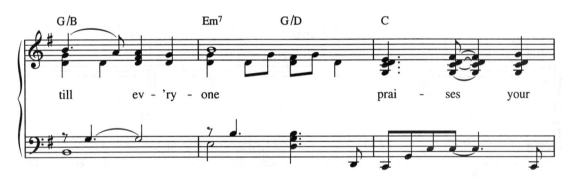

till ev - 'ry - one prai - ses your

name once more.

Words and Music: Robin Mark

377 Nothing shall separate us

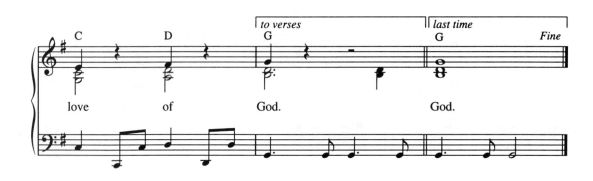

him to save us all. Sin's price was met

by Je - sus' death and hea - ven's mer - cy falls.

2. Up from the grave Jesus was raised
   to sit at God's right hand;
   pleading our cause in heaven's courts,
   forgiven we can stand.

3. Now by God's grace we have embraced
   a life set free from sin;
   we shall deny all that destroys
   our union with him.

Words and Music: Noel and Tricia Richards

378 Now unto the King
(Unto the King)

Now un-to the King e-ter - nal, un-to the King im-mor - tal, un-to the King in-vi - si-ble, the on - ly wise God, the on - ly wise God.

1. Now God.
2. Now God.

Un-to the King be glo-ry and hon - our, un-to the King for

Words and Music: Joey Holder

379 O Breath of Life

SPIRITUS VITAE 98 98

2. O Breath of Love, come breathe within us,
   renewing thought and will and heart;
   come, love of Christ, afresh to win us,
   revive your church in ev'ry part!

3. O Wind of God, come bend us, break us,
   till humbly we confess our need;
   then, in your tenderness remake us,
   revive, restore – for this we plead.

4. Revive us, Lord; is zeal abating
   while harvest fields are vast and white?
   Revive us, Lord, the world is waiting –
   equip thy church to spread the light.

Words: Elizabeth Ann Porter Head
Music: Mary Jane Hammond
© Copyright control.

380 O come, all ye faithful

ADESTE FIDELES Irregular and Refrain

1. O come, all ye faith-ful, joy-ful and tri-um-phant, O come ye, O come ye to Beth-le-hem; come and be-hold him, born the king of an-gels:

O come, let us a-dore him, O come, let us a-dore him, O come, let us a-dore him, Christ the Lord.

2. God of God,
   Light of Light,
   lo, he abhors not the Virgin's womb;
   very God, begotten not created:

3. See how the shepherds,
   summoned to his cradle,
   leaving their flocks, draw nigh with lowly fear;
   we too will thither bend our joyful footsteps:

4. Lo, star-led chieftains,
   Magi, Christ adoring,
   offer him incense, gold and myrrh;
   we to the Christ-child bring our hearts' oblations:

5. Sing, choirs of angels,
   sing in exultation,
   sing, all ye citizens of heav'n above;
   glory to God in the highest:

6. Yea, Lord, we greet thee,
   born this happy morning,
   Jesu, to thee be glory giv'n;
   Word of the Father, now in flesh appearing:

Words: possibly by John Francis Wade trans. Frederick Oakeley and others
Music: possibly by John Francis Wade

381 O come and join the dance

Words and Music: Graham Kendrick

382 O Father of the fatherless
(Father me)

1. O Father of the fatherless, in whom all fa-mi-lies are blessed, I love the way you father me.

You gave me life, for-gave the past, now in your arms I'm safe at last; I love the way you father me.

Father me,

2. When bruised and broken I draw near,
   you hold me close and dry my tears;
   I love the way you father me.
   At last my fearful heart is still,
   surrendered to your perfect will;
   I love the way you father me.

3. If in my foolishness I stray,
   returning empty and ashamed,
   I love the way you father me.
   Exchanging for my wretchedness
   your radiant robes of righteousness,
   I love the way you father me.

4. And when I look into your eyes,
   from deep within my spirit cries,
   I love the way you father me.
   Before such love I stand amazed
   and ever will through endless days;
   I love the way you father me.

Words and Music: Graham Kendrick

383 O for a thousand tongues to sing

LYNGHAM 86 86 extended

1. O for a thou - sand tongues to sing my dear Re-deem-er's praise, my dear Re - deem - er's praise, the glo - ries of my God and King, the the tri - umphs of his grace, the tri - umphs of his tri - umphs of his grace, the tri - umphs of his grace, the

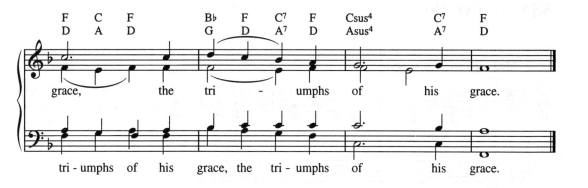

F	C	F		Bb	F	C⁷	F	Csus⁴		C⁷		F
D	A	D		G	D	A⁷	D	Asus⁴		A⁷		D

grace,   the   tri - umphs   of   his   grace.

tri - umphs   of   his   grace, the   tri - umphs   of   his   grace.

2. Jesus! the name that charms our fears,
   that bids our sorrows cease,
   that bids our sorrows cease;
   'tis music in the sinner's ears,
   'tis life and health and peace. *(3)*

3. He breaks the pow'r of cancelled sin,
   he sets the pris'ner free,
   he sets the pris'ner free;
   his blood can make the foulest clean;
   his blood availed for me. *(3)*

4. He speaks; and list'ning to his voice,
   new life the dead receive,
   new life the dead receive,
   the mournful broken hearts rejoice,
   the humble poor believe. *(3)*

5. Hear him, ye deaf; his praise, ye dumb,
   your loosened tongues employ,
   your loosened tongues employ;
   ye blind, behold your Saviour come;
   and leap, ye lame, for joy! *(3)*

6. My gracious Master and my God,
   assist me to proclaim,
   assist me to proclaim
   and spread through all the earth abroad
   the honours of thy name. *(3)*

Words: Charles Wesley
Music: Thomas Jarman

384 O give thanks

Medium fast, reggae style

O give thanks to the Lord, for his love will ne-ver end. O give thanks to the Lord, for his love it ne-ver will end.

(Leader) (Ev-'ry-bo-dy sing).

(All) O give thanks to the Lord, for his love will ne-

2. Give him thanks for the fruitful earth,
   for the sun, the seasons, the rain.
   For the joys of his good creation,
   the life and breath he sustains.

3. Let the heavens rejoice before him,
   the earth and all it contains.
   All creation in jubilation,
   join in the shout, 'The Lord reigns!'

4. Let the hearts of those who seek him
   be happy now in his love.
   Let their faces look up and gaze
   at his gracious smile from above.

Words and Music: Graham Kendrick

385 O God, Most High
(You have broken the chains)

1. O God, Most High, Almighty King, the champion of heaven, Lord of ev'ry-thing; you've fought, you've won, death's lost its sting, and standing in your victory we sing.

pow'r of hell has been un-done, the captivity held captive by the risen One, and in the name of God's great Son, we claim the mighty victory you've won.

Chorus
You have broken the chains that held our captive souls.
You have broken the chains and used them on

Words and Music: Jamie Owens-Collins

386 O God of burning, cleansing flame
(Send the fire)

1. O God of burn-ing, cleans-ing flame: send the fi-re! Your blood-bought gift to-day we claim: send the fire to-day! Look down and see this wait-ing host, and send the pro-mised Ho-ly Ghost; we need a-no-ther Pen-te-cost! Send the fire to-

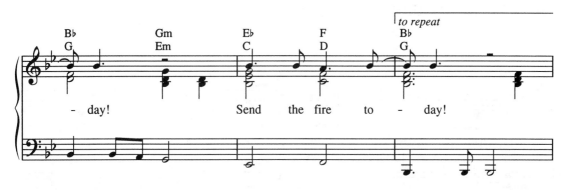

day!   Send   the   fire   to - day!

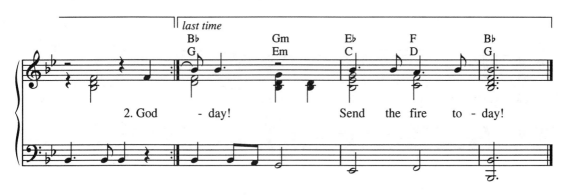

2. God - day!   Send   the   fire   to - day!

2. God of Elijah, hear our cry: send the fire!
    and make us fit to live or die: send the fire today!
    To burn up ev'ry trace of sin,
    to bring the light and glory in,
    the revolution now begin!
    Send the fire today! Send the fire today!

3. It's fire we want, for fire we plead: send the fire!
    The fire will meet our ev'ry need: send the fire today!
    For strength to always do what's right,
    for grace to conquer in the fight,
    for pow'r to walk the world in white.
    Send the fire today! Send the fire today!

4. To make our weak heart strong and brave: send the fire!
    To live, a dying world to save: send the fire today!
    O, see us on your altar lay,
    we give our lives to you today,
    so crown the off'ring now we pray:
    Send the fire today! Send the fire today! Send the fire today!

Words: William Booth
Music: Lex Loizides

387 O happy day

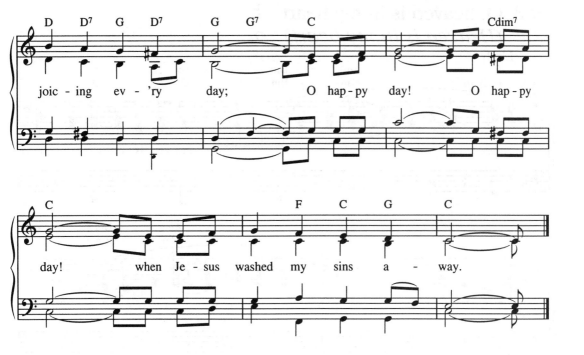

joic - ing ev - 'ry day;   O hap-py day!   O hap-py

day!   when Je - sus washed my sins a - way.

2. 'Tis done, the work of grace is done!
   I am the Lord's, and he is mine!
   He drew me, and I followed on,
   glad to confess the voice divine.

3. Now rest, my long-divided heart,
   fixed on this blissful centre, rest;
   nor ever from thy Lord depart,
   with him of ev'ry good possessed.

4. High heav'n, that heard the solemn vow,
   that vow renewed shall daily hear;
   till in life's latest hour I bow,
   and bless in death a bond so dear.

Words: Philip Doddridge, alt.
Music: Ron Jones

388 O, heaven is in my heart
(Heaven is in my heart)

O, heaven is in my heart.

O, heaven is in my heart.

(Leader) 1. The kingdom of our God is here, *(All)* heaven is in my heart.

(Leader) The pres-ence of his ma - jes-ty,

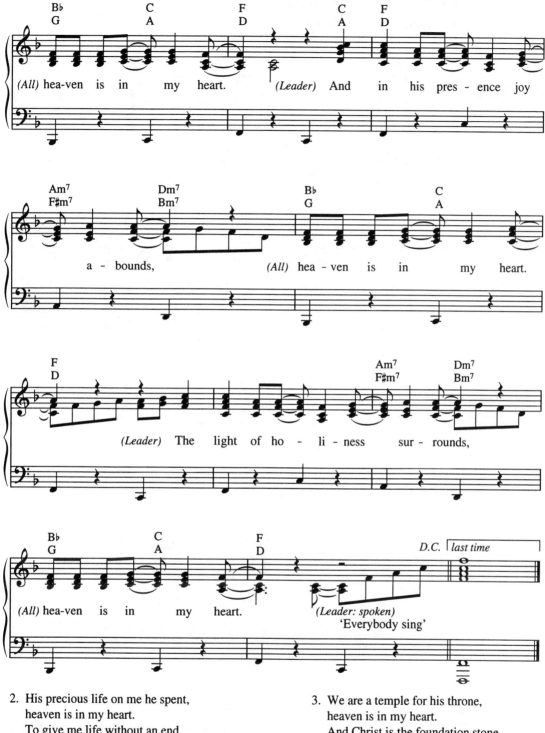

2. His precious life on me he spent,
heaven is in my heart.
To give me life without an end,
heaven is in my heart.
In Christ is all my confidence,
heaven is in my heart.
The hope of my inheritance,
heaven is in my heart.

3. We are a temple for his throne,
heaven is in my heart.
And Christ is the foundation stone,
heaven is in my heart.
He will return to take us home,
heaven is in my heart.
The Spirit and the Bride say, 'Come!',
heaven is in my heart.

Words and Music: Graham Kendrick

389 Oh, I was made for this
(I was made for this)

2. My feet were made to dance,
   my spirit made to soar;
   my life is not by chance,
   you give me more and more.
   For I was made for you,
   and I have made my choice,
   and all that stole my joy,
   I left it at the cross.

3. When I was far away,
   you ran to welcome me;
   I felt your warm embrace,
   I saw your smiling face.
   And when you rescued me,
   I saw my destiny:
   to worship you, my Lord,
   to be a friend of God.

Words and Music: Graham Kendrick

390 Oh, lead me

Oh, lead me to the place where I can

find you, oh, lead me

to the place where you'll be.

Lead me to the cross where we first met,

draw me to my knees so we can talk;

let me feel your breath, let me know you're

here with me. (Oh,)

Words and Music: Martin Smith

391 O Jesus, I have promised

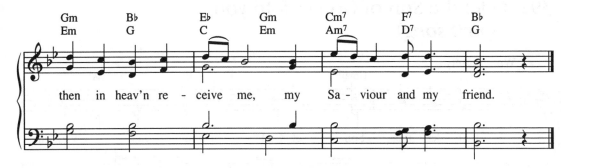

then in heav'n re - ceive me, my Sa - viour and my friend.

2. O let me feel thee near me:
the world is ever near;
I see the sights that dazzle,
the tempting sounds I hear;
my foes are ever near me,
around me and within;
but, Jesus, draw thou nearer,
and shield my soul from sin.

3. O let me hear thee speaking
in accents clear and still,
above the storms of passion,
the murmurs of self-will;
O speak to reassure me,
to hasten or control;
O speak and make me listen,
thou guardian of my soul.

4. O Jesus, thou hast promised
to all that follow thee,
that where thou art in glory
there shall thy servants be;
and, Jesus, I have promised
to serve thee to the end:
O give me grace to follow,
my Master and my friend.

5. O let me see thy footmarks,
and in them plant my own;
my hope to follow duly
is in thy strength alone:
O guide me, call me, draw me,
uphold me to the end;
and then in heav'n receive me,
my Saviour and my friend,
and then in heav'n receive me,
my Saviour and my friend.

Words: John Ernest Bode
Music: Geoffrey Beaumont, arr. Norman Warren

392 O let the Son of God enfold you
(Spirit song)

Worshipfully

1. O let the Son of God en-fold you with his Spi-rit and his love, let him fill your heart and sa-tis-fy your soul. O let him have the things that hold you, and his Spi-rit like a dove will des-cend up-on your life and make you whole. Je-

2. O come and sing this song with gladness
   as your hearts are filled with joy,
   lift your hands in sweet surrender to his name.
   O give him all your tears and sadness,
   give him all your years of pain,
   and you'll enter into life in Jesus' name.

Words and Music: John Wimber

393 O little town of Bethlehem

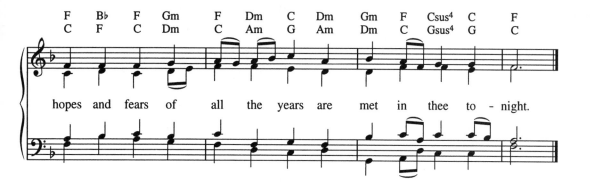

hopes and fears of all the years are met in thee to - night.

2. O morning stars, together
   proclaim the holy birth,
   and praises sing to God the King,
   and peace upon the earth.
   For Christ is born of Mary;
   and, gathered all above,
   while mortals sleep, the angels keep
   their watch of wond'ring love.

3. How silently, how silently,
   the wondrous gift is giv'n!
   So God imparts to human hearts
   the blessings of his heav'n.
   No ear may hear his coming;
   but in this world of sin,
   where meek souls will receive him, still
   the dear Christ enters in.

4. O holy child of Bethlehem,
   descend to us, we pray;
   cast out our sin, and enter in,
   be born in us today.
   We hear the Christmas angels
   the great glad tidings tell:
   O come to us, abide with us,
   our Lord Emmanuel.

Words: Phillips Brooks, alt.
Music: traditional English melody collected and arr. Ralph Vaughan Williams

To him who loves us
and has freed us from our sins by his blood,
and has made us to be a kingdom and priests
to serve his God and Father –
to him be glory and power for ever and ever!
Amen.

Revelation 1:5b-6

394 O Lord, hear my prayer

Words: from Scripture
Music: Jacques Berthier

© Copyright Ateliers et Presses de Taizé, Taizé-Communauté, F-71250,
France. Used by permission. This song is NOT covered by a CCl Licence. Permission
should be obtained from Calamus, 30 North Terrace, Mildenhall, Suffolk IP28 7AB.

395 O Lord, how majestic is your name
(How majestic)

Words and Music: Ben Lindquist and Don Moen

396 O Lord, my God
(How great thou art)

HOW GREAT THOU ART 11 10 11 10 and Refrain

1. O Lord, my God, when I, in awe-some won - der, con - si - der all the works thy hand has made, I see the stars, I hear the roll-ing thun - der, thy pow'r through - out the u - ni - verse dis - played.

Chorus Then sings my soul, my Sa-viour God, to thee: how great thou

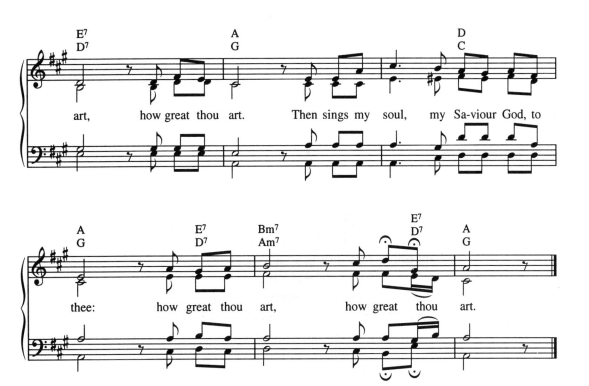

art,   how great thou art.   Then sings my soul,   my Sa-viour God, to

thee: how great thou art,   how great thou art.

2. When through the woods and forest glades I wander,
   and hear the birds sing sweetly in the trees;
   when I look down from lofty mountain grandeur,
   and hear the brook, and feel the gentle breeze.

3. And when I think that God, his Son not sparing,
   sent him to die, I scarce can take it in
   that on the cross, my burden gladly bearing,
   he bled and died to take away my sin.

4. When Christ shall come with shout of acclamation,
   and take me home, what joy shall fill my heart;
   then I shall bow in humble adoration,
   and there proclaim: my God, how great thou art.

Words: Stuart K. Hine
Music: Swedish folk melody arr. Stuart K. Hine

If I speak in the tongues of men and of angels,
but have not love,
I am only a resounding gong or a clanging cymbal.
If I have the gift of prophecy
and can fathom all mysteries and all knowledge,
and if I have a faith that can move mountains,
but have not love,
I am nothing.
If I give all I possess to the poor
and surrender my body to the flames,
but have not love,
I gain nothing.
Love is patient, love is kind.
It does not envy, it does not boast, it is not proud.
It is not rude, it is not self-seeking,
it is not easily angered, it keeps no record of wrongs.
Love does not delight in evil
but rejoices with the truth.
It always protects, always trusts,
always hopes, always perseveres.

1 Corinthians 13:1-7

397 O Lord, my heart is not proud

Words: Psalm 131
Music: Margaret Rizza

398 O Lord our God
(We will magnify)

1. O Lord our God, how ma-jes-tic is your name; the earth is filled with your glo-ry. O Lord our God, you are robed in ma-jes-ty; you've set your glo-ry a-bove the hea -

2. O Lord our God, you have established a throne,
   you reign in righteousness and splendour.
   O Lord our God, the skies are ringing with your praise;
   soon those on earth will come to worship.

3. O Lord our God, the world was made at your command,
   in you all things now hold together.
   Now to him who sits on the throne and to the Lamb
   be praise and glory and pow'r for ever.

Words and Music: Philip Lawson Johnston

399 O Lord, the clouds are gathering

2. O Lord, over the nations now,
   where is the dove of peace?
   Her wings are broken.
   O Lord, while precious children starve,
   the tools of war increase;
   their bread is stolen.

3. O Lord, dark pow'rs are poised to flood
   our streets with hate and fear;
   we must awaken!
   O Lord, let love reclaim the lives
   that sin would sweep away,
   and let your kingdom come.

4. Yet, O Lord, your glorious cross shall tower
   triumphant in this land,
   evil confounding.
   Through the fire your suffering church displays
   the glories of her Christ:
   praises resounding.

Words and Music: Graham Kendrick

400 O Lord, you lead me
(Have faith in God)

1. O Lord, you lead me by the still wa - ters,

quiet - ly res - tor - ing my soul. You

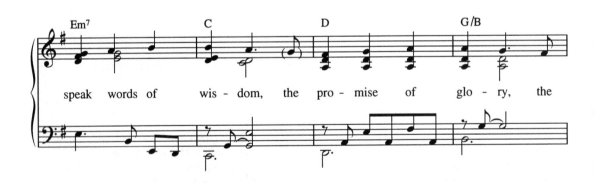

speak words of wis - dom, the pro - mise of glo - ry, the

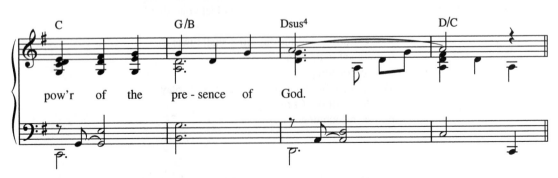

pow'r of the pre - sence of God.

2. O Lord, you guide me
   through all the darkness,
   turning my night into day;
   you'll never leave me,
   never forsake me
   the pow'r of the presence of God.

Words and Music: Geoff Bullock

401 O Lord, you're beautiful

Words and Music: Keith Green

402 O Lord, your tenderness

With feeling

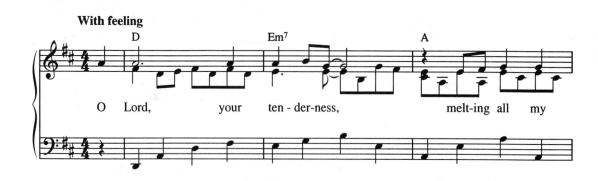

O Lord, your ten-der-ness, melt-ing all my

bit-ter-ness, O Lord, I re-ceive your

love. O Lord, your

love-li-ness, chang-ing all my ug-li-ness, O

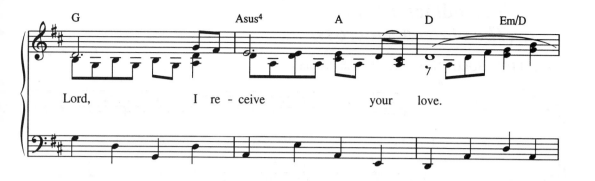

Lord, I re - ceive your love.

O Lord, I re - ceive your

love, O Lord, I re -

ceive your love.

Words and Music: Graham Kendrick

403 On a hill far away
(The old rugged cross)

THE OLD RUGGED CROSS Irregular and Refrain

1. On a hill far a-way stood an old rug-ged cross, the em-blem of suff-'ring and shame; and I loved that old cross where the dear-est and best for a world of lost sin-ners was slain. So I'll cher-ish the old rug-ged cross, till my tro-phies at last I lay down;

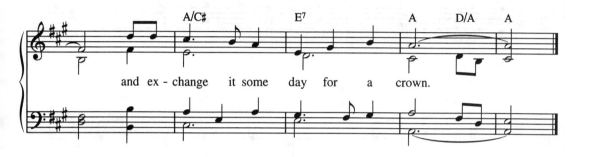

I will cling to the old rug - ged cross and ex - change it some day for a crown.

2. O, that old rugged cross, so despised by the world,
   has a wondrous attraction for me:
   for the dear Lamb of God left his glory above
   to bear it to dark Calvary.

3. In the old rugged cross, stained with blood so divine,
   a wondrous beauty I see.
   for 'twas on that old cross Jesus suffered and died
   to pardon and sanctify me.

4. To the old rugged cross I will ever be true,
   its shame and reproach gladly bear.
   Then he'll call me some day to my home far away;
   there his glory for ever I'll share.

Words and Music: George Bennard

404 Once in royal David's city

IRBY 87 87 77

2. He came down to earth from heaven,
   who is God and Lord of all,
   and his shelter was a stable,
   and his cradle was a stall;
   with the poor and meek and lowly,
   lived on earth our Saviour holy.

3. And through all his wondrous childhood
   day by day like us he grew;
   he was little, weak and helpless,
   tears and smiles like us he knew;
   and he feeleth for our sadness,
   and he shareth in our gladness.

4. Still among the poor and lowly
   hope in Christ is brought to birth,
   with the promise of salvation
   for the nations of the earth;
   still in him our life is found
   and our hope of heav'n is crowned.

5. And our eyes at last shall see him
   through his own redeeming love,
   for that child so dear and gentle
   is our Lord in heav'n above;
   and he leads his children on
   to the place where he is gone.

6. Not in that poor lowly stable,
   with the oxen standing by,
   we shall see him, but in heaven,
   set at God's right hand on high;
   when like stars his children crowned,
   all in white shall wait around.

Words: Cecil Frances Alexander; v.4: Michael Forster
Music: Henry John Gauntlett

405 One heart, one voice, one mind

One heart,   one voice,   one mind.

One in Spi – rit,   and one   in   love.

This will be   the hope   that we long   for,

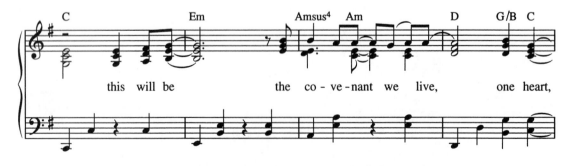

this will be   the co – ve – nant we live,   one heart,

Words and Music: David Hadden

406 One shall tell another
(The wine of the kingdom)

Lightly, with increasing pace

Verse

1. One shall tell a-no-ther, and he shall tell his friend, hus-bands, wives and child-ren shall come fol-low-ing on. From house to house in fa-mi-lies shall more be ga-thered in, and lights will shine in ev-'ry street, so warm and wel-com-ing.

Chorus

Come on in and taste the new wine,

the wine of the king-dom, the wine of the king-dom of God.

Here is heal - ing and for - give-ness,

the wine of the king-dom, the wine of the king-dom of God.

to verses | *last time*

2. Com-

2. Compassion of the Father
   is ready now to flow,
   through acts of love and mercy
   we must let it show.
   He turns now from his anger
   to show a smiling face,
   and longs that all should stand beneath
   the fountain of his grace.

3. He longs to do much more than
   our faith has yet allowed,
   to thrill us and surprise us
   with his sov'reign power.
   Where darkness has been darkest
   the brightest light will shine;
   his invitation comes to us,
   it's yours and it is mine.

Words and Music: Graham Kendrick

407 One thing I ask

One thing I ask, one thing I
Hear me, O Lord, hear me when I

seek, that I may dwell in your
cry; Lord, do not hide your

house, O Lord. All of my
face from me. You have been my

days, all of my life,
strength, you have been my shield,

Words and Music: Andy Park

408 Only by grace

Words and Music: Gerrit Gustafson

409 On this day

Verse

1. On this day we now come to stand be-fore the Fa - ther, en - ve - loped in his love.

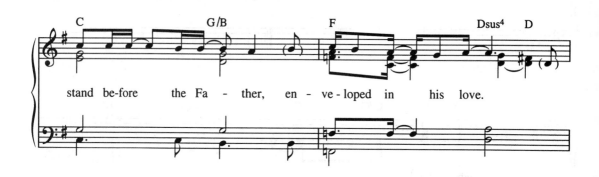

Hum - bly now off - 'ring all to live for the glo - ry of God.

Chorus

It is so

good to know, Lord, you are faith-ful, you love with-out end. We pledge our heart and soul to live for the glo-ry of God.

2. On this day we now come
   to kneel before the Saviour,
   Jesus Christ the Lord.
   With his word in our hearts
   we will live for the glory of God.

3. On this day we now come
   walking in the Spirit –
   the holy fire of God.
   Anointed with the living flame
   we will live for the glory of God.

Words and Music: Wes Sutton

410 On this day of happiness
(Three-part harmony)

Words and Music: Graham Kendrick

And I pray that you,
being rooted and established in love,
may have power, together with all the saints,
to grasp how wide and long and high and deep
is the love of Christ,
and to know this love that surpasses knowledge –
that you may be filled to the measure
of all the fullness of God.

Ephesians 3:17-19

411 Open the doors of praise

With energy
Chorus

O - pen the doors of praise. O - pen the doors of

praise. O - pen the doors of praise and

let the Lord come in. | 1. In the spi - rit world
2. And the de - mons will flee,

Fine *Verse*

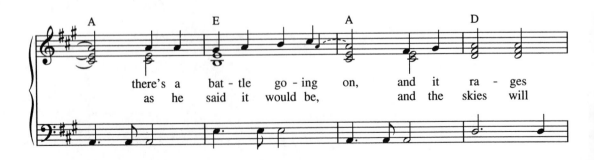

there's a bat - tle go - ing on, and it ra - ges
as he said it would be, and the skies will

Words and Music: Ian White

412 O the blood of Jesus

413 O the blood of my Saviour

Verse

1. O the blood of my Saviour, O the blood of the Lamb, O the blood of God's only Son has paid the price for my sin.

Chorus

It's the blood, it's the blood, the blood that my Lord shed for me. It's the blood, it's the blood, the blood of my Lord set me free.

2. O the blood shed at Calv'ry,
O the blood spilled for me,
O the blood of God's only Son,
Jesus, your blood set me free.

3. O the blood from the nail prints,
O the blood from the thorns,
O the blood from the spear in his side
has given me life evermore.

Words and Music: Colin Owen

414 O the deep, deep love of Jesus!

is the cur - rent of thy love; lead - ing on - ward,

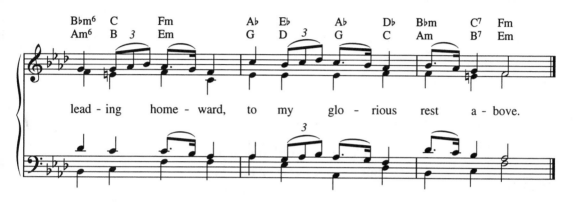

lead - ing home - ward, to my glo - rious rest a - bove.

2. O the deep, deep love of Jesus!
   Spread his praise from shore to shore,
   how he loveth, ever loveth,
   changeth never, nevermore;
   how he watches o'er his loved ones,
   died to call them all his own;
   how for them he intercedeth,
   watcheth o'er them from the throne.

3. O the deep, deep love of Jesus!
   Love of ev'ry love the best;
   'tis an ocean vast of blessing,
   'tis a haven sweet of rest.
   O the deep, deep love of Jesus!
   'Tis a heav'n of heav'ns to me;
   and it lifts me up to glory,
   for it lifts me up to thee.

Words: Samuel Trevor Francis
Music: from an anthem by Thomas Williams

Not to us, Lord, not to us
but to your name be the glory,
because of your love and faithfulness.

Psalm 115:1

415 O the glory of your presence

Words and Music: Steven Fry

416 O thou who camest from above (Tune 1)

HEREFORD LM

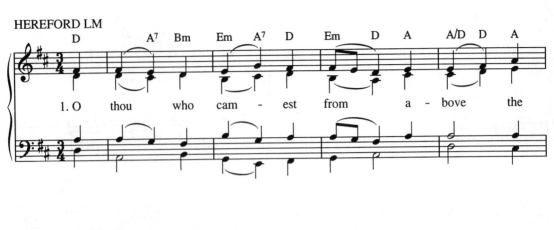

1. O thou who cam - est from a - bove the

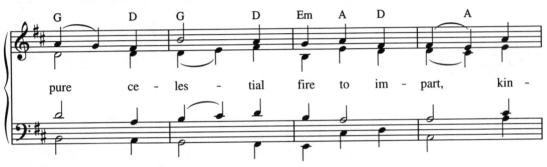

pure ce - les - tial fire to im - part, kin -

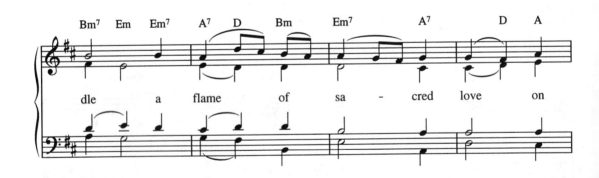

dle a flame of sa - cred love on

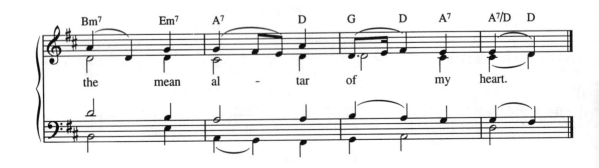

the mean al - tar of my heart.

416a O thou who camest from above (Tune 2)

AFFECTION LM

1. O thou who ca - mest from a - bove the
pure ce - les - tial fire to im-part, kin - dle a flame of
sa - cred love on the mean al - tar of my heart.

2. There let it for thy glory burn
   with inextinguishable blaze,
   and trembling to its source return
   in humble prayer and fervent praise.

3. Jesus, confirm my heart's desire
   to work and speak and think for thee;
   still let me guard the holy fire
   and still stir up thy gift in me.

4. Ready for all thy perfect will,
   my acts of faith and love repeat,
   till death thy endless mercies seal,
   and make the sacrifice complete.

Words: Charles Wesley
Music – Tune 1: Samuel Sebastian Wesley
Tune 2: *Greenwood's Psalmody*, Halifax

417 Our confidence is in the Lord

Words and Music: Noel and Tricia Richards

Great and marvellous are your deeds,
Lord God Almighty.
Just and true are your ways,
King of the ages.
Who will not fear you, O Lord,
and bring glory to your name?
For you alone are holy.
All nations will come
and worship before you,
for your righteous acts have been revealed.

Revelation 15:3-4

418 Our God is an awesome God
(Awesome God)

With strength

Our God is an awe-some God, he reigns from

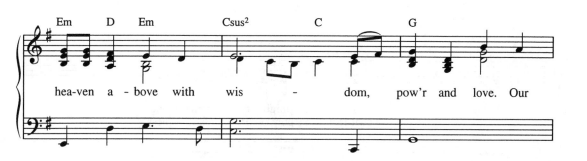

hea-ven a-bove with wis - dom, pow'r and love. Our

God is an awe-some God! Our God!

Words and Music: Rich Mullins

419 Our God is awesome in power
(Warrior)

Rocky

1. Our God is awe-some in pow-er, scat-ters his e - ne - mies;
2. Wa-ken the war - ri - or spi - rit, ar-my of God, a - rise;

our God is migh - ty in bring - ing the
chal-lenge the pow - ers of dark - ness, there

pow - er-ful to their knees. He has put on his ar-
must be no com - pro - mise. We shall at-tack their strong-

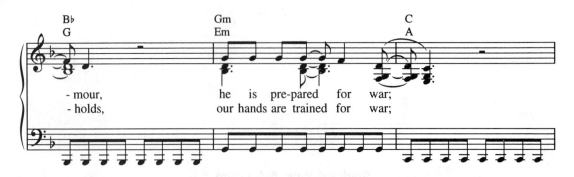

- mour, he is pre-pared for war;
- holds, our hands are trained for war;

Words and Music: Noel and Tricia Richards

420 Our God is so great

421 Over the mountains and the sea
(I could sing of your love for ever)

O-ver the moun-tains and the sea your ri-ver runs with love for me,

and I will o - pen up my heart and let the Heal - er set me free.

I'm hap-py to be in the truth, and I will dai - ly lift my hands,

for I will al - ways sing of when your love came down.

I could sing of your love for e - ver, I could sing of your love

Words and Music: Martin Smith

Be imitators of God, therefore,
as dearly loved children
and live a life of love,
just as Christ loved us
and gave himself up for us
as a fragrant offering and sacrifice to God.

Ephesians 5:1-2

422 Overwhelmed by love

Words and Music: Noel Richards

423 O, we are more than conquerors

2. For he's within to finish what's begun in me,
   he opens doors that no one can deny,
   he makes a way where there's no other way
   and gives me wings to fly.

Words and Music: Steven Fry

No, in all these things
we are more than conquerors
through him who loved us.
For I am convinced that neither death nor life,
neither angels nor demons,
neither the present nor the future,
nor any powers,
neither height nor depth,
nor anything else in all creation,
will be able to separate us
from the love of God
that is in Christ Jesus our Lord.

Romans 8:37-39

424 O, what a morning
(Christ is risen)

Joyfully

1. O, what a morn - ing, O, how glo - ri - ous, O, what a light has bro -

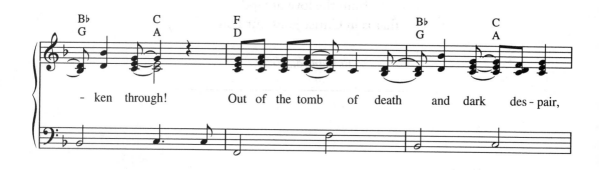

- ken through! Out of the tomb of death and dark des - pair,

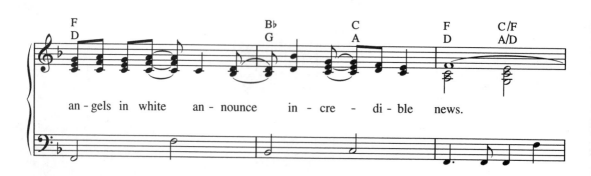

an - gels in white an - nounce in - cre - di - ble news.

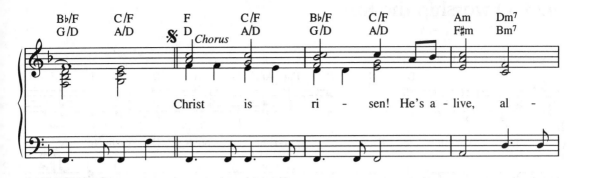

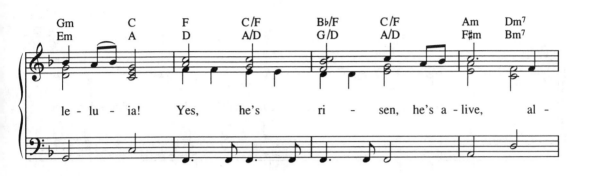

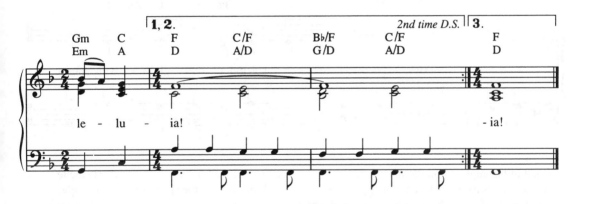

2. Suddenly hope has filled our darkest night,
suddenly life has blossomed here;
suddenly joy has rushed like rivers,
he is alive and love has conquered our fear.

Words and Music: Graham Kendrick

425 O worship the King

HANOVER 10 10 11 11

1. O worship the King all glorious above; O gratefully sing his pow'r and his love: our shield and defender, the Ancient of Days, pavilioned in splendour, and girded with praise.

2. O tell of his might, O sing of his grace,
   whose robe is the light, whose canopy space;
   his chariots of wrath the deep thunder-clouds form,
   and dark is his path on the wings of the storm.

3. This earth with its store of wonders untold,
   almighty, thy pow'r hath founded of old:
   hath stablished it fast by a changeless decree,
   and round it hath cast, like a mantle, the sea.

4. Thy bountiful care what tongue can recite?
   It breathes in the air, it shines in the light;
   it streams from the hills, it descends to the plain,
   and sweetly distils in the dew and the rain.

5. Frail children of dust, and feeble as frail,
   in thee do we trust, nor find thee to fail;
   thy mercies how tender, how firm to the end!
   Our maker, defender, redeemer, and friend.

6. O measureless might, ineffable love,
   while angels delight to hymn thee above,
   thy humbler creation, though feeble their lays,
   with true adoration shall sing to thy praise.

Words: Robert Grant
Music: melody and bass by William Croft

426 O worship the Lord in the beauty of holiness

WAS LEBET 13 10 13 10

1. O worship the Lord in the beauty of holiness; bow down before him, his glory proclaim; with gold of obedience, and incense of lowliness, kneel and adore him: the Lord is his name.

2. Low at his feet lay thy burden of carefulness:
   high on his heart he will bear it for thee,
   comfort thy sorrows, and answer thy prayerfulness,
   guiding thy steps as may best for thee be.

3. Fear not to enter his courts in the slenderness
   of the poor wealth thou wouldst reckon as thine:
   truth in its beauty, and love in its tenderness,
   these are the off'rings to lay on his shrine.

4. These, though we bring them in trembling and fearfulness,
   he will accept for the name that is dear;
   mornings of joy give for evenings of tearfulness,
   trust for our trembling and hope for our fear.

5. O worship the Lord in the beauty of holiness;
   bow down before him, his glory proclaim;
   with gold of obedience, and incense of lowliness,
   kneel and adore him: the Lord is his name.

Words: John Samuel Bewley Monsell
Music: melody from the *Rheinhardt MS*, Üttingen

427 Peace be to these streets

Verse

1. & 2. Peace be to these streets, peace be to these streets,

peace be to these streets in the name of Je - sus.

Chorus

Walk here, Lord, draw near, Lord, pass through these

streets to - day. Bring heal - ing, for - give - ness;

here   let   your   liv - ing   wa - ters   flow.

last time

Peace   be   to   these   streets!

3. Love come to these streets,
   love come to these streets,
   love come to these streets in the name of Jesus.

4. Joy come to these streets,
   joy come to these streets,
   joy come to these streets in the name of Jesus.

Words and Music: Graham Kendrick

428 Peace I give to you

2. Love I give to you . . .

3. Hope I give to you . . .

4. Joy I give to you . . .

5. Grace I give to you . . .

6. Pow'r I give to you . . .

Words and Music: Graham Kendrick

429 Peace like a river

Words and Music: John Watson

© Copyright 1989 Ampelos Music. Administered by CopyCare,
P.O. Box 77, Hailsham, East Sussex, BN27 3EF, UK. Used by permission.

430 Peace, perfect peace

1. Peace, per-fect peace, is the gift of Christ our

Lord. Peace, per-fect peace, is the

gift of Christ our Lord. Thus, says the

Lord, will the world know my friends.

Peace, per - fect peace, is the gift of Christ our Lord.

2. Love, perfect love, is the gift of Christ our Lord.
   Love, perfect love, is the gift of Christ our Lord.
   Thus, says the Lord, will the world know my friends.
   Love, perfect love, is the gift of Christ our Lord.

3. Faith, perfect faith, is the gift of Christ our Lord.
   Faith, perfect faith, is the gift of Christ our Lord.
   Thus, says the Lord, will the world know my friends.
   Faith, perfect faith, is the gift of Christ our Lord.

4. Hope, perfect hope, is the gift of Christ our Lord.
   Hope, perfect hope, is the gift of Christ our Lord.
   Thus, says the Lord, will the world know my friends.
   Hope, perfect hope, is the gift of Christ our Lord.

5. Joy, perfect joy, is the gift of Christ our Lord.
   Joy, perfect joy, is the gift of Christ our Lord.
   Thus, says the Lord, will the world know my friends.
   Joy, perfect joy, is the gift of Christ our Lord.

Words and Music: Kevin Mayhew

431 Peace to you

Words and Music: Graham Kendrick

432 Praise God from whom all blessings flow

Steady rock feel

Praise God from whom all bless - ings flow, praise him, all crea - tures here

be - low. Praise him a - bove, you hea - v'nly host, praise

Fa - ther, Son and Ho - ly Ghost. Praise - ly Ghost. Give

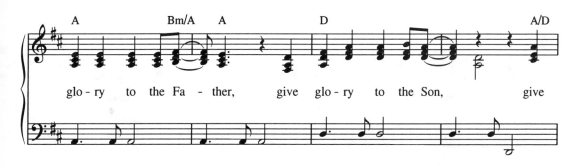

glo - ry to the Fa - ther, give glo - ry to the Son, give

Words and Music: Andy Piercy and Dave Clifton arr. Alison Berry

433 Praise, my soul, the King of heaven

PRAISE, MY SOUL 87 87 87

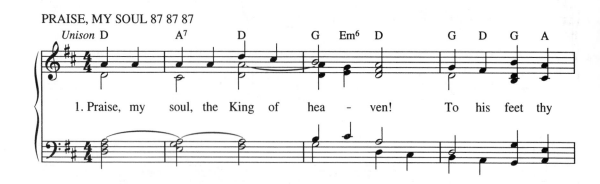

1. Praise, my soul, the King of hea - ven! To his feet thy

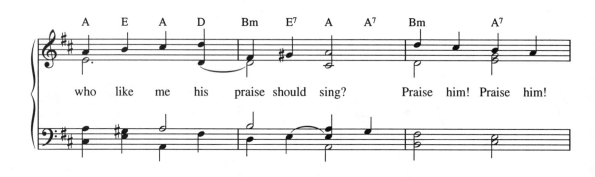

tri - bute bring; ran - somed, healed, re - stored, for - gi - ven,

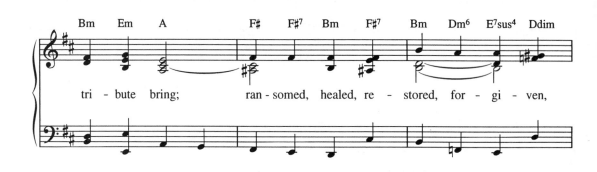

who like me his praise should sing? Praise him! Praise him!

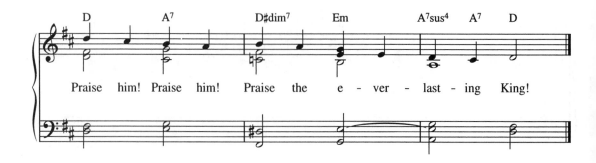

Praise him! Praise him! Praise the e - ver - last - ing King!

2. Praise him for his grace and favour
   to our fathers in distress;
   praise him still the same as ever,
   slow to chide and swift to bless.
   Praise him! Praise him! Praise him! Praise him!
   Glorious in his faithfulness.

3. Father-like, he tends and spares us;
   well our feeble frame he knows;
   in his hands he gently bears us,
   rescues us from all our foes.
   Praise him! Praise him! Praise him! Praise him!
   Widely as his mercy flows.

4. Angels, help us to adore him;
   ye behold him face to face;
   sun and moon, bow down before him,
   dwellers all in time and space.
   Praise him! Praise him! Praise him! Praise him!
   Praise with us the God of grace!

Words: Henry Francis Lyte, alt.
Music: John Goss

434 Praise the Lord, O my soul

Chorus

Praise the Lord, O my soul, praise his ho – ly name.

. Praise the Lord, O my soul,

to end | *to verses* | *Verse*

praise his ho – ly name. 1. All of my in –

– most be – ing, praise his ho – ly name,

2. He forgives me all my sins, praise his holy name . . .
   He heals all my diseases . . .

3. He redeems my life from the pit . . .
   He crowns me with love and compassion . . .

4. He satisfies your desires with good things . . .
   So my youth is renewed like the eagles' . . .

Words and Music: Jeannie Hall and Carol Owen

I will proclaim the name of the Lord.
Oh, praise the greatness of our God!
He is the Rock, his works are perfect,
and all his ways are just.
A faithful God who does no wrong,
upright and just is he.

Deuteronomy 32:3-4

435 Praise the name of Jesus

Worshipfully

Praise the name of Je - sus, praise the name of
Je - sus, he's my rock, he's my for - tress,
he's my de - li - ve - rer, in him will I trust.
Praise the name of Je - sus.

Words and Music: Roy Hicks

436 Purify my heart
(Refiner's fire)

Prayerfully

1. Pu - ri - fy my heart, let me be as gold and pre-cious sil - ver. Pu - ri - fy my heart, let me be as gold,

Chorus

pure gold. Re - fin - er's fire, my heart's one de-sire is to be ho - ly,

2. Purify my heart,
   cleanse me from within and make me holy.
   Purify my heart,
   cleanse me from my sin, deep within.

Words and Music: Brian Doerksen

Therefore, I urge you, brothers,
in view of God's mercy,
to offer your bodies as living sacrifices,
holy and pleasing to God –
this is your spiritual act of worship.

Romans 12:1

437 Reign in me

Reign in me, Sov'reign Lord, reign in me.
Reign in me, Sov'reign Lord, reign in me.
Cap-ti-vate my heart, let your king-dom come, es-tab-lish there your throne, let your will be done.

Words and Music: Chris Bowater

438 Rejoice!

hands   he will   give   the   ground   we   claim.

He rides in   ma - jes - ty   to   lead us in - to   vic - to - ry,

the   world   shall   see   that   Christ   is   Lord!   Re -

2. God is at work in us
   his purpose to perform,
   building a kingdom
   of power not of words,
   where things impossible
   by faith shall be made possible;
   let's give the glory to him now.

3. Though we are weak, his grace
   is ev'rything we need;
   we're made of clay
   but this treasure is within.
   He turns our weaknesses
   into his opportunities,
   so that the glory goes to him.

Words and Music: Graham Kendrick

My soul glorifies the Lord
and my spirit rejoices in God my Saviour.

Luke 1:46b-47

439 Restore, O Lord

2. Restore, O Lord,
   in all the earth your fame,
   and in our time revive
   the church that bears your name.
   And in your anger,
   Lord, remember mercy,
   O living God,
   whose mercy shall outlast the years.

3. Bend us, O Lord,
   where we are hard and cold,
   in your refiner's fire:
   come purify the gold.
   Though suff'ring comes
   and evil crouches near,
   still our living God
   is reigning, he is reigning here.

4. *as verse 1*

Words and Music: Graham Kendrick and Chris Rolinson

440 Righteousness, peace, joy in the Holy Ghost

With an 'island' feel

Right-eous-ness, peace, joy in the Ho-ly Ghost,

right-eous-ness, peace, and joy in the Ho-ly Ghost: that's the king-dom of God.

Don't you want to be a part of the king-dom, don't you want to be a

part of the king-dom, don't you want to be a part of the king-dom?

Come on, ev-'ry-bo-dy. Don't you want to be a part of the king-dom,

2. There's peace in the kingdom . . .

3. There's joy in the kingdom . . .

4. I'm an heir of the kingdom,
   I'm an heir of the kingdom,
   I'm an heir of the kingdom.
   Come on, ev'rybody!

Words and Music: Helena Barrington

But when the kindness and love
of God our Saviour appeared,
he saved us,
not because of righteous things we had done,
but because of his mercy.
He saved us through the washing of rebirth and renewal
by the Holy Spirit,
whom he poured out on us generously
through Jesus Christ our Saviour,
so that, having been justified by his grace,
we might become heirs
having the hope of eternal life.

Titus 3:4-7

441 River, wash over me

Unhurried, with strength

1. Ri - ver, wash o - ver me,
cleanse me and make me new.
Bathe me, re - fresh me and fill me a - new.
Ri - ver, wash o - ver me.

2. Spirit, watch over me,
   lead me to Jesus' feet.
   Cause me to worship and fill me anew.
   Spirit, watch over me.

3. Jesus, rule over me,
   reign over all my heart.
   Teach me to praise you and fill me anew.
   Jesus, rule over me.

Words and Music: Dougie Brown

© Copyright 1980 Kingsway's Thankyou Music, P.O. Box 75, Eastbourne,
East Sussex, BN23 6NW, UK. Used by permission.

442 Ruach

With a sense of awe

Ru - ach, Ru -
ach, ho-ly wind of God, blow on me.
Touch the fad - ing
em - bers, breathe on me.
Fan in-to a flame all that you've placed in me.

Words and Music: David Fellingham

443 Salvation belongs to our God

1. Sal - va - tion be - longs to our God, who

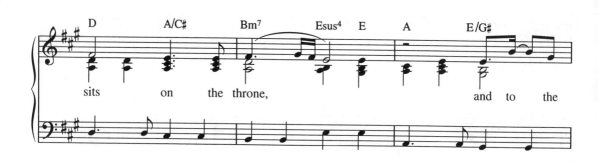

sits on the throne, and to the

Lamb. Praise and glo - ry, wis - dom and thanks,

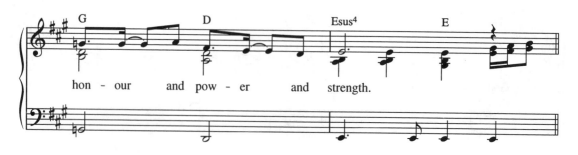

hon - our and pow - er and strength.

2. And we, the redeemed, shall be strong
   in purpose and unity,
   declaring aloud,
   praise and glory, wisdom and thanks,
   honour and power and strength.

Words and Music: Adrian Howard and Pat Turner

444 Save the people

1. Save the peo-ple, save the peo-ple now;
save the peo-ple, save the peo-ple now.
Lord, have mer-cy.
Christ, have mer-cy. Fa - ther, hear our prayer:

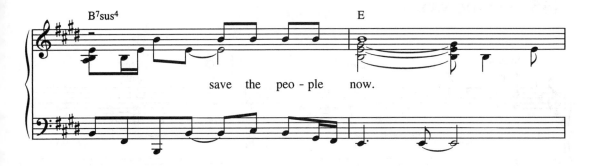

save the peo - ple now.

2. Save the children, save the children now. *(x4)*
   Lord, have mercy. Christ, have mercy.
   Father, hear our prayer: save the children now.

3. Send your Spirit, send your Spirit now. *(x4)*
   Lord, have mercy. Christ, have mercy.
   Father, hear our prayer: send your Spirit now.

4. Send revival, send revival now. *(x4)*
   Lord, have mercy. Christ, have mercy.
   Father, hear our prayer: send revival now.

   Add extra verses as required, for example:
   Send the fire . . .
   Save the nation . . .

Words and Music: Graham Kendrick

445 Say the word

each drop a fresh re-ve-la - tion. I will re-turn to the place

of the cross, where grace and mer-cy pour from hea-ven's throne.

last time

3. Say the word,

say the word.

2. Say the word, I will be filled;
   my hands reach out to heaven,
   where striving is stilled.
   Say the word, I will be changed;
   where I am dry and thirsty,
   send cool, refreshing rain,
   say the word.

3. Say the word, I will be poor,
   that I might know the riches
   that you have in store.
   Say the word, I will be weak;
   your strength will be the power
   that satisfies the meek,
   say the word.

   The Lord will see the travail of his soul,
   and he and I will be satisfied.
   Complete the work you have started in me:
   O come, Lord Jesus, shake my life again.

Words and Music: Stuart Townend

446 See his glory

Slow and worshipful

See his glo - ry, see his glo - ry, see his

glo - ry now ap - pear. See his glo - ry, see his

glo - ry, see his glo - ry now ap -pear. God of light,

ho - li-ness and truth, pow'r and might, see his

glo - ry, see it now ap-pear. Now we de - clare our God is

good, and his mer - cies en-dure for e - ver. Now we de -

clare our God is good, and his mer - cies en-dure for-

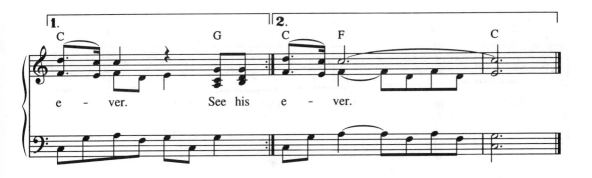

1. e - ver. See his **2.** e - ver.

Words and Music: Chris Bowater

447 Seek ye first

Brightly

Verse

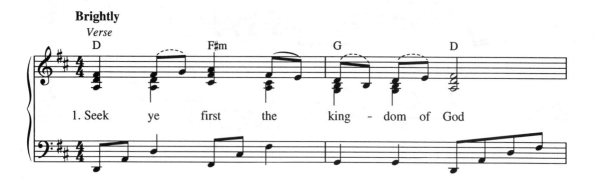

1. Seek ye first the king - dom of God

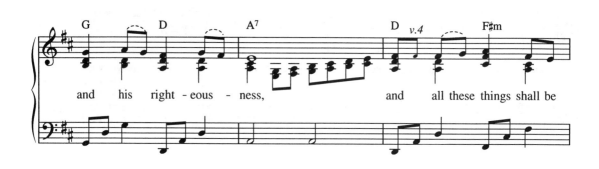

and his right - eous - ness, and all these things shall be

ad-ded un-to you, hal - le - lu, hal-le-lu - jah!

Chorus

Hal - le - lu - jah! Hal - le -

lu - jah! Hal - le - lu - jah!

Hal - le - lu, hal - le - lu - jah!

2. You shall not live by bread alone,
   but by ev'ry word
   that proceeds from the mouth of God,
   hallelu, hallelujah!

3. Ask and it shall be given unto you,
   seek and you shall find.
   Knock and it shall be opened unto you,
   hallelu, hallelujah!

4. If the Son shall set you free,
   you shall be free indeed.
   You shall know the truth
     and the truth shall set you free,
   hallelu, hallelujah!

5. Let your light so shine before men
   that they may see your good works
   and glorify your Father in heaven,
   hallelu, hallelujah!

6. Trust in the Lord with all your heart,
   he shall direct your paths,
   in all your ways acknowledge him,
   hallelu, hallelujah.

Words and Music: Karen Lafferty

448 See, your Saviour comes

See, your Saviour comes;
see, your Saviour comes.

1. Desolate cities, desolate homes,
desolate lives on the streets, angry and restless. When will you know the

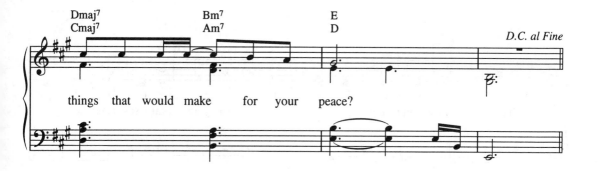

Dmaj⁷ / Cmaj⁷   Bm⁷ / Am⁷   E / D   *D.C. al Fine*

things that would make for your peace?

2. Father of mercy, hear as we cry
   for all who live in this place;
   show here your glory, come satisfy
   your longing that all should be saved.

3. Where lives are broken, let there be hope,
   where there's division bring peace;
   where there's oppression, judge and reprove,
   and rescue the crushed and the weak.

4. Lord, let your glory dwell in this land,
   in mercy restore us again:
   pour out salvation, grant us your peace,
   and strengthen the things that remain.

Words and Music: Graham Kendrick

449 Shout for joy

1. Shout for joy and sing, let your prai-ses ring;

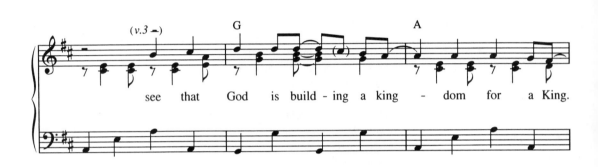

see that God is build-ing a king - dom for a King.

His dwell-ing -place with men, the new Je -

ru - sa-lem; where Je - sus is Lord o - ver all.

2. A work so long concealed,
   in time will be revealed,
   as the sons of God shall rise and take their stand.
   Clothed in his righteousness,
   the church made manifest,
   where Jesus is Lord over all.

3. Sov'reign over all,
   hail him risen Lord.
   He alone is worthy of our praise.
   Reigning in majesty,
   ruling in victory,
   Jesus is Lord over all.

Words and Music: Dave Bilbrough

450 Shout for joy and sing

Words and Music: David Fellingham

451 Shout, shout for joy

Words and Music: Dave Bell

452 Shout! The Lord is risen
(The day of his power)

day   of   his   pow - er,   (woa - oh)   his   pow - er,   (woa -

oh)   his   pow - er.   SHOUT!

2. Shout! He has ascended, he reigns at God's right hand.
   Shout! Till death is ended. This is the day of his power, his power.

3. Shout! With fire from heaven, he sent his Spirit down.
   Shout! And gifts were given. This is the day of his power, his power.

4. Shout! Proclaim the kingdom! Announce the Jubilee.
   Shout! The year of freedom! This is the day of his power, his power.

5. Shout! A new generation rises across the land.
   Shout! A new demonstration. This is the day of his power, his power.

6. Go! Tell ev'ry nation. Our hearts are willing now.
   Go! He is our passion. This is the day of his power, his power.

7. Come! O come, Lord Jesus. We cry, O Lord, how long?
   Come! And end injustice. This is the day of his power, his power.

8. Come! If you are thirsty, while living waters flow.
   Come! And taste his mercy. This is the day of his power, his power.

9. Shout! In expectation the whole creation yearns.
   Shout! For liberation. This is the day of his power, his power.

Words and Music: Graham Kendrick

453 Shout unto God

Words and Music: Collette Dallas and Deborah Page

454 Show your power, O Lord

1. Show your pow'r, O Lord, de-mon-strate the jus-tice of your king-dom. Prove your migh-ty word, vin-di-cate your name be-fore a watch-ing world.

2. Show your pow'r, O Lord,
   cause your church to rise and take action.
   Let all fear be gone,
   powers of the age to come
   are breaking through.
   We your people are ready to serve,
   to arise and to obey.
   Show your pow'r, O Lord,
   and set the people free.

   Show your pow'r, O Lord,
   and set the people –
   show your pow'r, O Lord,
   and set the people –
   show your pow'r, O Lord,
   and set the people free.

Words and Music: Graham Kendrick

455 Silent night

STILLE NACHT Irregular

2. Silent night, holy night.
   Shepherds quake at the sight,
   glories stream from heaven afar,
   heav'nly hosts sing alleluia:
   Christ the Saviour is born,
   Christ the Saviour is born.

3. Silent night, holy night.
   Son of God, love's pure light,
   radiant beams from thy holy face,
   with the dawn of redeeming grace:
   Jesus, Lord, at thy birth,
   Jesus, Lord, at thy birth.

Words: Joseph Mohr trans. John Freeman Young
Music: Franz Grüber arr. Colin Hand

456 Silent, surrendered

1. Si - lent, sur - ren - dered, calm and still, o - pen to the

word of God. Heart hum - bled to his will,

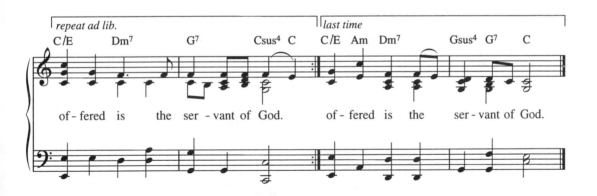

of - fered is the ser - vant of God. of - fered is the ser - vant of God.

2. Come, Holy Spirit, calm and still,
   teach us, heal us, give us life.
   Come, Lord, O let our hearts
   flow with love and all that is true.

Words: Pamela Hayes

Music: Margaret Rizza

Words © Copyright Sister Pamela Hayes RSCJ. Used by permission.
Music © Copyright 1997 Kevin Mayhew Ltd.

457 Sing a song of celebration
(We will dance)

With strength

Capo 3 A

Sing a song of ce - le - bra-tion, lift up a shout of
Dance with all your might, lift up your hands and clap for

praise, for the Bride-groom will come, the
joy: the time's draw - ing near when

glo - ri -ous One. And O,
he will ap - pear. And O,

we will look on his face;
we will stand by his side;

we'll go
a strong,

to a much bet - ter

Words and Music: David Ruis

458 Sing, praise and bless the Lord
(Laudate Dominum)

Words: Taizé Community
Music: Jacques Berthier

459 Soften my heart, Lord

460 Soon and very soon

2. No more crying there, we are going to see the King,
   no more crying there, we are going to see the King,
   no more crying there, we are going to see the King,
   hallelujah, hallelujah, we're going to see the King.

3. No more dying there, we are going to see the King,
   no more dying there, we are going to see the King,
   no more dying there, we are going to see the King,
   hallelujah, hallelujah, we're going to see the King.

Words and Music: Andraé Crouch

461 Sound the trumpet

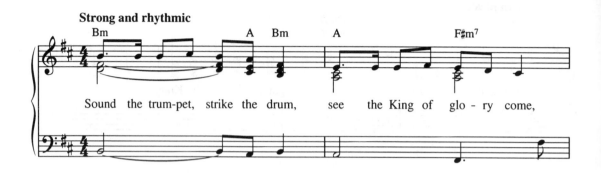

Sound the trum-pet, strike the drum, see the King of glo - ry come,

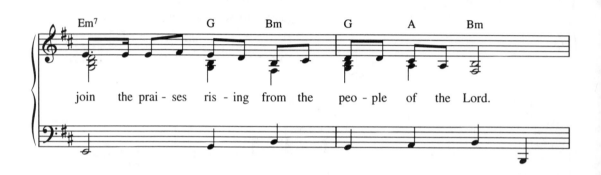

join the prai - ses ris - ing from the peo - ple of the Lord.

Let your voi - ces now be heard, un - re - strained and un - re - served, pre -

pare the way for his re - turn, you peo - ple of the Lord. Sing

Words and Music: Dave Bilbrough

462 Spirit of the living God (Iverson)

Words and Music: Daniel Iverson

463 Spirit of the living God (Armstrong)

Words and Music: Paul Armstrong

464 Streams of worship

1. Streams of wor - ship and ri - vers of praise, a - scend-ing to the One who is the An - cient of Days: to him who is wor -thy, to him who was slain, to him who sits up - on the throne and to the Lamb.

to with the Lamb:

2. Thousands upon thousands
   encircle the throne,
   singing a new song
   to the One who is to come:
   to him who is worthy,
   to him who was slain,
   to him who sits upon the throne
   and to the Lamb:

3. Streams of worship
   and rivers of praise
   flowing from the lips of those
   who never cease to be amazed
   with him who is worthy,
   with him who was slain,
   with him who sits upon the throne
   and with the Lamb:

Words and Music: David Hadden

My command is this:
Love each other as I have loved you.
Greater love has no one than this,
that he lay down his life for his friends.
You are my friends if you do what I command.
I no longer call you servants,
because a servant does not know his master's business.
Instead, I have called you friends,
for everything that I learned from my Father
I have made known to you.

John 15:12-15

465 Such love

Flowing

1. Such love, pure as the whit-est snow;
such love weeps for the shame I know;
such love, pay-ing the debt I owe;
O Je-sus, such love.

2. Such love, stilling my restlessness;
such love, filling my emptiness;
such love, showing me holiness;
O Jesus, such love.

3. Such love springs from eternity;
such love, streaming through history;
such love, fountain of life to me;
O Jesus, such love.

Words and Music: Graham Kendrick

466 Surely our God
(Revealer of mysteries)

Sure-ly our God is the God of gods and the Lord of kings, a re-veal-er of mys-te-ries. Sure-ly our God is the God of gods and the Lord of kings, a re-veal-er of my-ste-ries.

1. He chan-ges the times and the sea-sons, he gives

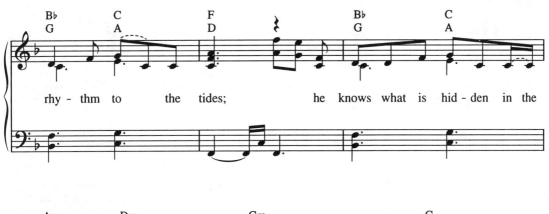

rhy - thm to the tides; he knows what is hid - den in the

dark - est of pla - ces, brings the sha - dows in - to his light.

2. I will praise you always, my Father,
   you are Lord of heaven and earth,
   you hide your secrets from the wise and the learnèd
   and reveal them to this your child.

3. Thank you for sending your only Son,
   we may know the myst'ry of God;
   he opens the treasures of wisdom and knowledge
   to the humble, not to the proud.

Words and Music: David and Liz Morris

467 Take me past the outer courts
(Take me in)

Take me past the out - er courts, and through the ho - ly place,

past the bra - zen al - tar, Lord, I want to see your face.
Pass me

by the crowds of peo - ple, and the priests who sing their praise;
I

hun - ger and thirst for your right - eous - ness, but it's

Words and Music: Dave Browning

468 Take my life, and let it be

INNOCENTS 77 77

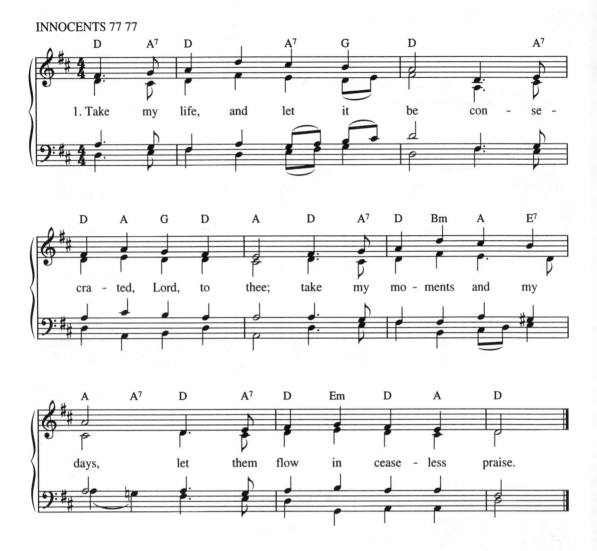

1. Take my life, and let it be con-se-crated, Lord, to thee; take my moments and my days, let them flow in cease-less praise.

2. Take my hands, and let them move
   at the impulse of thy love;
   take my feet, and let them be
   swift and beautiful for thee.

3. Take my voice, and let me sing
   always, only, for my King;
   take my lips, and let them be
   filled with messages from thee.

4. Take my silver and my gold;
   not a mite would I withhold;
   take my intellect, and use
   ev'ry pow'r as thou shalt choose.

5. Take my will, and make it thine:
   it shall be no longer mine;
   take my heart: it is thine own;
   it shall be thy royal throne.

6. Take my love; my Lord, I pour
   at thy feet its treasure-store;
   take myself, and I will be
   ever, only, all for thee.

468a Take my life, and let it be

2. Take my feet, and let them be
swift and beautiful for thee.
Take my voice, and let me sing
always, only, for my King,
always, only, for my King.

3. Take my lips, and let them be
filled with messages from thee.
Take my silver and my gold,
not a mite would I withhold,
not a mite would I withhold.

4. Take my love; my God, I pour
at thy feet its treasure-store.
Take myself, and I will be
ever, only, all for thee,
ever, only, all for thee.

5. Take my life, and let it be
consecrated, Lord, to thee.
Take myself, and I will be
ever, only, all for thee,
ever, only, all for thee.

Words: Frances Ridley Havergal
Music – Tune 1: *The Parish Choir*
Tune 2: Henri A. Cesar Malan arr. Terry Butler.

469 Teach me to dance

Teach me to dance to the beat of your heart,
teach me to move in the pow'r of your Spi - rit, teach me to walk in the light of your pre -
sence, teach me to dance to the beat of your heart.

Teach me to love with your heart of com - pas - sion,
teach me to trust in the word of your pro - mise, teach me to hope in the day of your com -
ing, teach me to dance to the beat of your heart.

1. You wrote the rhy - thm of life,

cre - a - ted hea-ven and earth, in you is joy with-out mea - sure.

So, like a child in your sight, I dance to see your de-light, for I was made for your

plea - sure, plea - sure.

2. Let all my movements express
a heart that loves to say 'yes',
a will that leaps to obey you.
Let all my energy blaze
to see the joy in your face;
let my whole being praise you,
praise you.

Words and Music: Graham Kendrick and Steve Thompson

470 Teach me your ways
(Purify my heart)

Teach me your ways, O Lord, my God, and I will walk in your truth. Give me a totally un-di-vi-ded heart that I may fear your name. Pu-ri-fy my heart,

Words and Music: Eugene Greco

471 Tell out, my soul

2. Tell out, my soul,
   the greatness of his name:
   make known his might,
   the deeds his arm has done;
   his mercy sure,
   from age to age the same;
   his holy name:
   the Lord, the Mighty One.

3. Tell out, my soul,
   the greatness of his might:
   pow'rs and dominions
   lay their glory by;
   proud hearts and stubborn wills
   are put to flight,
   the hungry fed,
   the humble lifted high.

4. Tell out, my soul,
   the glories of his word:
   firm is his promise,
   and his mercy sure.
   Tell out, my soul,
   the greatness of the Lord
   to children's children
   and for evermore.

Words: Timothy Dudley-Smith
Music: Walter Greatorex

472 Thank you for saving me

With a steady rhythm

1. Thank you for sav-ing me; what can I say?

You are my ev-'ry-thing, I will sing your praise.

You shed your blood for me; what can I say?

You took my sin and shame, a sin-ner called by name.

Great

2. Mercy and grace are mine, forgiv'n is my sin;
   Jesus, my only hope, the Saviour of the world.
   'Great is the Lord,' we cry; God, let your kingdom come.
   Your word has let me see, thank you for saving me.

Words and Music: Martin Smith

473 Thank you for the cross
(O I love you, Lord)

2. For our healing there,
   Lord, you suffered,
   and to take our fear
   you poured out your love,
   precious Lord (precious Lord).
   Calvary's work is done,
   you have conquered,
   able now to save
   so completely,
   thank you, Lord (thank you, Lord).

Words and Music: Graham Kendrick

474 Thank you for your mercy
(Great is your mercy)

1. Thank you for your mer - cy, thank you for your grace;
thank you for your blood that's made a way to
come in-to your pre - sence and glo-ri-fy your name.
Lord, I stand a-mazed at what I see. Great is your
mer - cy to-ward me, your lov-ing kind - ness to-ward me,
faith - ful to me, al-ways pro-vid - ing for me,

Words and Music: Don Moen

475 Thank you, Jesus

2. You rose up from the grave,
   to me new life you gave,
   thank you, Lord, for loving me.
   You rose up from the grave,
   to me new life you gave,
   thank you, Lord, for loving me.

3. You're coming back again,
   and we with you shall reign.
   Thank you, Lord, for loving me.
   You're coming back again,
   and we with you shall reign.
   Thank you, Lord, for loving me.

Words and Music: Unknown

476 The angels, Lord, they sing

1. The angels, Lord, they sing around your throne; and we will join their song: praise you a - lone. The lone. Ho - ly, ho - ly, ho - ly, Lord our God, who was and is and is to come. come. 2. The come. A - men. A - men.

2. The living creatures, Lord, speak endless praise;
   and joining at your throne, we'll sing their sweet refrain. *(Repeat)*

3. The elders, Lord, they fall before your throne;
   our hearts we humbly bow to you alone. *(Repeat)*

Words and Music: Matt Redman

© Copyright 1993 Kingsway's Thankyou Music, P.O. Box 75, Eastbourne,
East Sussex, BN23 6NW, UK. Used by permission.

477 The church's one foundation

AURELIA 76 76 D

The church's one foundation is Jesus Christ, her Lord; she
is his new creation, by water and the word; from
heav'n he came and sought her to be his holy bride, with
his own blood he bought her, and for her life he died.

2. Elect from ev'ry nation, yet one o'er all the earth,
   her charter of salvation, one Lord, one faith, one birth;
   one holy name she blesses, partakes one holy food,
   and to one hope she presses, with ev'ry grace endued.

3. 'Mid toil and tribulation, and tumult of her war,
   she waits the consummation of peace for evermore;
   till with the vision glorious her longing eyes are blest,
   and the great church victorious shall be the church at rest.

4. Yet she on earth hath union with God the Three in One,
   and mystic sweet communion with those whose rest is won:
   O happy ones and holy! Lord, give us grace that we
   like them, the meek and lowly, on high may dwell with thee.

Words: Samuel John Stone
Music: Samuel Sebastian Wesley

478 The cross has said it all

1. The

cross has said it all, the cross has said it all.
cross has said it all, the cross has said it all.

I can't de-ny what you have shown, the
I ne-ver re-cog-nised your touch, un-

cross speaks of a God of love;
til I met you at the cross.
there dis-played for all
We are fall – en, dust

to see,
to dust,
Je – sus Christ, our on – ly hope, a
how could you do this for us?

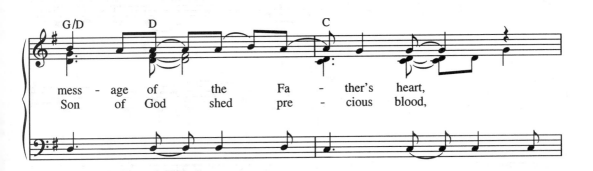

mess – age of the Fa – ther's heart,
Son of God shed pre – cious blood,

'Come, my child – ren, come on home.'
who can com – pre – hend this love?
As
As

Words and Music: Matt Redman and Martin Smith

479 The crucible for silver

Chorus

Je - sus, Ho - ly One, you

are my heart's de - sire.

King of kings, my ev - 'ry - thing, you've

set this heart on fire.

Fa - ther, take our of – fer- ing, with our

song we hum - bly praise you. you have brought your ho – ly fi – re to our

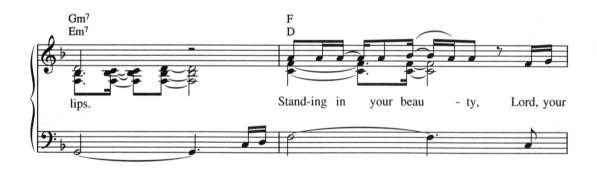

lips. Stand-ing in your beau – ty, Lord, your

gift to us is ho - li - ness; lead us to the place where we can

Words and Music: Martin Smith

480 The heavens shall declare

Words and Music: Geoff Bullock

481 The Lord is a mighty King
(Creation creed)

SHOUT:
For by him
all things were created.
Things in heaven
and on earth.
Visible and invisible.
Whether thrones
or powers
or rulers
or authorities;
all things were created by him,
and for him.

Words and Music: Graham Kendrick

482 The Lord is marching out
(O give thanks)

1. The Lord is march-ing out in splen - dour,

in awe-some ma-jes-ty he rides, for truth, hu-mi-li-ty and

jus-tice, his might-y ar-my fills the skies. O give

thanks to the Lord for his love en - dures, O give thanks to the Lord for his

love en-dures, O give thanks to the Lord for his love en-dures for e - ver, for e - ver.

1. **2.** for e - ver,

2. His army marches out with dancing
   for he has filled our hearts with joy.
   Be glad the kingdom is advancing,
   the love of God, our battle cry!

Words and Music: Graham Kendrick

483 The Lord is moving across this land
(We're in God's army)

1. The Lord is mov - ing a - cross this land, it's
Spi - rit's lead - ing us out to war, but we're
De - vil's sha - kin', his time has come, the

time to rise up and take our stand be - hind the ban - ner of
not the same as we were be - fore, we are a - noin - ted to
pow'rs of dark - ness are on the run; we're stand - ing firm by faith in our au -

Je - sus Christ and claim the vic - to - ry that's
mul - ti - ply; the Lord has called us and
tho - ri - ty, de - feat - ing all our foes and bring - ing

ours by right; we're in God's ar - my, we're in God's
that is why we're in God's ar - my, we're in God's
li - ber - ty; we're in God's ar - my, we're in God's

Words and Music: Colin Owen

484 The Lord is our strength

2. We give thanks to you, Lord,
and call on your name;
we proclaim that your name is exalted on high.
(Repeat)
So we sing to you, Lord,
you've done glorious things,
we shout aloud and dance for joy,
for great is the Holy One.
So we sing to you, Lord,
you've done glorious things,
we rejoice in our God
for the things you have done.

Words and Music: Carol Owen

485 The Lord reigns

2. The heav'ns declare his righteousness,
   the peoples see his glory;
   for you, O Lord, are exalted over all the earth,
   over all the earth.

Words and Music: Dan C. Stradwick

The Lord is my shepherd, I shall not be in want.
He makes me lie down in green pastures,
he leads me beside quiet waters.

Psalm 23:1-2

486 The Lord's my shepherd

CRIMOND CM

1. The Lord's my shep - herd, I'll not want. He makes me down to lie in pas - tures green. He lead - eth me the qui - et wa - ters by.

2. My soul he doth restore again,
   and me to walk doth make
   within the paths of righteousness,
   e'en for his own name's sake.

3. Yea, though I walk in death's dark vale,
   yet will I fear none ill.
   For thou art with me, and thy rod
   and staff me comfort still.

4. My table thou hast furnishèd
   in presence of my foes:
   my head thou dost with oil annoint,
   and my cup overflows.

5. Goodness and mercy all my life
   shall surely follow me.
   And in God's house for evermore
   my dwelling-place shall be.

Words: *The Scottish Psalter*
Music: melody by Jessie Seymour Irvine

487 The price is paid

ev - 'ry part, I live to thank you for the price you paid.

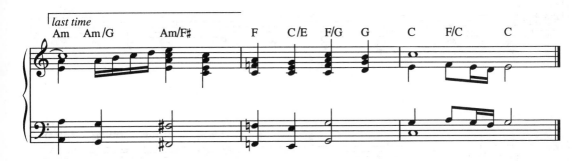

to verses

2. The price is

last time

2. The price is paid,
   see Satan flee away;
   for Jesus crucified
   destroys his pow'r.
   No more to pay,
   let accusation cease,
   in Christ there is
   no condemnation now.

3. The price is paid
   and by that scourging cruel
   he took our sicknesses
   as if his own.
   And by his wounds
   his body broken there,
   his healing touch
   may now by faith be known.

4. The price is paid,
   'Worthy the Lamb!' we cry,
   eternity shall never
   cease his praise.
   The church of Christ
   shall rule upon the earth,
   in Jesus' name
   we have authority.

Words and Music: Graham Kendrick

488 The promise of the Holy Spirit
(Acts chapter 2, verse 39)

With energy

The pro-mise of the Ho - ly Spi - rit is for you.

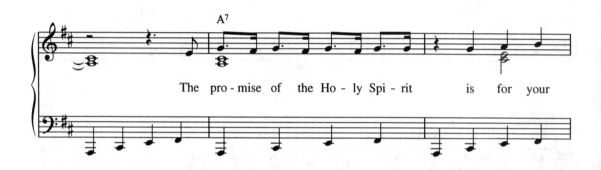

The pro-mise of the Ho - ly Spi - rit is for your

child - ren. The pro-mise of the Ho - ly Spi - rit

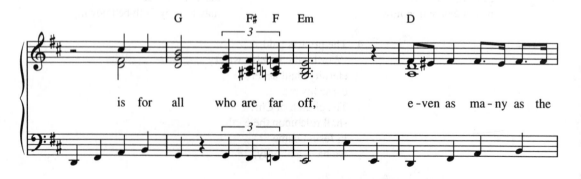

is for all who are far off, e - ven as ma - ny as the

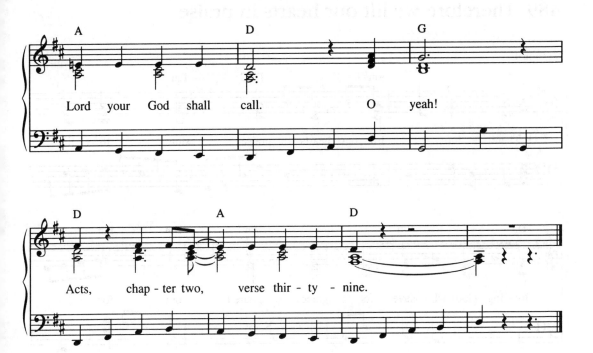

Lord your God shall call. O yeah!

Acts, chap - ter two, verse thir - ty - nine.

Words and Music: Richard Hubbard

489 Therefore we lift our hearts in praise

Version 1

Version 2

1. There - fore we lift our hearts in praise, sing to the

liv-ing God who saves, for grace poured out for you and me.

2. There for ev'ryone to see,
   there on the hill at Calvary,
   Jesus died for you and me.

3. For our sad and broken race,
   he arose with life and grace,
   and reigns on high for you and me.

4. There for such great pain and cost
   the Spirit came at Pentecost
   and comes in pow'r for you and me.

5. Therefore we lift our hearts in praise,
   sing to the living God who saves,
   for grace poured out for you and me.

Words and music: Unknown
Version 2 arr. Norman Warren

490 There is a louder shout to come

2. Now we see a part of this,
   one day we shall see in full;
   all the nations with one voice,
   all the people with one love.
   No one else will share your praise,
   nothing else can take your place;
   all the nations with one voice,
   all the people with one Lord.
   And what a song we'll sing upon that day!

3. Even now upon the earth
   there's a glimpse of all to come;
   many people with one voice,
   harmony of many tongues.
   We will all confess your name,
   you will be our only praise;
   all the nations with one voice,
   all the people with one God.
   And what a song we'll sing upon that day!

Words and Music: Matt Redman

491 There is a place of commanded blessing
(Break dividing walls)

There is a place of com-man-ded bless-ing where breth-ren in u-ni-ty dwell, a place where a-noint-ing oil is flow-ing, where we live as one. You have called us to be a bo-dy, you have called us as

Words and Music: David Ruis

492 There is a Redeemer

1. There is a Redeem-er, Je-sus, God's own Son,
pre-cious Lamb of God, Mes-si-ah, Ho - ly One.

Chorus

Thank you, O my Fa - ther, for giv-ing us your Son, and
leav-ing your Spi-rit till the work on earth is done. done.

2. Jesus, my Redeemer,
   Name above all names,
   precious Lamb of God, Messiah,
   O for sinners slain.

3. When I stand in glory,
   I will see his face.
   And there I'll serve my King for ever,
   in that Holy Place.

Words and Music: Melody Green

493 There is none like you

There is none like you,
no one else can touch my heart like you do.
I could search for all e-ter-ni-ty long and find
there is none like you.

Your mer - cy flows like a ri -

- ver wide, and heal - ing comes from your hands.

Suf - fer - ing child - ren are safe

D.C. al Fine

in your arms; there is none like you.

Words and Music: Lenny LeBlanc

494 There is only one Lord

Words and Music: Morris Chapman and Claire Cloninger

495 There is power in the name of Jesus

2. There is pow'r in the name of Jesus,
   like a sword in our hands.
   We declare in the name of Jesus
   we shall stand! We shall stand!
   At his name God's enemies
   shall be crushed beneath our feet,
   for there is no other name that is higher
   than Jesus!

Words and Music: Noel Richards

496 There's a blessed time that's coming
(We shall see the King)

1. There's a bless-ed time that's com-ing, com-ing, soon, it may be eve-ning, morn-ing or at noon. There'll be a wed-ding of the Bride, u-ni-ted with the Groom. We shall see the King when he comes.

2. Are you ready should the Saviour call today?
   Would Jesus say, 'Well done' or 'Go away'?
   He's building a home for the pure, the vile can never stay.
   We shall see the King when he comes.

3. O my brother, are you ready for the call?
   We'll crown our Saviour King and Lord of all.
   All the kingdoms of this world shall soon before him fall.
   We shall see the King when he comes.

Words and Music: J.B. Vaughn

497 There's an awesome sound
(Send revival)

Building in strength

1. There's an awe - some sound
   mor - tal King

on the
who will

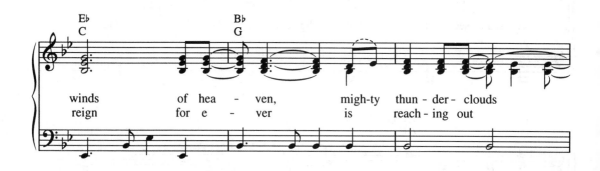

winds   of hea - ven,   migh-ty thun-der-clouds
reign   for e - ver   is   reach-ing out

in   the   skies   a - bove.   The im-
with   his   arms   of

love, his arms of   love,

2. All creation sings of the Lamb of glory
   who laid down his life for all the world.
   What amazing love, that the King of heaven
   should be crucified, stretching out his arms,
   his arms of love, his arms of love.

Words and Music: Richard Lewis

498 There's a place where the streets shine
(Because of you)

Strongly rhythmic

1. There's a place where the streets shine with the
   pain, no more sad - ness, with no more
   joy e - ver - last - ing, there is

glo - ry of the Lamb. There's a way, we can
suf - f'ring, no more tears. No more sin, no more
glad - ness, there is peace. There is wine e - ver -

go there, we can live there be - yond
sick - ness, no in -
flow - ing, there's a

time. Be - cause of you, jus - tice, no more
wed - ding, there's a

to next section

now we have this hope, be - cause of you.

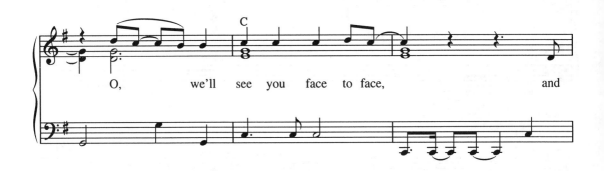

O, we'll see you face to face, and

we will dance to - ge - ther, in the ci - ty of our God,

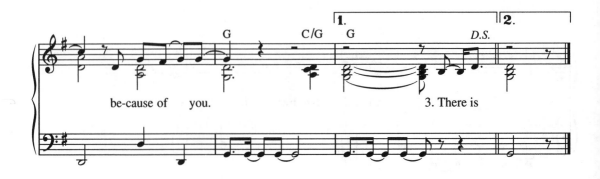

be-cause of you. 3. There is

Words and Music: Paul Oakley

Then I saw a new heaven and a new earth,
for the first heaven and the first earth had passed away,
and there was no longer any sea.
I saw the Holy City, the new Jerusalem,
coming down out of heaven from God,
prepared as a bride beautifully dressed for her husband.
And I heard a loud voice from the throne saying,
'Now the dwelling of God is with men,
and he will live with them.
They will be his people,
and God himself will be with them and be their God.
He will wipe every tear from their eyes.
There will be no more death or mourning
or crying or pain,
for the old order of things has passed away.

I did not see a temple in the city,
because the Lord God Almighty and the Lamb are its temple.
The city does not need the sun or the moon to shine on it,
for the glory of God gives it light,
and the Lamb is its lamp.
The nations will walk by its light,
and the kings of the earth will bring their splendour into it.
On no day will its gates ever be shut,
for there will be no night there.
The glory and honour of the nations will be brought into it.
Nothing impure will ever enter it,
nor will anyone who does what is shameful or deceitful,
but only those whose names are written
in the Lamb's book of life.

Revelation 21:1-4, 22-27

499 There's a river of joy

With energy

Chorus

There's a ri-ver of joy that flows from your throne, O

ri-ver of joy, flow through me. There's a ri-ver of joy that flows

from your throne: come, Ho-ly Spi – rit, with joy,

last time to Coda

come, Ho-ly Spi – rit, with joy. **1.** There's a **2.**

Verse

I will rise up on the wings of an ea-

Words and Music: Taran Ash, James Mott and Matthew Pryce

500 There's a sound of singing

1. There's a sound of sing - ing in our midst, there's an
of - fer - ing of praise. We set our hearts to - wards
you, Lord, with our lips our songs we raise. There is
ju - bi - la - tion in the camp for your pro - mi - ses are true,
and by your grace sal - va - tion comes to

lives we hum - bly bow to you and
stand - ing in this place our songs ex - press our hearts'
de - sire to serve you all our days. We will
hon - our you and mag - ni - fy your name a - bove all names,
for we know there is no o - ther God, yes, you

Words and Music: Matt Redman and Paul Donnelly

As I looked,
thrones were set in place,
and the Ancient of Days took his seat.
His clothing was as white as snow;
the hair of his head was white like wool.
His throne was flaming with fire,
and its wheels were all ablaze.
A river of fire was flowing,
coming out from before him.
Thousands upon thousands attended him;
ten thousand times ten thousand stood before him.

Daniel 7:9-10a

501 There's a wind a-blowing
(Sweet wind)

Rhythmically

1. There's a wind a-blow- ing
2. There's a rain a-pour- ing
3. There's a fi- re burn- ing

all a-cross the land;
sho- wers from a-bove;
fall- ing from the sky;

fra- grant breeze of hea- ven
mer- cy drops are com- ing,
awe- some tongues of fi- re, con-

blow- ing once a-gain.
mer- cy drops of love.
sum- ing you and I.

Don't know where it comes from,
Turn your face to hea- ven,
Can you feel it burn- ing,

Words and Music: David Ruis

502 There's no one like you

1. There's no one like you, my Lord, no one could take your place; my heart beats to wor - ship you, I live just to

I long for your pre - sence, Lord, to serve you is

Words and Music: Eddie Espinosa

God is spirit,
and his worshippers must worship in spirit
and in truth.

John 4:24

503 These are the days
(Days of Elijah)

1. These are the days of E-li-jah, de-clar-ing the word of the Lord; and these are the days of your ser-vant, Mo-ses, right-eous-ness be-ing re-stored. And though these are days of great tri-al, of fa-mine and dark-ness and

2. These are the days of E-ze-kiel, the dry bones be-com-ing as flesh; and these are the days of your ser-vant, Da-vid, re-build-ing a tem-ple of praise. These are the days of the har-vest, the fields are as white in the

sword, still we are the voice in the de-sert cry-ing, 'Pre-
world, and we are the lab-'rers in your vine-yard, de-

Chorus

pare ye the way of the Lord.' Be-hold, he comes rid-ing on the
clar-ing the word of the Lord.

clouds, shin-ing like the sun at the trum-pet call; lift your

voice, it's the year of ju-bi-lee, out of Zi-on's hill sal-va-tion comes.

last time

Words and Music: Robin Mark

504 The Spirit of the sovereign Lord

1. The Spi-rit of the sov-'reign Lord is up-on you/us because he has a-noin-ted you/us to preach good news; the
Spi-rit of the sov-'reign God is up-on you/us because he has a-noin-ted you/us to preach good news.

(Leader) He has sent you to the poor, (All) this is the year,
He will com-fort all who mourn,

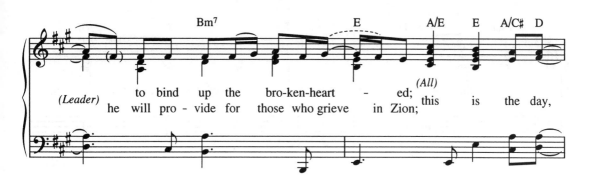

(Leader) to bind up the bro-ken-heart - ed;
(Leader) he will pro - vide for those who grieve in Zion; *(All)* this is the day,

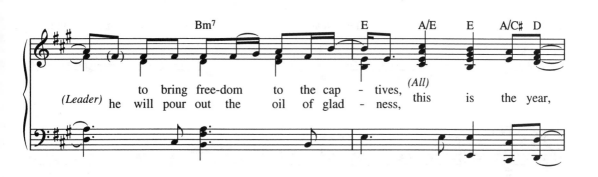

(Leader) to bring free-dom to the cap - tives,
(Leader) he will pour out the oil of glad - ness, *(All)* this is the year,

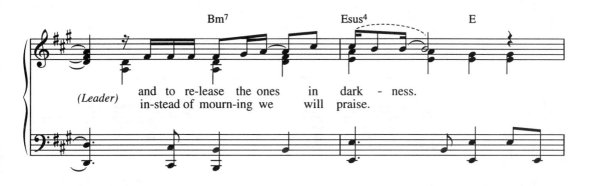

(Leader) and to re-lease the ones in dark - ness.
in-stead of mourn-ing we will praise.

(All) This is the year of the fa - vour of the Lord,

Words and Music: Andy Park

505 The steadfast love of the Lord

Worshipfully

The stead-fast love of the Lord ne-ver cea-ses, his mer-cies ne-ver come to an end. They are new ev-'ry morn-ing, new ev-'ry morn-ing; great is thy faith-ful-ness, O Lord, great is thy faith-ful-ness.

Words and Music: Edith McNeil

506 The trumpets sound, the angels sing
(The feast is ready)

(Leader, spoken) In Jesus, God has prepared a feast of good things for all who will accept his invitation. Come on: the feast is ready!

1. The trumpets sound, the angels sing, the feast is ready to begin; the gates of heav'n are open wide, and Jesus

2. Tables are laden with good things, O taste the peace and joy he brings; he'll fill you up with love divine, he'll turn your

3. The hungry heart he satisfies, offers the poor his paradise; now hear all heav'n and earth applaud the amazing

Words and Music: Graham Kendrick

I consider everything a loss
compared to the surpassing greatness
of knowing Christ Jesus my Lord,
for whose sake I have lost all things.
I consider them rubbish,
that I may gain Christ and be found in him,
not having a righteousness of my own
that comes from the law,
but that which is through faith in Christ –
the righteousness that comes from God
and is by faith.

Philippians 3:8-9

507 The Word made flesh
(We await a Saviour from heaven)

1. The Word made flesh, full of truth and grace, the light of men, God in-car-nate came. He lived, he loved, a ser-vant hum-ble, meek, and in his voice we hear the Fa-ther speak. We a-wait a Sa-viour from hea-

- ven, and he will sure - ly come, in his glo - ry and with the an - gels and the pow - er of his throne. The Christ from hea - ven re - turn - ing, his pro - mise to ful - fil be - fore the splen-dour of his pre - sence, let the earth be still.

2. Such hate, such scorn, and a traitor's kiss
   led to the cross for such a world as this.
   The death he died, the grave in which he laid
   could not hold him; to life again he came.

3. Now death destroyed, the grave left open wide,
   our Saviour reigns at the Father's side.
   Where death your sting, where your pow'r, O grave?
   The Son of God prepares to come again.

Words and Music: Wes Sutton

508 The world is looking for a hero
(Champion)

With strength

Verse

1. The world is look-ing for a he-ro;

we know the great-est one of all:

the migh-ty ru-ler of the na-tions,

King of kings and Lord of lords,

who took the na-ture of a ser-vant,

2. The Lord Almighty is our hero,
   he breaks the stranglehold of sin.
   Through Jesus' love we fear no evil;
   pow'rs of darkness flee from him.
   His light will shine in ev'ry nation,
   a sword of justice he will bring.

Words and Music: Noel and Tricia Richards

Praise the Lord.
Praise the Lord, O my soul.
I will praise the Lord all my life;
I will sing praise to my God as long as I live.

Do not put your trust in princes,
in mortal men, who cannot save.
When their spirit departs, they return to the ground;
on that very day their plans come to nothing.

Blessed is he whose help is the God of Jacob,
whose hope is in the Lord his God,
the Maker of heaven and earth,
the sea, and everything in them –
the Lord, who remains faithful for ever.
He upholds the cause of the oppressed
and gives food to the hungry.
The Lord sets prisoners free,
the Lord gives sight to the blind,
the Lord lifts up those who are bowed down,
the Lord loves the righteous.
The Lord watches over the alien
and sustains the fatherless and the widow,
but he frustrates the ways of the wicked.

The Lord reigns for ever,
your God, O Zion, for all generations.

Praise the Lord.

Psalm 146

509 They that wait

Words and Music: Kevin Prosch

510 Thine be the glory

MACCABAEUS 10 11 11 11 and Refrain

1. Thine be the glo - ry, ri - sen, con-qu'ring Son,

end - less is the vic - t'ry thou o'er death hast won;

an - gels in bright rai - ment rolled the stone a - way,

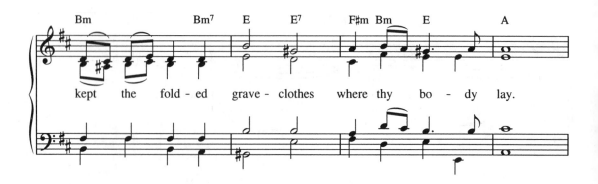

kept the fold - ed grave - clothes where thy bo - dy lay.

Chorus (unison)

Thine be the glo - ry, ri - sen, con-qu'ring Son,

end - less is the vic - t'ry thou o'er death hast won.

2. Lo! Jesus meets us, risen from the tomb;
   lovingly he greets us, scatters fear and gloom.
   Let the church with gladness hymns of triumph sing,
   for her Lord now liveth; death hast lost its sting.

3. No more we doubt thee, glorious Prince of Life;
   life is naught without thee: aid us in our strife.
   Make us more than conqu'rors through thy deathless love;
   bring us safe through Jordan to thy home above.

Text: Edmond Louis Budry trans. Richard Birch Hoyle
Music: George Frideric Handel

511 This Child

Calypso

1. This Child, se-cret-ly comes in the night, O this Child, hid-ing a hea-ven-ly light, O this Child, com-ing to us like a stran-ger, this hea-ven-ly Child. This

Child, hea-ven come down now to be with us here, hea-ven-ly love

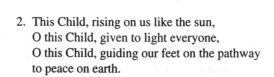

2. This Child, rising on us like the sun,
   O this Child, given to light everyone,
   O this Child, guiding our feet on the pathway
   to peace on earth.

3. This Child, raising the humble and poor,
   O this Child, making the proud ones to fall;
   O this Child, filling the hungry with good things,
   this heavenly Child.

Words and Music: Graham Kendrick

512 This grace is mine
(The power and the glory)

1. This grace is mine, this glo-ry, earth-bound hea-ven sent

this plan di-vine, this life, this light that breaks my night,

the Spi-rit of God hea-ven falls like a dove to my heart.

to verse 2

The pow-er and the glo-ry of your name.

2. This love is mine, so undeserved, this glorious name,
   this Son, this God, this life, this death, this vict'ry won,
   forgiveness has flowed and this grace that is mine finds my heart.

3. This life is mine, so perfect and so pure, this God in me,
   this glorious hope from earth to heaven, death to life,
   this future assured and secured by this love in my heart.

Words and Music: Geoff Bullock

513 This, in essence, is the message
(God is light)

This, in es - sence, is the mes - sage we

heard from Christ. This, in es -

- sence, is the mes - sage we heard from

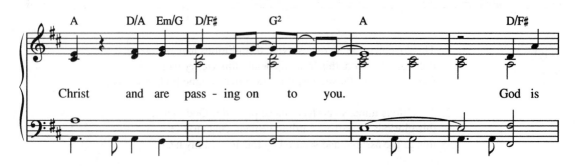

Christ and are pass - ing on to you. God is

light, God is light, pure

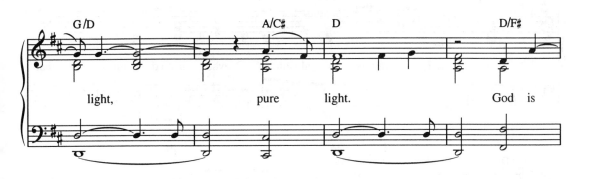

light, pure light. God is

light, pure light. There's

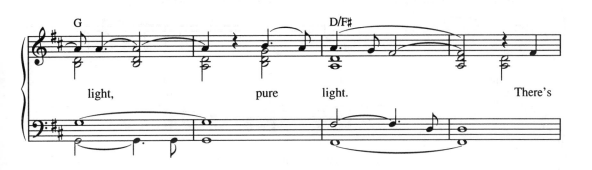

not a trace of dark - ness in him.

Words and Music: Gary Sadler and Lynn DeShazo

514 This is my beloved Son
(That the Lamb who was slain)

1. This is my be-lov-ed Son who tast-ed death that you, my child, might live. See the blood he shed for you, what suf-fer-ing, say what more could he give? Cloth'd in his per-fec-tion bring praise, a fra-grance sweet,

2. Look, the world's great harvest fields
   are ready now
   and Christ commands us: 'Go!'
   Countless souls are dying
   so hopelessly,
   his wondrous love unknown.
   Lord, give us the nations
   for the glory of the King.
   Father, send more lab'rers
   the lost to gather in.

3. Come the day when we will stand
   there face to face,
   what joy will fill his eyes.
   For at last his bride appears
   so beautiful,
   her glory fills the skies.
   Drawn from every nation,
   people, tribe and tongue;
   all creation sings,
   the wedding has begun.

Words and Music: Graham Kendrick

515 This is my desire
(I give you my heart)

Words and Music: Reuben Morgan

516 This is the day that the Lord has made

Words and Music: Bob Fitts

517 This is the day

Brightly, with pace

This is the day, this is the day that the Lord has made, that the
Lord has made; we shall re-joice, we shall re-joice and be
glad in it, and be glad in it. This is the day that the
Lord has made, we shall re-joice and be glad in it;
this is the day, this is the day that the Lord has made.

Words and Music: Les Garrett

518 This is the message of the cross
(Message of the cross)

1. This is the mes-sage of the cross,
2. This is the mes-sage of the cross,
3. This is the mes-sage of the cross,

that we can be free, to live in the
that we can be free, to lay all our
that we can be free, to hun-ger for

vic - to - ry and turn from our sin.
bur-dens here, at the foot of the tree.
hea-ven, to hun-ger for thee.

My pre - cious Lord Je - sus,
The cross was the shame of the world,
The cross is such fool - ish - ness

Words and Music: Martin Smith

519 This is the mystery
(Let the Bride say, 'Come')

With strength

1. This is the mys - te - ry, that Christ has cho - sen you and me, to
2. She's crowned in splen - dour and a roy - al di - a - dem, the
3. Now hear the Bride - groom call, 'Be - lov - ed, come a - side; the

be the re - vel - a - tion of his glo - ry;
King is en - thralled by her beau - ty.
time of be - tro - thal is at hand.

a cho - sen, roy - al, ho - ly peo - ple set a - part and loved, a
A - dorned in right - eous - ness, ar - rayed in glo - rious light, the
Lift up your eyes and see the dawn - ing of the day, when as

bride pre - par - ing for her King.
Bride is wait - ing for her King. Let the Bride say, 'Come', let the
King, I'll re - turn to claim my Bride.'

Bride say, 'Come', let the Bride of the Lamb say,

'Come, Lord Je - sus!' Let the Bride say, 'Come', let the

Bride say, 'Come', let the Bride of the Lamb say,

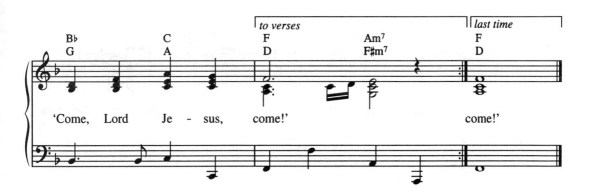

to verses *last time*

'Come, Lord Je - sus, come!' come!'

Words and Music: Philip Lawson Johnston and Chris Bowater

520 This is the sweetest mystery

of Man, and yet with-in this won - drous plan the

Spi - rit with us here.

2. Lord, may this truth become a flame
   that burns within our hearts again,
   that we may glorify your name
   in all we do and say.
   And so, dear Lord, we gladly come
   to stand before the Three in One,
   and worship Father, Spirit, Son;
   accept the praise we bring.

Words and Music: Andy Piercy and Dave Clifton

This is the time
(Distant thunder)

see 610

In order to keep *The Source* as relevant and up to date as possible, we added this new song to the collection after the contents had been finalised. For this reason it is included out of alphabetical order and will be found at number 610.

521 This love
(Now is the time)

This love, this hope, this peace

of God, this right - eous - ness, this faith, this joy,

this life, com-plete in me. Now healed

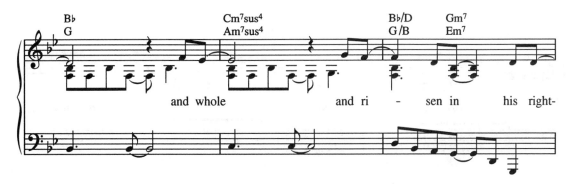

and whole and ri - sen in his right-

Words and Music: Geoff Bullock

522 Though I feel afraid
(All I know)

Moderately

Verse

1. Though I feel a-fraid of ter - ri - t'ry un-known, I know that I can say that I do not stand a - lone. For Je - sus, you have pro - mised your pre-sence in my heart; I can - not see the end - ing, but it's here that I must start. And

Chorus

all I know is you have called me, and that I will fol - low is all

I can say. I will go where you will send me, and your fire lights my way.

1.

2. What your fire lights my way.

Your fire lights my way.

2. What lies across the waves
   may cause my heart to fear;
   will I survive the day,
   must I leave what's known and dear?
   A ship that's in the harbour
   is still and safe from harm,
   but it was not built to be there,
   it was made for wind and storm.

Words and Music: Ian White

523 Though the earth should tremble
(I worship you, eternal God)

2. Though earth's kingdoms crumble
   and the nations rage
   and rulers and kings come and go,
   yours is the kingdom unshaken,
   and you've never forsaken your own.

Words and Music: Mark Altrogge

524 To be in your presence
(My desire)

2. To rest in your presence, not rushing away,
   to cherish each moment, here I would stay.

Words and Music: Noel Richards

525 To every good thing God is doing
(Amen)

To ev-'ry good thing God is do-ing with-in me that I can-not see, a-men. And to the heal-ing vir-tue of Je-sus that's flow-ing in me, a-

Words and Music: Bob Fitts

526 To God be the glory!

TO GOD BE THE GLORY 11 11 11 11 and Refrain

1. To God be the glory! great things he hath done; so loved he the world that he gave us his Son; who yield-ed his life an a-tone-ment for sin, and o-pened the life-gate that all may go in. Praise the Lord, praise the Lord! let the earth hear his

voice; praise the Lord, praise the Lord! let the peo - ple re - joice: O come to the Fa - ther, through Je - sus the Son, and give him the glo - ry; great things he hath done!

2. O perfect redemption, the purchase of blood!
   to ev'ry believer the promise of God;
   the vilest offender who truly believes
   that moment from Jesus a pardon receives.

3. Great things he hath taught us, great things he hath done,
   and great our rejoicing through Jesus the Son;
   but purer, and higher, and greater will be
   our wonder, our rapture, when Jesus we see.

Text: Frances Jane van Alstyne (Fanny J. Crosby)
Music: William Howard Doane

One thing I ask of the Lord,
this is what I seek:
that I may dwell in the house of the Lord
all the days of my life,
to gaze upon the beauty of the Lord
and to seek him in his temple.

Psalm 27:4

527 To keep your lovely face

Words and Music: Graham Kendrick

528 Tonight
(Glory to God)

Words and Music: Graham Kendrick

529 To you, O Lord, I bring my worship
(Release my soul)

Words and Music: Craig Musseau

530 To you, O Lord, I lift up my soul

1. To you, O Lord, I lift up my soul.
2. Show me your ways and teach me your paths.

In you I trust, O my God.
Guide me in truth, lead me on;

Do not let me be put to shame,
for you're my God, you are my Sa - viour.

nor let my e - ne - mies tri - umph o - ver me.
My hope is in you each mo - ment of the day.

Chorus
No one whose hope is in you

Words and Music: Graham Kendrick

I will extol the Lord at all times;
his praise will always be on my lips.
My soul will boast in the Lord;
let the afflicted hear and rejoice.
Glorify the Lord with me:
let us exalt his name together.
I sought the Lord, and he answered me;
he delivered me from all my fears.
Those who look to him are radiant;
their faces are never covered with shame.
This poor man called, and the Lord heard him;
he saved him out of all his troubles.
The angel of the Lord encamps
around those who fear him,
and he delivers them.
Taste and see that the Lord is good;
blessed is the man who takes refuge in him.

Psalm 34:1-8

531 Turn our hearts

Turn our hearts, turn our

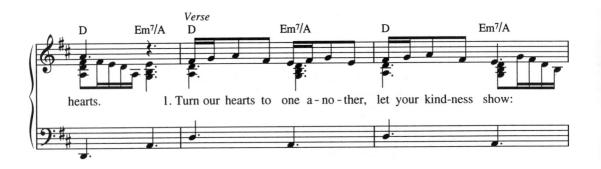

hearts. 1. Turn our hearts to one a-no-ther, let your kind-ness show:

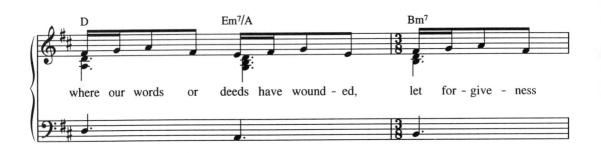

where our words or deeds have wound-ed, let for-give-ness

flow. Turn our hearts,

change   our   hearts,   join   our

hearts,   turn   our   hearts.

2. Turn our hearts from pride and anger
   to your ways of peace,
   for you died and shed your blood
   that enmity may cease.

3. Turn the hearts of generations
   that we may be one:
   make us partners in the kingdom
   till your work is done.

4. As we all have been forgiven,
   so must we forgive;
   as we all have found acceptance,
   so let us receive.

Words and Music: Graham Kendrick

532 Turn to me and be saved

o-ther. For you are God, and there is no

o - ther. For you are God, and there is no

All sing own prayers

12 times

o - ther.

SHOUT

Leader	Now, Lord, send your Holy Spirit.
All	Now, Lord, send your Holy Spirit.
Leader	Drench this land with your awesome presence.
All	Drench this land with your awesome presence.
Leader	Send your Holy Spirit more powerfully.
All	Send your Holy Spirit more powerfully.
Leader	Let grace and mercy flood this land.
All	Let grace and mercy flood this land.
Leader	Let mercy triumph over judgement.
All	Let mercy triumph over judgement.
Leader	Let mercy triumph over judgement.
All	Let mercy triumph over judgement.

Words and Music: Graham Kendrick

533 Turn your eyes upon Jesus

Turn your eyes up-on Je -
sus, look full in his won-der-ful face,
and the things of earth will grow strange - ly
dim in the light of his glo - ry and grace.

to repeat

last time
grace.

Words and Music: Helen H. Lemmel

534 Wake up, my soul

Words and Music: Matt Redman

535 Wake up, O sleeper

Wake up, O sleep-er   and   rise from the dead,

and Christ will shine on   you.

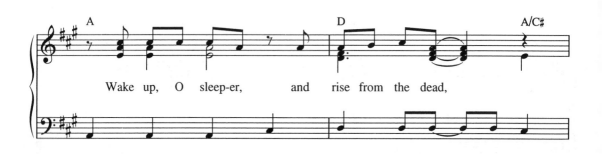

Wake up, O sleep-er,   and   rise from the dead,

and Christ will shine on   you.

1. Once you were dark-ness, but now you are light,
now you are light in the Lord.
So as true child-ren of light you must live,
show-ing the glo-ry of God.

2. This is the beautiful fruit of the light,
the good, the righteous, the true.
Let us discover what pleases the Lord
in everything we do.

3. As days get darker, take care how you live,
not as unwise, but as wise,
making the most of each moment he gives,
and pressing on for the prize.

Words and Music: Graham Kendrick

536 We are a people of power

Driving rock

We are a people of power,
we are a people of praise;
we are a people of promise,
Je-sus has ri-sen, he's con-quered the grave!

Words and Music: Trevor King

537 We are his children
(Go forth in his name)

With life

Verse

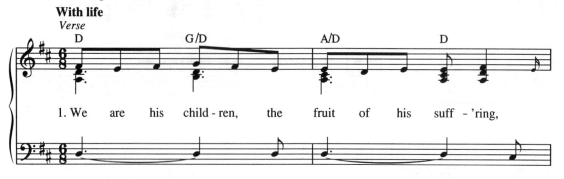

1. We are his child-ren, the fruit of his suff-'ring,

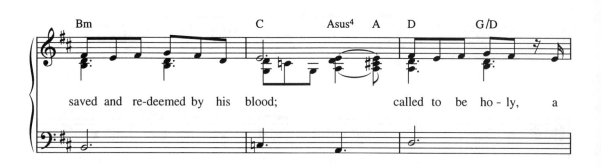

saved and re-deemed by his blood; called to be ho-ly, a

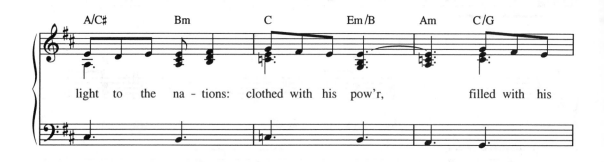

light to the na-tions: clothed with his pow'r, filled with his

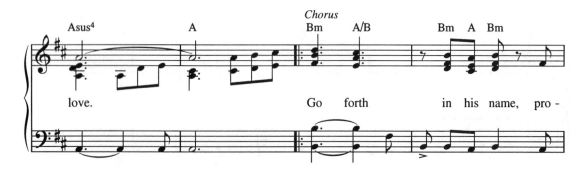

love. Go forth in his name, pro-

claim - ing, 'Je - sus reigns!' Now is the time for the

church to a - rise and pro - claim him 'Je - sus,

1.

Sa-viour, Re-deem – er and Lord'.

2.

Lord'.

2. Countless the souls that are stumbling in darkness;
   why do we sleep in the light?
   Jesus commands us to go make disciples,
   this is our cause, this is our fight.

3. Listen, the wind of the Spirit is blowing,
   the end of the age is so near;
   powers in the earth and heavens are shaking,
   Jesus our Lord soon shall appear!

Words and Music: Graham Kendrick

Therefore God exalted him to the highest place
and gave him the name that is above every name,
that at the name of Jesus every knee should bow,
in heaven and on earth and under the earth,
and every tongue confess that Jesus Christ is Lord,
to the glory of God the Father.

Philippians 2:9-11

538 We are his people
(Shout to the Lord)

In a steady half-time

Lyrics:

We are his peo - ple, he gives us mu -
But there is a cry in our hearts, like when deep calls un -

- sic to sing. There is a sound now, like the
- to the deep, for your breath of de - liv - 'rance, to

sound of the Lord when his e - ne - mies flee.
breathe on the mu - sic we so des-p'rate-ly need.

But with-out your

Words and Music: Kevin Prosch

539 We are marching

1. We are march - ing in the light of God, we are march-ing in the light of God. We are march-ing in the light of God. We are march-ing, march-ing, we are march-ing, oh, we are march-ing in the light of God.

2. We are living in the love of God . . .

3. We are moving in the pow'r of God . . .

Words and Music: Traditional African

540 We are the army of God
(Army of God)

With a steady rhythm

We are the ar-my of God, child-ren of A-bra-ham,

we are a cho - sen ge-ne-ra - tion.

Un - der a co-ve-nant, washed by his pre-cious blood,

filled with the migh - ty Ho - ly Ghost. And I

hear the sound of the com-ing rain,

Words and Music: Kevin Prosch

541 We believe

1. We believe in God the Father, Maker of the universe, and in Christ his Son, our Saviour, come to us by virgin birth. We believe he died to save us, bore our sins, was crucified. Then from death he rose victorious, ascended to the Father's side.

2. We believe he sends his Spirit
   on his church with gifts of pow'r.
   God, his word of truth affirming,
   sends us to the nations now.
   He will come again in glory,
   judge the living and the dead.
   Ev'ry knee shall bow before him,
   then must ev'ry tongue confess.

Words and Music: Graham Kendrick

I will sacrifice a thank-offering to you
and call on the name of the Lord.
I will fulfil my vows to the Lord
in the presence of all his people,
in the courts of the house of the Lord –
in your midst, O Jerusalem.
Praise the Lord.

Psalm 116:17-19

542 We bring the sacrifice of praise

Words and Music: Kirk Dearman

543 We come into your presence
(Father of creation)

We come in-to your pre-sence to sing a song to you, a song of praise and hon-our for all the things you've helped us through; you gave a life worth liv-ing, a life in love with you, and now I just love giv-ing all my prai-ses back to you. You're the

Words and Music: Robert Eastwood

544 We declare your majesty

Words and Music: Malcolm du Plessis

545 We do not presume
(Prayer of humble access)

Meditatively

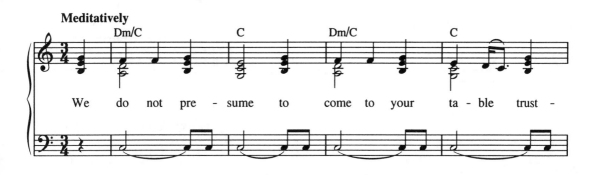

We do not pre - sume to come to your ta - ble trust -

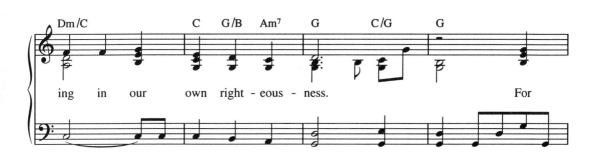

ing in our own right - eous - ness. For

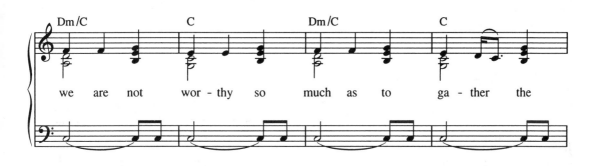

we are not wor - thy so much as to ga - ther the

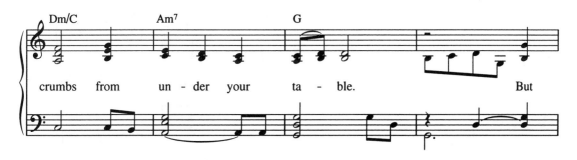

crumbs from un - der your ta - ble. But

Words and Music: Andy Piercy

546 We have a great priest

he who pro-mised is faith - ful, for

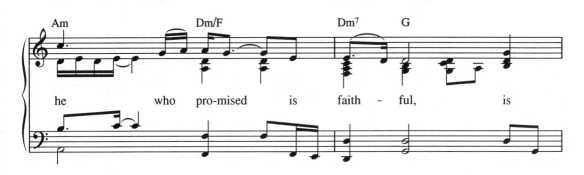

he who pro-mised is faith - ful, is

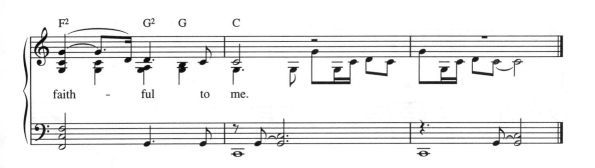

faith - ful to me.

2. Give me a pure heart,
   holding to your hope,
   the hope I profess, Lord,
   lead me in your way;
   be now my strength, Lord,
   and all of my trust, Lord,
   I will fear no one,
   for you are with me.

Words and Music: Dave Clifton

547 We have prayed that you would have mercy
(Let it rain)

We have prayed that you would have mer - cy;
we be - lieve from hea - ven you've heard.
Heal our land, so dry and so thir - sty;
we have strayed so far from you, Lord.
Your cloud ap - peared on the ho - ri - zon,

Words and Music: Paul Oakley

548 Welcome, King of kings

Brightly, with strength

Wel - come, King of kings! How great is your name. You come in ma-jes-ty for e -ver to reign. reign.

1. You rule the na - tions, they shake at the sound of your name. To you is gi - ven all pow'r and you shall reign.

2. Let all creation bow down
   at the sound of your name.
   Let ev'ry tongue now confess,
   the Lord God reigns.

Words and Music: Noel Richards

549 Welcome the King

1. Wel-come the King, wel-come the King, wel-come the King, wel-come the King,
2. Who is this King, who is this King, who is this King, who is this King,

wel-come the King who comes in the name of the Lord.
who is this King who comes in the name of the Lord?

Wel-come the King, wel-come the King, wel-come the King, wel-come the King,
Who is this King, who is this King, who is this King, who is this King,

wel-come the King who comes in the name of the Lord.
who is this King who comes in the name of the Lord?

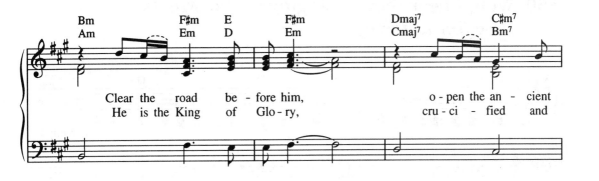

Clear the road be - fore him, o - pen the an - cient
He is the King of Glo - ry, cru - ci - fied and

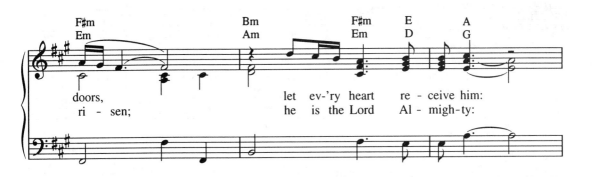

doors, let ev-'ry heart re - ceive him:
ri - sen; he is the Lord Al - migh-ty:

1.

wel-come the King who comes in the name of the Lord.

2.

Lord; wel-come the King who comes in the name of the Lord.

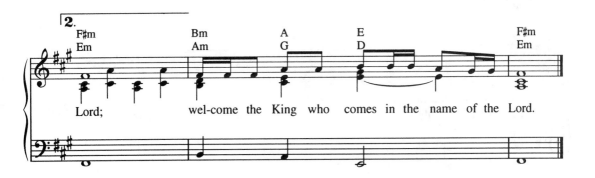

Words and Music: Graham Kendrick

550 Well, I hear they're singing in the streets
(I've found Jesus)

lift – ed me from where I was, set my feet up - on a rock,

hum-bled that you e – ven know 'bout me. Now

I have cho-sen to be - lieve, be - liev - ing that you've cho - sen me;

I was lost but now I've found– I've found

Words and Music: Martin Smith arr. L. Hills

Praise be to the God and Father of our Lord Jesus Christ!
In his great mercy he has given us new birth into a living hope
through the resurrection of Jesus Christ from the dead.

1 Peter 1:3

551 We'll walk the land
(Let the flame burn brighter)

With a strong rhythm

1. We'll walk the land with hearts on fire; and ev-'ry
   years, and still the flame is burn-ing
   truth, speak out for love; in Je - sus'

step will be a prayer. Hope is ris - ing, new day
bright a-cross the land. Hearts are wait - ing, long-ing,
name we shall be strong, to lift the fall - en, to save the

dawn - ing; sound of sing - ing fills the air.
ach - ing, for a - wak - 'ning once a - gain.
child - ren, to fill the na - tion with your song.

1.

2. Two thou - sand

2, 3. *Chorus*

Let the flame burn

Let the flame burn bright-er in the heart of the dark - ness, turn-ing night to glo-rious

Words and Music: Graham Kendrick

552 We march to the tune of a love-song
(We lift up a shout)

Words and Music: Steven Fry

553 We must work together
(We'll see it all)

Words and Music: Ian Mizen and Andy Pressdee

554 We rejoice in the goodness of our God

We re-joice in the good-ness of our God,

we re-joice in the won-ders of your fa-vour.

You've set the cap-tives free,

you've caused the blind to see,

hal-le-lu-jah, you give us li-ber-ty,

2. You give us hope, you give us joy,
   you give us fullness of life to enjoy.
   Our shepherd and provider,
   our God who's always there,
   never failing, always true.

Words and Music: Carol Owen

555 We serve a God of miracles
(We serve a God of power)

Words and Music: Mark Altrogge

556 We shall stand

to verses

1. Lord, you have cho – sen me for fruit – ful-ness, to be trans-formed in-to your like – ness. I'm gon-na fight on through till I see you face to face.

2. Lord, as your witnesses
   you've appointed us.
   And with your Holy Spirit
   anointed us.
   And so I'll fight on through
   till I see you face to face.

Words and Music: Graham Kendrick

Blessed are they whose ways are blameless,
who walk according to the law of the Lord.
Blessed are they who keep his statutes
and seek him with all their heart.

Psalm 119:1-2

557 We've had a light
(Surely the time has come)

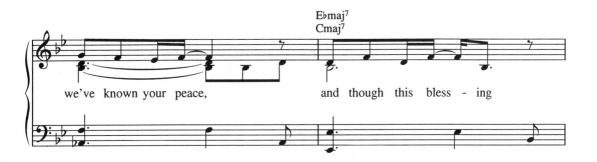

Words and Music: Matt Redman

Dear friends, let us love one another,
for love comes from God.
Everyone who loves
has been born of God and knows God.

Dear friends, since God so loved us,
we also ought to love one another.

1 John 4:7, 11

558 We want to remain in your love

Love is pa - tient, love is kind, does not en -

- vy, does not boast, is not proud, is not

rude; love does not re - joice in e - vil, but re - joi -

- ces with the truth. Love pro - tects, al - ways

trusts, al - ways hopes, and per - se - veres,

is slow to an - ger, ne - ver fails; love does

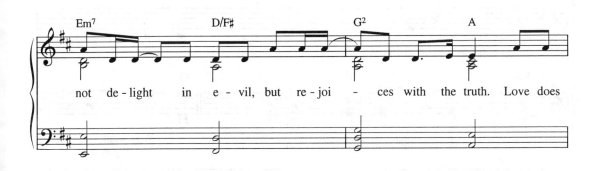

not de - light in e - vil, but re - joi - ces with the truth. Love does

not de - light in e - vil, but re - joi - ces with the truth.

Words and Music: Andy Piercy and Dave Clifton

559 We want to see Jesus lifted high

Words and Music: Doug Horley

O God, you are my God,
earnestly I seek you;
my soul thirsts for you,
my body longs for you,
in a dry and weary land
where there is no water.

I have seen you in the sanctuary
and beheld your power and your glory.
Because your love is better than life,
my lips will glorify you.
I will praise you as long as I live,
and in your name I will lift up my hands.

Psalm 63:1-4

560 We will cross every border
(Cross every border)

Fairly slow, with strength

1. We will cross ev-'ry bor-der, throw wide ev-'ry door, join-ing our hands a-cross the na-tions, we'll pro-claim Je-sus is Lord. -ward. Then we'll pro-claim Je-sus is Lord. We shall pro-claim Je-sus is Lord.

2. We will break sin's oppression,
   speak out for the poor,
   announce the coming of Christ's kingdom
   from east to west and shore to shore.

3. We will gather in the harvest,
   and work while it's day,
   though we may sow with tears of sadness,
   we will reap with shouts of joy.

4. Soon our eyes shall see his glory,
   the Lamb, our risen Lord,
   when he receives from ev'ry nation
   his blood-bought Bride, his great reward.
   Then we'll proclaim Jesus is Lord.
   We shall proclaim Jesus is Lord.

Words and Music: Graham Kendrick

561 We will run and not grow weary
(We will wait)

Words and Music: Tricia Allen and Martin J. Nystrom

562 We will turn the hearts

Calypso feel

We will turn the hearts of the fa - thers so they will look a - gain to their child - ren. We will turn the hearts of the child - ren so that to - ge - ther we can look to you. We will

1. to repeat *to end*

2. to continue The young and the old now, stand-ing to - ge - ther,

The walls have been broken, we stand as one now,
one in the Spirit and won by your blood.
We're moving forwards under your banner,
telling the world of your glory.
And we take on your promise,
together we'll welcome the Day of the Lord!

Words and Music: Kath Hall

563 We will worship the Lamb of glory

2. Bless the name of the Lamb of glory,
I bless the name of the King of kings;
bless the name of the Lamb of glory,
bless the name of the King.

Words and Music: Dennis Jernigan

564 We worship and adore you

We wor-ship and a-dore you, Lord, hear us when we call,

for there is no god a-bove you, you

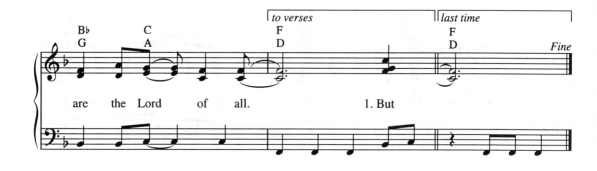

are the Lord of all. 1. But

how can we be-gin to ex-press what's on our hearts?
of men and an - gels we need, to sing your praise,

Words and Music: Andy Piercy (v.3 Cecil Frances Alexander) arr. Alison Berry

565 What a friend I've found
(Jesus, friend for ever)

1. What a friend I've found, clo-ser than a bro-ther.

I have felt your touch, more in-ti-mate than lo-vers.

Je - sus, Je - sus,

Je - sus, friend for e - ver.

2. What a hope I've found,
more faithful than a mother.
It would break my heart,
to ever lose each other.

Words and Music: Martin Smith

© Copyright 1996 Curious? Music UK. Administered by Kingsway's
Thankyou Music, P.O. Box 75, Eastbourne, East Sussex, BN23 6NW, UK. Used by permission.

566 What a friend we have in Jesus

WHAT A FRIEND (CONVERSE) 87 87 D

1. What a friend we have in Jesus, all our sins and griefs to bear!
What a privilege to carry ev-'ry-thing to him in prayer!
O what peace we of-ten for-feit, O what need-less pain we bear,
all be-cause we do not carry ev-'ry-thing to God in prayer!

2. Have we trials and temptations?
Is there trouble anywhere?
We should never be discouraged:
take it to the Lord in prayer!
Can we find a friend so faithful,
who will all our sorrows share?
Jesus knows our ev'ry weakness –
take it to the Lord in prayer!

3. Are we weak and heavy-laden,
cumbered with a load of care?
Jesus is our only refuge,
take it to the Lord in prayer!
Do thy friends despise, forsake thee?
Take it to the Lord in prayer!
In his arms he'll take and shield thee,
thou wilt find a solace there.

Words: Joseph Medlicott Scriven
Music: Charles Crozat Converse

567 What kind of greatness

O what else can I do but kneel and wor - ship you, and come just as I am, my whole life an of - fer - ing.

2. The One in whom we live and move
   in swaddling cloths lies bound.
   The voice that cried, 'Let there be light',
   asleep without a sound.
   The One who strode among the stars,
   and called each one by name,
   lies helpless in a mother's arms
   and must learn to walk again.

3. What greater love could he have shown
   to shamed humanity,
   yet human pride hates to believe
   in such deep humility.
   But nations now may see his grace
   and know that he is near,
   when his meek heart, his words, his works
   are incarnate in us here.

Words and Music: Graham Kendrick

568 What kind of love is this

1. What kind of love is this that

gave it-self for me? I

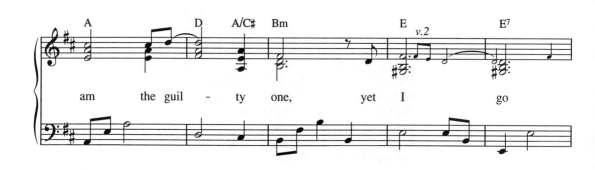

am the guil - ty one, yet I go

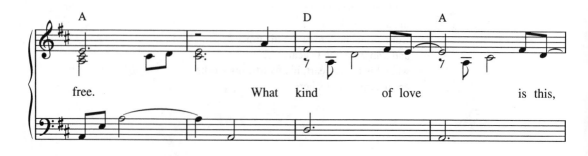

free. What kind of love is this,

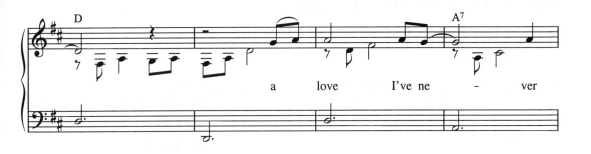

a love I've ne - ver

known? I did - n't e - ven know his

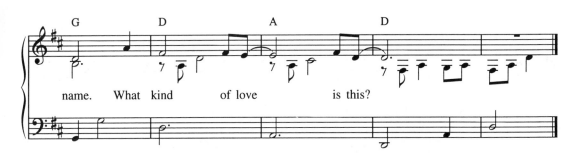

name. What kind of love is this?

2. What kind of man is this
   that died in agony?
   He who had done no wrong
   was crucified for me.
   What kind of man is this
   who laid aside his throne,
   that I may know the love of God?
   What kind of man is this?

3. By grace I have been saved;
   it is the gift of God.
   He destined me to be his child,
   such is his love.
   No eye has ever seen,
   no ear has ever heard,
   nor has the heart of man conceived
   what kind of love is this.

Words and Music: Bryn and Sally Haworth

569 What noise shall we make

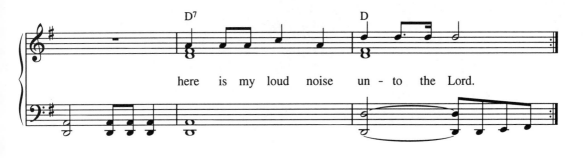

here is my loud noise un-to the Lord.

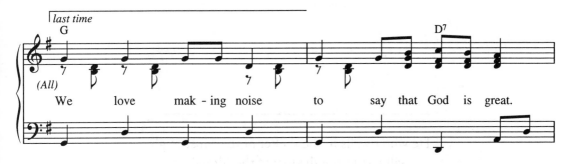

last time

(All) We love mak-ing noise to say that God is great.

We love mak-ing noise un-to the Lord.

2. Let's make a quiet noise . . .
   Here is my quiet noise . . .

3. Let's make a fast noise . . .
   Here is my fast noise . . .

4. Let's make a slow noise . . .
   Here is my slow noise . . .

5. Let's make a joyful noise . . .
   Here is my joyful noise . . .

6. Let's make a praising noise . . .
   Here is my praising noise . . .

   We love making noise
   to say that God is great.
   We love making noise
   unto the Lord.

Words and Music: Lucy East

He who dwells in the shelter of the Most High
will rest in the shadow of the Almighty.
I will say of the Lord,
'He is my refuge and my fortress,
my God, in whom I trust.'

Psalm 91:1-2

570 When I feel the touch

Words and Music: Keri Jones and David Matthew

571 When I look into your holiness

Words and Music: Wayne and Cathy Perrin

572 When I survey the wondrous cross (Tune 1)

ROCKINGHAM LM

1. When I sur-vey the won-drous cross on which the Prince of Glo-ry died, my rich-est gain I count but loss, and pour con-tempt on all my pride.

572a When I survey the wondrous cross (Tune 2)

O WALY WALY LM

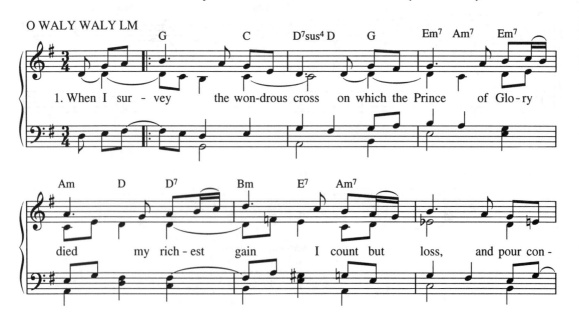

1. When I sur-vey the won-drous cross on which the Prince of Glo-ry died my rich-est gain I count but loss, and pour con-

2. Forbid it, Lord, that I should boast,
   save in the death of Christ, my God:
   all the vain things that charm me most,
   I sacrifice them to his blood.

3. See from his head, his hands, his feet,
   sorrow and love flow mingling down:
   did e'er such love and sorrow meet,
   or thorns compose so rich a crown?

4. Were the whole realm of nature mine,
   that were an off'ring far too small;
   love so amazing, so divine,
   demands my soul, my life, my all.

Words: Isaac Watts
Music – Tune 1: adapted by Edward Miller
Tune 2: Somerset folk song collected by Cecil Sharp arr. Richard Lloyd

573 When my heart is overwhelmed
(Lead me to the rock)

1. When my heart is o-ver-whelmed, hear my cry, give heed to my prayer; and my eyes are dim with tears, O Fa - ther, make them clear; from the ends of all the earth, when my heart is faint - ing,

2. You, O Lord, have been for me a ref - uge from my e - ne - mies; let me live with- in your strength, in the shel - ter of your wings:

Words and Music: Lynn DeShazo

574 When peace like a river

soul. It is well (it is well) with my soul (with my

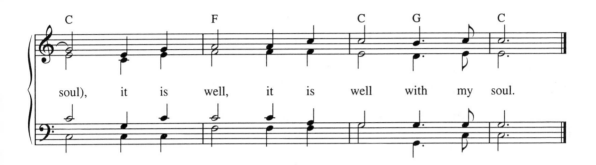

soul), it is well, it is well with my soul.

2. Though Satan should buffet, though trials should come,
   let this blest assurance control,
   that Christ hath regarded my helpless estate,
   and hath shed his own blood for my soul.

3. For me be it Christ, be it Christ, hence to live!
   If Jordan above me shall roll,
   no pang shall be mine, for in death as in life,
   thou wilt whisper thy peace to my soul.

4. But, Lord, 'tis for thee, for thy coming we wait,
   the sky, not the grave, is our goal;
   oh, trump of the angel! O voice of the Lord!
   Blessed hope! blessed rest of my soul!

Words: Horatio G. Spafford
Music: Philipp Bliss

575 When the Lord brought us back
(Psalm 126)

When the Lord brought us back and re-stored our free - dom, we felt so good, we felt so strong, at first we thought we were dream - ing. How we laughed! How we sang, we were o - ver - flow - ing; then we heard the na - tions say,

Words and Music: Graham Kendrick

576 When the music fades
(The heart of worship)

1. When the mu - sic fades, all is stripped a - way,
2. King of end - less worth, no one could ex - press

and I simp - ly come. Long - ing just to bring
how much you de - serve. Though I'm weak and poor

some - thing that's of worth, that will bless your heart.
all I have is yours, ev - 'ry sin - gle breath.

I'll bring you more than a song, for a song in it - self

is not what you have re - quired.

Words and Music: Matt Redman

577 Where there once was only hurt
(Mourning into dancing)

Words and Music: Tommy Walker

578 Where two or three

Words and Music: Graham Kendrick

579 Who can sound the depths of sorrow

With feeling

1. Who can sound the depths of sor - row in the Fa - ther heart of God, for the child - ren we've re - jec - ted, for the lives so deep - ly scarred? And each light that we've ex - tin - guished has brought dark - ness to our land:

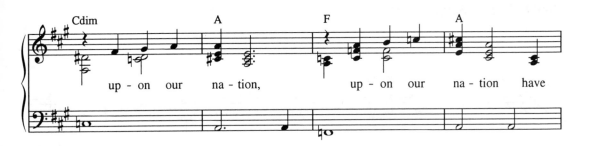

up - on our na - tion, up - on our na - tion have

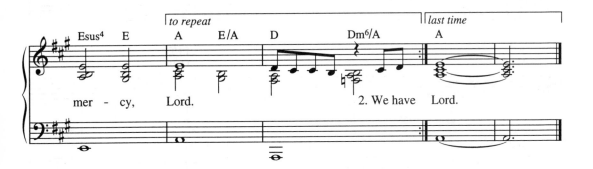

mer - cy, Lord.　　2. We have Lord.

2. We have scorned the truth you gave us,
   we have bowed to other lords.
   We have sacrificed the children
   on the altar of our gods.
   O let truth again shine on us,
   let your holy fear descend:
   upon our nation, upon our nation
   have mercy, Lord.

   (Men)
3. Who can stand before your anger?
   Who can face your piercing eyes?
   For you love the weak and helpless,
   and you hear the victims' cries.
   (All)
   Yes, you are a God of justice,
   and your judgement surely comes:
   upon our nation, upon our nation
   have mercy, Lord.

   (Women)
4. Who will stand against the violence?
   Who will comfort those who mourn?
   In an age of cruel rejection,
   who will build for love a home?
   (All)
   Come and shake us into action,
   come and melt our hearts of stone:
   upon your people, upon your people
   have mercy, Lord.

5. Who can sound the depths of mercy
   in the Father heart of God?
   For there is a Man of sorrows
   who for sinners shed his blood.
   He can heal the wounds of nations,
   he can wash the guilty clean:
   because of Jesus, because of Jesus
   have mercy, Lord.

Note: some congregations may wish to add to the effectiveness of this song by
transposing the final verse up a semitone, into Bb major.

Words and Music: Graham Kendrick

580 Who sees it all

3. Who knows the fears that drive a choice,
   unburies pain and gives it voice?
   And who can wash a memory,
   or take the sting of death away?

4. Whose anger burns at what we've done,
   then bears our sin as if his own?
   Who will receive us as we are,
   whose arms are wide and waiting now?

5. Whose broken heart upon a cross
   won freedom, joy and peace for us?
   Whose blood redeems, who ever lives
   and all because of love forgives?

Words and Music: Graham Kendrick

581 With all my heart

2. Nothing compares to your faithfulness,
   no greater love in earth or above:
   so I'll declare, my heart is safe in your arms.

Words and Music: Steve McGregor

582 With my whole heart

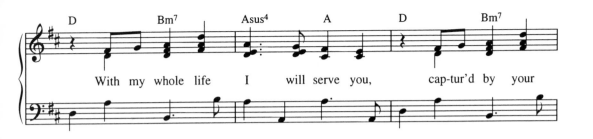

With my whole life I will serve you, cap-tur'd by your

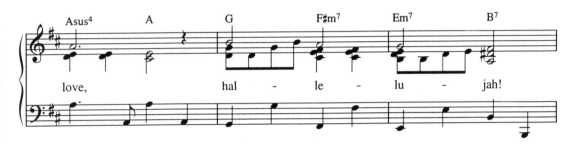

love, hal - le - lu - jah!

O a-maz - ing love! O a-maz - ing love!

last time

2. Lord, your heart is overflowing
   with a love divine, hallelujah!
   And this love is mine for ever.
   Now your joy has set you laughing
   as you join the song, hallelujah!
   Heaven sings along, I hear the
   voices swell to great crescendos,
   praising your great love, hallelujah!
   O amazing love! O amazing love!

3. Come, O Bridegroom, clothed in splendour,
   my Beloved One, hallelujah!
   How I long to run and meet you.
   You're the fairest of ten thousand,
   you're my life and breath, hallelujah!
   Love as strong as death has won me.
   All the rivers, all the oceans
   cannot quench this love, hallelujah!
   O amazing love! O amazing love!

Words and Music: Graham Kendrick

While they were eating,
Jesus took bread, gave thanks and broke it,
and gave it to his disciples,
saying, 'Take it; this is my body.'
Then he took the cup,
gave thanks and offered it to them,
and they all drank from it.
'This is my blood of the covenant,
which is poured out for many,'
he said to them.
'I tell you the truth,
I will not drink again of the fruit of the vine
until that day when I drink it anew
in the kingdom of God.'

Mark 14:22-25

583 With this bread

1. With this bread we will re-mem-ber him,
Son of God, bro-ken and suf-fer-ing;
for our guilt – in-no-cent of-fer-ing.
As we eat, re-mem-ber him.

2. With this wine we will remember him,
on the cross, paying the price for sin –
blood of Christ cleansing us deep within.
As we drink, remember him.

Words and Music: Geoff Baker

584 Worthy is the Lamb

Words and Music: Eddie Espinosa

585 Worthy, O worthy are you, Lord

Words and Music: Mark S. Kinzer

Let us acknowledge the Lord;
let us press on to acknowledge him.
As surely as the sun rises,
he will appear;
he will come to us like the winter rains,
like the spring rains that water the earth.

Hosea 6:3

586 Yahweh

Words and Music: Andy Park

587 Yet this will I call to mind
(Because of the Lord's great love)

Smoothly

this will I call to mind, and there - fore I will

hope, be - cause of the Lord's great love I've been re -

deemed. The Lord is gra - cious and

kind to all who call on his name,

1. Yet

2. I know of his steadfast love,
   his mercy renewed each day,
   because of the Lord's great love I've been redeemed.
   Washed in the blood of the Lamb,
   guiltless for ever I stand,
   because of the Lord's great love I've been redeemed.

Words and Music: Carl Tuttle

588 You alone, Lord, are wonderful

Words and Music: Carol Owen

589 You are beautiful
(I stand in awe)

You are beau - ti - ful be - yond de - scrip - tion, too

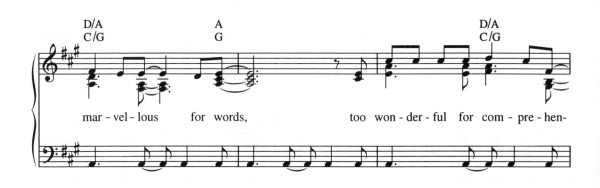

mar - vel - lous for words, too won - der - ful for com - pre - hen-

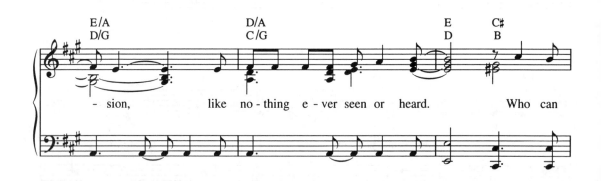

- sion, like no - thing e - ver seen or heard. Who can

grasp your in - fi - nite wis - dom? Who can

Words and Music: Mark Altrogge

590 You are crowned with many crowns

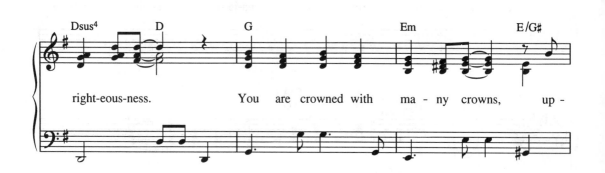

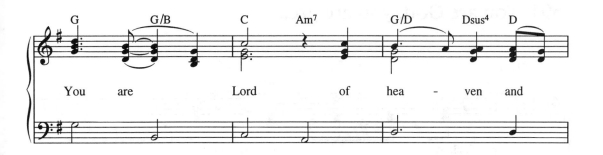

You are   Lord   of   hea   –   ven   and

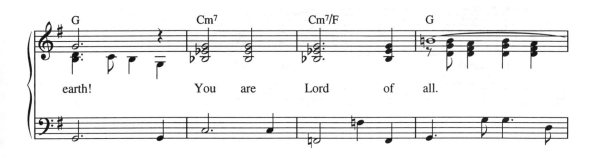

earth!   You   are   Lord   of   all.

You   are   Lord   of

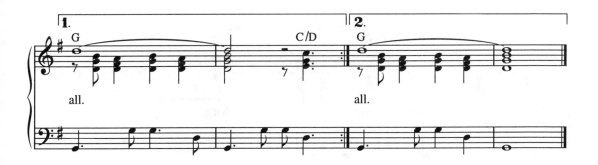

all.   all.

Words and Music: John Sellers

591 You are God, you are great

2. You're the God of wisdom and of majesty,
   the earth is like a footstool at your feet,
   yet you came down and dwelt
   among the sons of men in Jesus.

Words and Music: Carol Owen

592 You are Lord

You are Lord   of our hearts,

you are Lord   of our lives,

and you reign,   and you reign.

His wave of love

will wash a - way our pre - ju - dice and shame, our bro - ken - ness and pain. Faith will rise, faith in-stead of fear, con - nec - ted in his love, a - noin - ted from a - bove.

Words and Music: Trish Morgan

593 You are merciful to me

Words and Music: Ian White

594 You are mighty

You are migh - ty, you are ho - ly, you are awe-

- some in your pow - er; you have ri -

- sen, you have con - quered, you have bea -

- ten the pow'r of death.

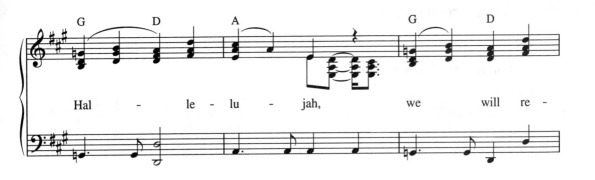

Hal - le - lu - jah, we will re -

joice; hal - le - lu - jah,

we will re - joice! You are migh-

- joice! You are migh - ty!

Words and Music: Craig Musseau

595 You are my King

Tenderly, building in strength

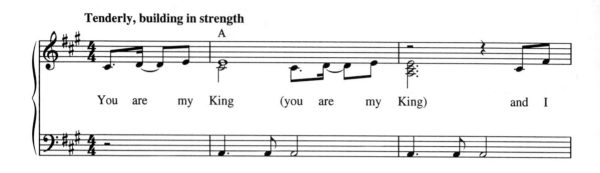

You are my King (you are my King) and I

love you. You are my King (you are my

King) and I wor-ship you, kneel-ing be-fore you now,

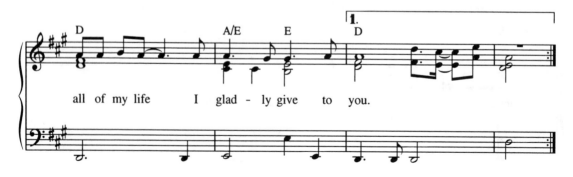

all of my life I glad-ly give to you.

Words and Music: Brian Doerksen

596 You are my passion

Gently, with feeling

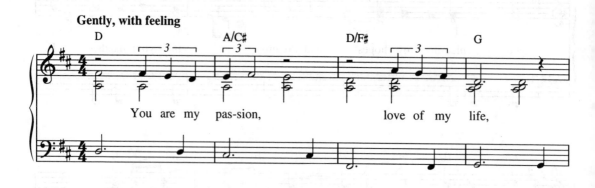

You are my pas-sion, love of my life,

friend and com-pan-ion, my Lo-ver.

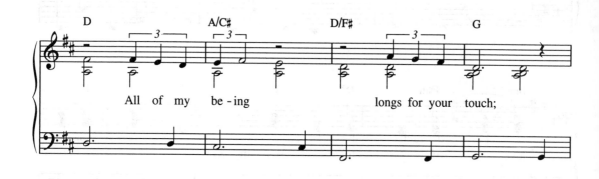

All of my be-ing longs for your touch;

with all my heart I love you.

Words and Music: Noel and Tricia Richards

597 You are my rock

1. You are my rock, you are my fort - ress, you are my strength, I will not fear. You are my shield and my strong tow - er, you are my ref - uge in the storm. You are the in - vin - ci - ble God,

2. You are my light and my salvation,
   I run to you, my hiding-place.
   Your name is Jesus and you are mighty.
   You are my stronghold, you are my life.

Words and Music: Jarrod Cooper and Sharon Pearce

598 You have called us

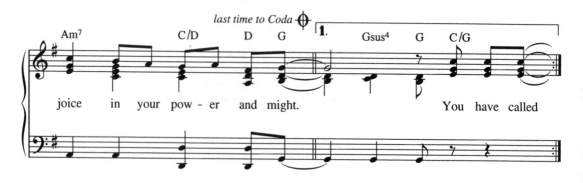

2. We are to take your light
   to ev'ry nation, tongue and tribe;
   so they may see your glory
   shining through our lives.

Words and Music: Lynn DeShazo and Martin J. Nystrom

599 You have shown me
(I give thanks)

1. You have shown me fa - vour un - end - ing;
2. You have poured out your heal - ing up - on us;

you have giv - en your life for me.
you have set the cap - tives free.

And my heart knows of your good - ness,
And we know it's not what we've done,

your blood has cov - ered me. I will a -
but by your hand a - lone. We will a -

Words and Music: Brian Thiessen

600 You have taken the precious
(So come)

1. You have ta - ken the pre - cious from the worth - less and

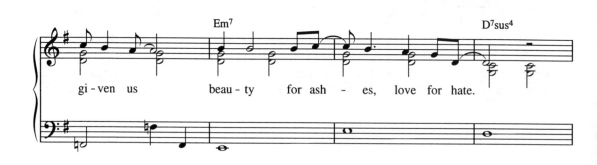

gi - ven us beau - ty for ash - es, love for hate.

You have cho - sen the weak things of the world to shame

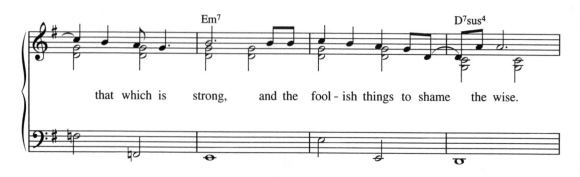

that which is strong, and the fool - ish things to shame the wise.

2. You are help to the helpless,
   strength to the stranger,
   and a father to the child that's left alone.
   And the thirsty are invited
   to come to the waters,
   and those who have no money come and buy.

3. Behold, the days are coming,
   for the Lord has promised
   that the ploughman will overtake the reaper.
   And our hearts shall be the threshing floor,
   and the move of God we've cried out for
   will come, it will surely come.

4. For you will shake the heavens,
   and fill your house with glory,
   and turn the shame of the outcast into praise.
   And all creation groans and waits
   for the Spirit and the bride to say
   the word that your heart has longed to hear.

Words and Music: Kevin Prosch and Tom Davis

601 You laid aside your majesty
(I really want to worship you, my Lord)

Words and Music: Noel Richards

602 You love me as you found me
(Your love keeps following me)

Bright

You love me as you found me;
By grace I'm what I should be;
your love keeps fol - low - ing me.

You wrapped your arms
You saw me as
a - round me,
I could be;
your love keeps fol - low - ing me.

1. fol - low - ing me.

2. And it's high - er, (reach - es from

Words and Music: Russell Fragar

603 You make my heart feel glad

With a steady rock rhythm

Chorus

You make my heart feel glad,

you make my heart feel glad;

Je - sus, you bring me joy,

you make my heart feel glad. *Fine*

Verse

1. Lord, your love brings heal - ing and a peace in - to my heart;

I want to give my-self in praise to you.

Though I've been through heart-ache, you have un-der-stood my tears: O Lord, I will give thanks to you.

2. When I look around me
   and I see the life you made,
   all creation shouts aloud in praise;
   I realise your greatness –
   how majestic is your name!
   O Lord, I love you more each day.

Words and Music: Patricia Morgan and Sue Rinaldi

604 You make your face to shine on me
(And that my soul knows very well)

2. Joy and strength each day I find,
   and that my soul knows very well.
   Forgiveness, hope, I know is mine,
   and that my soul knows very well.

Words and Music: Darlene Zschech and Russell Fragar

605 You rescued me

Words and Music: Geoff Bullock

606 You're the Lion of Judah
(Lion of Judah)

1. You're the Li - on of Ju - dah, the Lamb that was
2. There's a shield in our hand and a sword at our

slain, you as - cend - ed to hea - ven and e - ver - more will reign; at the end of the
side, there's a fire in our spi - rit that can - not be de - nied; as the Fa - ther has

age when the earth you re - claim, you will ga - ther the na - tions be - fore you.
told us: for these you have died, for the na - tions that ga - ther be - fore you.

And the eyes of all men will be fixed on the Lamb who was
And the ears of all men need to hear of the Lamb who was

cru - ci - fied, for with wis - dom and mer - cy and jus - tice he
cru - ci - fied, who des - cen - ded to hell yet was raised up to

Words and Music: Robin Mark

607 Your love flows like a river

Words and Music: Scott Brenner and Michele Brenner

608 Your mercy flows

Majestically

Verse

1. Your mer - cy flows up - on us like a ri - ver. Your mer - cy stands un - shak - a - ble and true. Most ho - ly God, of all good things the gi - ver, we turn and lift our fer - vent prayer to you. Hear our

Chorus

(Men) Hear our

(Women) Hear our cry, O Lord,

cry, O Lord, be

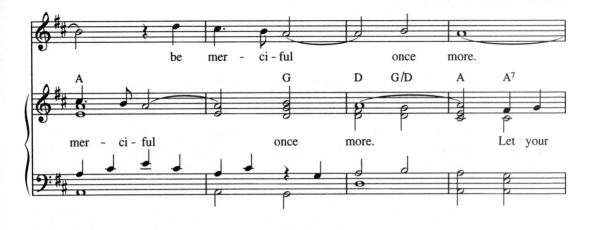

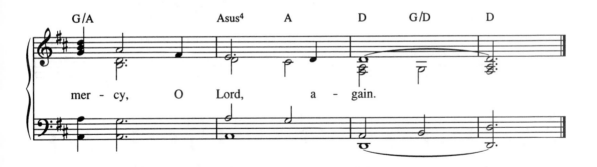

2. Your church once great, though standing clothed in sorrow,
   is even still the bride that you adore;
   revive your church, that we again may honour
   our God and King, our Master and our Lord.

3. As we have slept, this nation has been taken
   by ev'ry sin we have ever known,
   so at its gates, though burnt by fire and broken,
   in Jesus' name we come to take our stand.

Words and Music: Wes Sutton

609 You shall go out with joy
(The trees of the field)

Words and Music: Steffi Geiser Rubin and Stuart Dauermann

610 This is the time
(Distant thunder)

This is the time,

this is the place; we're liv-ing in a

sea - son of a - maz - ing grace.

We are the peo - ple, born for this

Words and Music: David Palmer

Indexes

Guitar Chords

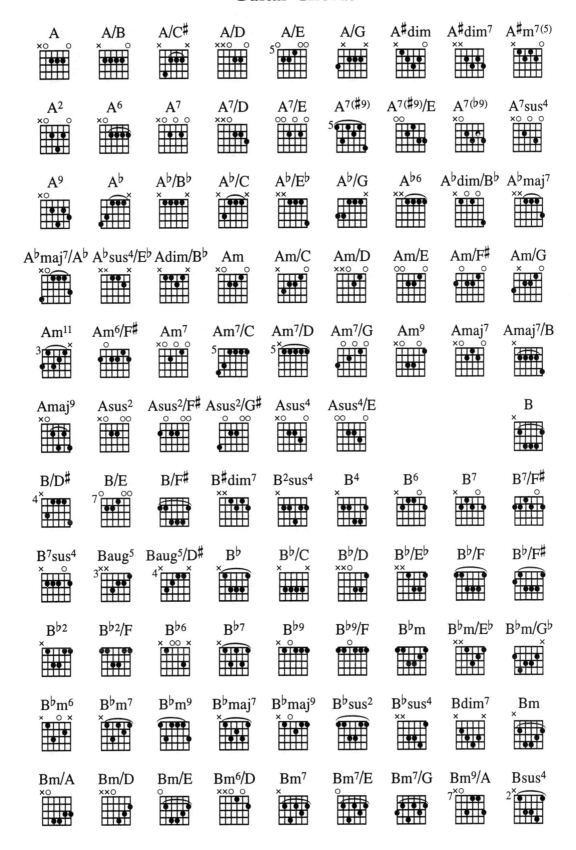

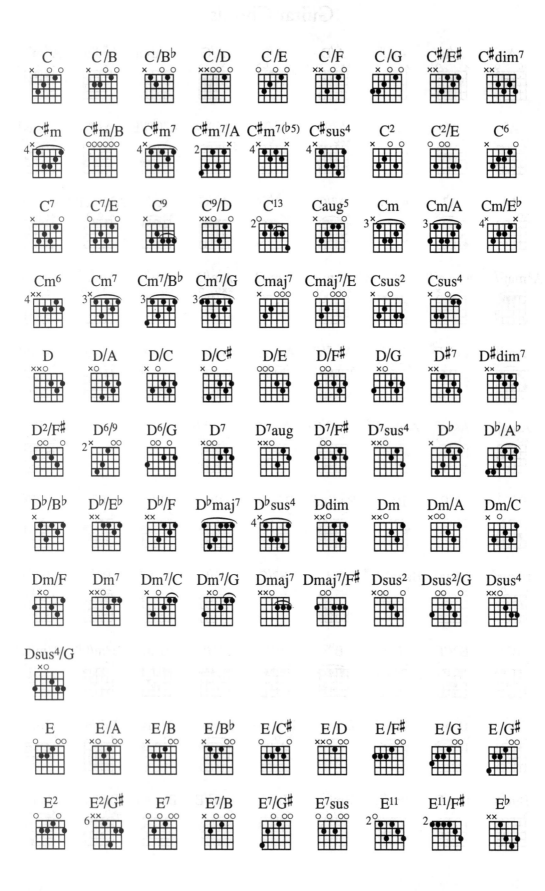

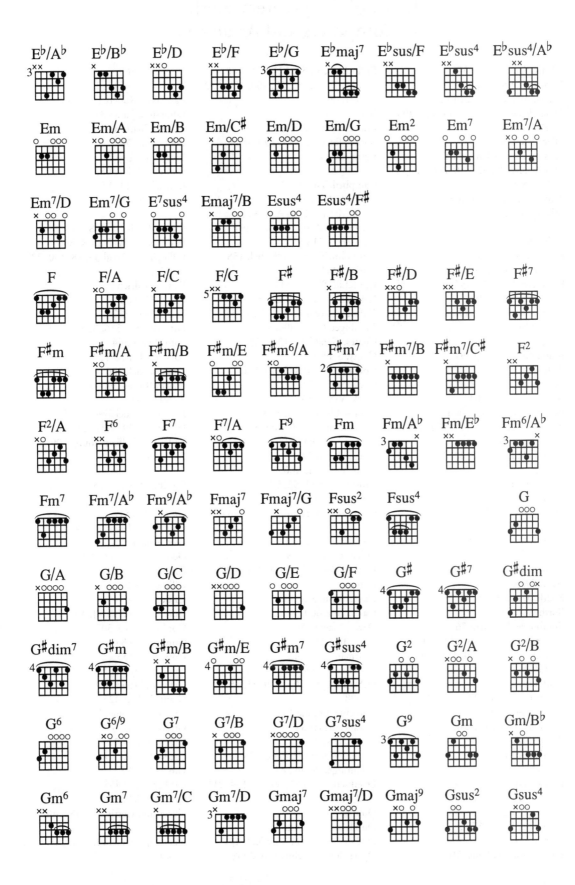

Index of Songwriters, Authors, Composers and Arrangers

Adams, Sarah Flower 372
Adkins, Donna 103
Ainger, Arthur Campbell 128
Alexander, Cecil Frances 14, 14a, 404, 564
Allen, Tricia 561
Alstyne, Frances Jane van 52, 526
Altrogge, Mark 232, 256, 266, 523, 555, 589
Armstrong, Paul 236, 463
Ash, Taran 499

Bailey, Judy 235, 336
Baker, Geoff 43, 583
Baloche, Paul 30, 213
Bankhead, Dave 75, 337
Barnett, John 95, 286
Barrington, Helena 440
Batya, Naomi 307
Baughen, Michael 327
Beaumont, Geoffrey 391
Bell, Dave 215, 451
Bell, John L. 151
Bennard, George 403
Berry, Alison 93, 432, 564
Berthier, Jacques 56, 119, 394, 458
Bieg, Loren 192
Bilbrough, Dave 1, 6, 20, 31, 41, 191, 317, 449, 461
Billington, Dave 26
Black, Richard 257
Bliss, Philipp 350, 574
Boberg, Karl 396
Bode, John Ernest 391
Bolton, Dave 279
Bonar, Horatius 206, 206a
Bond, Derek 32
Booth, William 386
Borthwick, Jane L. 49
Bourbouze, Elizabeth 76
Bowater, Chris 82, 88, 132, 161, 181, 273, 287, 296, 310, 351, 356, 437, 446, 519
Bradbury, W. B. 365
Brenner, Michele 607
Brenner, Scott 607
Brethorst, Leona von 262
Bridges, Matthew 77
Brierley, Michael 33
Broadwater, Lucy 206
Brooks, Phillips 393
Brown, Arthur Henry 306a
Brown, Dougie 441
Browning, Dave 467
Bryant, Dave 297
Budry, Edmond Louis 510

Bullock, Geoff 55, 121, 179, 180, 263, 264, 278, 329, 400, 480, 512, 521, 605
Butler, D. J. 260
Butler, Randy 209
Butler, Terry 12, 141, 209, 468a
Byrne, Mary 50

Campbell, Thomas 21
Cennick, John 324
Cesar Malan, Henri A. 468a
Chapman, Morris 38, 304, 494
Chesser, B. 218
Chisholm, Thomas Obadiah 138
Christ, Michael 250
Churchill, Wendy 283
Clephane, Elizabeth C. 45
Clifton, Dave 432, 520, 546, 558
Cloninger, Claire 304, 494
Coates, Gerald 44, 136, 155
Conty, Sophie 307
Converse, Charles Crozat 566
Cook, Steve 153
Cook, Vicki 153
Cooley, Lindell 226, 360
Cooper, Jarrod 139, 309, 597
Corbett, Sondra 271
Craig, Shawn 225
Crouch, Andraé 460
Crosby, Fanny J. 52, 526
Cullen, Tim 143
Cummings, William Hayman 144

Da Siena, Bianco 71
Dallas, Collette 453
Daniels, Danny 53, 94, 120, 173, 175
Daniels, John 29
Dauermann, Stuart 609
Davis, Tom 600
Dawn, Maggi 169
Day, Mike 215
Dearman, Kirk 542
Del Hierro, Jude 359
DeShazo, Lynn 205, 339, 513, 573, 598
Deuschle, Bonnie 197
Devane, Stuart 84
Dixon, Jessy 332
Doane, William Howard 526
Doddridge, Philip 387
Doerksen, Brian 81, 89, 98, 174, 211, 258, 361, 436, 595
Donnelly, Paul 500
Du Plessis, Malcolm 544
Dudley-Smith, Timothy 327, 471
Dykes, John Bacchus 176, 206a

East, Lucy 569
Eastwood, Debbie 198
Eastwood, Robert 198, 543
Edmeston, James 311
Elliott, Charlotte 306, 306a
Ellor, James 7a
Elvey, George Job 77
Espinosa, Eddie 68, 502, 584
Evans, David J. 47
Ezzy, John 290

Falson, Chris 10, 238, 253
Featherston, William R. 366
Fellingham, David 35, 78, 130, 227, 422, 450
Filitz, Friedrich 311
Fishel, Donald 4
Fisher, Lucy 333
Fitts, Bob 96, 516, 525
Ford, Mavis 244
Forster, Michael 128, 404
Founds, Rick 330
Fragar, Russell 39, 40, 86, 196, 251, 602, 604
Francis, Samuel Trevor 414
Fry, Steven 59, 415, 423, 552
Fullerton, William Young 199
Funk, Billy 42

Gardner, Daniel 315, 368
Garrard, Stuart 146
Garrett, Les 517
Gauntlett, Henry John 404
Gay, Robert 374
Geiser Rubin, Steffi 609
Gibson, John 299
Gillman, Bob 51
Gisbey, Mick 145
Gordon, Adoniram J. 366
Gordon, Nancy 302
Gore, Glenn 84
Goss, John 433
Goudie, Ray 337
Graham, David 229
Grant, Robert 425
Greatorex, Walter 471
Greco, Eugene 357, 470
Green, Keith 401
Green, Melody 492
Groves C. 165
Gruber, Franz 455
Grul, Daniel 290
Gustafson, Gerrit 277, 357, 408

Hadden, David 113, 166, 288, 323, 405, 464

Hall, Jeannie 434
Hall, Kath 562
Hammond, Mary Jane 379
Hanby, Mark David 326
Hand, Colin 50, 455
Handel, George Frideric 305, 510
Harris, Don 115, 281
Harvill, Jamie 54, 302
Hatch, Edwin 57, 57a
Havergal, Frances Ridley 468, 468a
Hawkins, Edwin 347
Haworth, Bryn 316, 568
Haworth, Sally 568
Hayes, Pamela 456
Hayford, Jack W. 346
Haynes, Bruce 226, 360
Hayward, Rob 217
Head, Elizabeth Ann Porter 379
Hearn, Naida 291
Heber, Reginald 176
Hewer, Jenny 97
Hewitt, E. E. 358
Hicks, Roy 435
Hills, L. 550
Hine, Stuart K. 396
Holder, Joey 378
Horley, Doug 254, 255, 559
Howard, Adrian 443
Hoyle, Richard Birch 510
Hubbard, Richard 224, 488
Hull, Eleanor 50
Hutchinson, Gill 282

Iliff, David 327
Irvine, Jessie Seymour 486
Israel, Steve 277
Iverson, Daniel 462

Jackson, Robert 57a
Jarman, Thomas 383
Jernigan, Dennis 108, 563
Johnson, Helen 356
Johnson, Mark 356
Jones, Keri 570
Jones, Ron 387

Keen, Richard 186
Kempen, Andre 212
Kendrick, Graham 3, 9, 11, 22, 34,
    37, 46, 65, 66, 70, 72, 73, 85,
    90, 92, 110, 111, 114, 116, 117,
    122, 124, 126, 148, 149, 150, 157,
    163, 167, 168, 183, 187, 202, 219,
    222, 234, 237, 259, 272, 275, 289,
    292, 295, 308, 312, 313, 321, 322,
    325, 328, 335, 340, 344, 349, 352,
    353, 363, 370, 375, 381, 382, 384,
    388, 389, 399, 402, 406, 410, 424,
    427, 428, 431, 438, 439, 444, 448,
    452, 454, 459, 465, 469, 473, 481,

482, 487, 506, 511, 514, 527, 528,
530, 531, 532, 535, 537, 541, 549,
551, 556, 560, 567, 575, 578, 579,
580, 582
Kenoly, Ron 142, 178
Kerr, Duke 247
Kerr, Ed 213
Kethe, William 13
Kilpatrick, Bob 230
King, Trevor 536
Kingham, Millicent 128
Kinzer, Mark S. 585
Kirkbride, Mary 25
Kirkpatrick, William James 36
Klein, Laurie 214
Knapp, Phoebe Palmer 52
Koch, Don 225
Kyle, Paul 300

Lafferty, Karen 447
Lawson Johnson, Philip 101, 285,
    398, 519
LeBlanc, Lenny 493
Lemmel, Helen H. 533
Lewis, Richard 28, 177, 338, 497
Lindquist, Ben 395
Ling, Matthew 245
Littledale, Richard F. 71
Lloyd, Richard 18, 36, 572a
Locke, Mary Lou 25
Lockhart, Charles 57
Lockwood, Matthew 267
Loizides, Lex 386
Lowry, Robert 164, 345
Lunt, Janet 58
Lyte, Henry Francis 2, 433

MacAlmon, Terry 240
Madan, Martin 144, 324
Maker, Frederick C. 45
Mansell, David 284
Mark, Robin 320, 364, 376, 503, 606
Martin, Austin 16
Mason, Lowell 372
Matthew, David 570
Maule, Graham 151
Mayhew, Kevin 430
McClellan, Sue 69
McEwan, Steve 137
McGregor, Steve 581
McIntosh, Claire 87
McIntosh, Mike 87
McNeil, Edith 505
McPherson, Stephen 290
Mendelssohn, Felix 144
Miller, Edward 572
Mizen, Ian 553
Moen, Don 125, 133, 162, 194, 207,
    357, 395, 474
Mohr, Joseph 455

Monk, William Henry 2, 14a
Monsell, John Samuel Bewley 426
Moody, Dave 5
Morgan, Patricia 75, 603
Morgan, Reuben 221, 303, 371, 515
Morgan, Trish 337, 592
Morris, David 466
Morris, Liz 466
Mote, Edward 365, 365a
Mott, James 499
Mullins, Rich 418
Musseau, Craig 201, 239, 529, 594

Nelson, Marc 195
Newton, John 18, 190
Noel, Maria Caroline 33
Nystrom, Martin J. 27, 281, 561, 598

Oakeley, Frederick 380
Oakley, Paul 106, 498, 547
Oliver, Gary 67
Overstreet, Paul 125
Owen, Carol 19, 160, 293, 434, 484,
    554, 588, 591
Owens, Carol 123
Owens-Collins Jamie 228, 385

Paculabo, John 69
Page, Deborah 453
Palmer, David 610
Paris, Twila 156
Park, Andy 83, 104, 154, 193, 231,
    233, 373, 407, 504, 586
Parry, Charles Hubert Hastings 79
Pearce, Sharon 597
Perrin, Cathy 571
Perrin, Wayne 571
Perronet, Edward 7, 7a
Pettygrove, Todd 135
Phillips, Thomas 298
Piercy, Andy 93, 165, 432, 520, 545,
    558, 564
Pigott, Sophia Jean 280
Pons, Fabienne 216
Pott, Joel 314
Pressdee, Andy 553
Price, Captain Alan J. 218
Prosch, Kevin 53, 152, 159, 223, 509,
    538, 540, 600
Pryce, Matthew 499

Redman, Matt 62, 63, 64, 147, 188,
    204, 249, 252, 261, 265, 274, 476,
    478, 490, 500, 534, 557, 576
Rees, John 18
Rees, William 164
Reidy, Dave 55
Reinagle, Alexander Robert 190
Richards, Dave 109

Richards, Noel 8, 44, 60, 61, 105, 136, 155, 172, 255, 268, 319, 369, 377, 417, 419, 422, 495, 508, 524, 548, 596, 601
Richards, Tricia 8, 60, 61, 105, 155, 172, 268, 319, 369, 377, 417, 419, 508, 596
Riches, Tanya 301
Rinaldi, Sue 603
Rizza, Margaret 397, 456
Robertson, Judith 216
Rogers, H. 304
Rolinson, Chris 9, 439
Rowlands, William Penfro 343a
Ruis, David 99, 171, 248, 270, 355, 457, 491, 501
Runyan, William Marion 138
Ryecroft, Keith 69

Sadler, Gary 54, 115, 513
Sanchez, Pete 112
Schlegal, Katharina Von 49
Schutte, Dan 246
Scriven, Joseph Medlicott 566
Scruggs, Randy 332, 334
Sellers, John 590
Sharp, Cecil 572a
Shrubsole, William 7
Sibelius, Jean 49
Silvester, Bob 323

Smale, Ian 91, 107, 127, 269, 342
Smart, Henry 306
Smith, Leonard E. 189
Smith, Henry 118
Smith, Louis 178
Smith, Martin 74, 80, 200, 241, 249, 341, 354, 390, 421, 472, 478, 479, 518, 550, 565
Smith, Walter Chalmers 220
Spifford, Horatio G. 574
Stainer, John 343
Stone, Samuel John 477
Stradwick, Dan C. 485
Sutton, Wes 184, 409, 507, 608
Sweney, J. R. 358

Taizé Community 56, 119, 294, 458
Tambling, Christopher 1, 288
Tannous, Arthur 208
Temple, Sebastian 348
Thiessen, Brian 599
Thomas, Donn Charles 24
Thompson, John 332, 334
Thompson, Steve 126, 183, 469
Townend, Ian 337
Townend, Stuart 133, 170, 185, 362, 445
Triffitt, Simon 131
Triffitt, Tina 131
Turner, Pat 443

Tuttle, Carl 102, 182, 203, 587

Van De Venter, J. W. 15
Vaughan Williams, Ralph 71, 206, 393
Vaughn J. B. 496
Vogels, Joseph 140

Wade, John Francis 380
Walker, Tommy 577
Warren, Norman 391, 489a
Watson, John 318, 429
Watts, Isaac 305, 572, 572a
Weedon, W. S. 15
Wesley, Charles 21, 144, 298, 324, 343, 343a, 383, 416, 416a
Wesley, Samuel Sebastian 416, 477
West, Peter 25
White, Ian 411, 522, 593
Whitefield, George 144
Whittier, John Greenleaf 79
Williams, Thomas 414
Wimber, John 129, 242, 392

Young, John Freeman 455

Zschech, Darlene 17, 100, 210, 331, 367, 604

Scriptural Index

GENESIS

1:1	Mighty is our God	357
	The Lord is a mighty King	481
1:3	He is the Lord	159
	Lord, the light of your love	335
1:26	The Lord is a mighty King	481
2:24	On this day of happiness	410
3:4	The Lord is a mighty King	481
18:17	I want to serve the purpose of God	256
22:14	Shout for joy and sing	450
28:10-22	Nearer, my God, to thee	372

EXODUS

3:5	Be still, for the presence of the Lord	47
3:14	I lift my hands	212
	Lord of lords	332
	We are the army of God	540
15:3	The Lord is moving across this land	483
15:11	Father, we adore you, you've drawn us	102
	He is the Lord	159
	I worship you, Almighty God	271
	Our God is an awesome God	418
	Our God is awesome in power	419
15:18	He is the Lord	159
15:26	Be still and know	48
	I am the God that healeth thee	194
	Jesus, your name is power	304
	Shout for joy and sing	450
19:20-21	Can I ascend	63
20:3	I lift my hands	212
28:36	Holiness unto the Lord	175
33:11	I will change your name	260
	Lord, we long to see your glory	338
	More love, more power	359
33:17-19	Yahweh	586
33:18	Here in your presence	162
	Lord, we long to see your glory	338
	More of your glory	360
39:30	Holiness unto the Lord	175
40:1-35	Take me past the outer courts	467
40:34-35	See his glory	446
40:34-38	O the glory of your presence	415

LEVITICUS

6:13	O thou who camest from above	416
18:21	Who can sound the depths of sorrow	579
25:10	Day of favour	78
	Shout! The Lord is risen!	452
	These are the days	503
26:13	We are his people	538

NUMBERS

6:24-26	Peace to you	431
6:25	I stand before your throne	245
	You make your face to shine on me	604
10:35-36	O the glory of your presence	415
13:1-33	Can we walk upon the water	64
14:1-45	Can we walk upon the water	64
21:4-9	Beneath the cross of Jesus	45

DEUTERONOMY

5:7	I lift my hands	212
6:5	I love you, Lord, with all of my heart	215
	I will worship	270
	More love, more power	359
	My life is in you, Lord	368
7:21	Our God is an awesome God	418
8:3	Seek ye first	447
10:17	Our God is an awesome God	418
11:14	Let it rain	314
	There's a wind a-blowing	501
	We are the army of God	540
32:3-4	Ascribe greatness	25

JOSHUA

1:5	Abide with me	2
	God is good all the time	125
	O Lord, you lead me	400
1:9	Be bold, be strong	38
6:2	Rejoice!	438
6:7	Rejoice!	438
6:16	Shout, shout for joy	451
24:15	Here I am	161
	O happy day	387

1 SAMUEL

7:12	Look what God has done	325
17:47	In heavenly armour	228
30:18-20	I went to the enemy's camp	257

2 SAMUEL

6:12	These are the days	503
6:14	Teach me to dance	469
6:22	I will dance, I will sing	261
7:12-13	These are the days	503

1 KINGS

18:1	Let it rain	314
18:36-39	O God of burning, cleansing flame	386
18:41	Let it rain	314
	This is the time	610
18:41-46	We have prayed that you would have mercy	547

1 CHRONICLES

16:8-10	O give thanks	384
16:25	I sing praises	240
16:29	The crucible for silver	479
16:31	O give thanks	384

2 CHRONICLES

7:13-14	We have prayed that you would have mercy	547
7:14	Can a nation be changed?	62
	Here we stand in total surrender	165
	Lord, have mercy	328
	Lord, we long for you	337
16:9	We serve a God of miracles	555

2 CHRONICLES continued

20:12	I will worship	270	
20:25	In heavenly armour	228	

NEHEMIAH

2:3	Your mercy flows	608	
8:10	In every circumstance	227	
	We will run and not grow weary	561	

JOB

38:7	Though the earth should tremble	523	

PSALMS

1:3	I want to be a tree that's bearing fruit	254
2:6	Lift up your heads	321
2:8	He is the Lord	159
	This is my beloved Son	514
3:3	Lord, my heart cries out	331
4:1	Father, hear our prayer	93
4:7	Almighty God, my Redeemer	17
	Come on and celebrate	75
8:1	King of kings, majesty	309
	O Lord, how majestic is your name	395
	You make my heart feel glad	603
8:1-2	O Lord our God	398
	What noise shall we make	569
8:9	King of kings, majesty	309
9:1	I will praise you all my life	266
9:7-8	O Lord our God	398
9:8	King of kings	308
10:14	You have taken the precious	600
15:1	Can I ascend	63
16:10	He has risen	155
	Jesus, your name is power	304
16:11	Lord, I come to you	329
	O, heaven is in my heart	388
	We will run and not grow weary	561
17:1	To you, O Lord, I bring my worship	529
18:1	In moments like these	229
	I've got a love song	252
	My Jesus, I love thee	366
	To you, O Lord, I bring my worship	529
	When I feel the touch	570
	You are my King	595
	You are my passion	596
18:1-3	My Jesus, my Saviour	367
18:1-2	This is the day that the Lord has made	516
18:2	Almighty God, my Redeemer	17
	Ascribe greatness	25
	Blessed be the name of the Lord	53
	Faithful One	89
	I will seek you	267
	King of kings, majesty	309
	My hope is built	365
	My spirit rests in you alone	371
	Praise the name of Jesus	435
	Shout for joy and sing	450
	Shout, shout for joy	451
	You are my rock	597
18:19	Thank you for the cross	473
18:30	Ascribe greatness	25

	God will make a new way	134
	Hail, Jesus, you're my King	140
18:32	God will make a new way	134
19:1	All heaven declares	8
	The heavens shall declare	480
	You make my heart feel glad	603
19:1-4	From the ends of the earth	115
	Joy to the world	305
	No scenes of stately majesty	375
19:1-6	O Lord, my God	396
19:14	May our worship be as fragrance	351
20:5	Come on, all us singers, sing	74
	We march to the tune of a love-song	552
	We want to see Jesus lifted high	559
22:1	Filled with compassion	105
22:3	Father in heaven, how we love you	96
	Jesus, we enthrone you	300
	Open the doors of praise	411
	Reign in me	437
23:1	Shout for joy and sing	450
	We rejoice in the goodness of our God	554
23:1-6	The Lord's my shepherd	486
	This is the day that the Lord has made	516
23:2-3	To be in your presence	524
23:2-4	O Lord, you lead me	400
23:3	My lips shall praise you	369
	Restore, O Lord	439
23:4	For the joys and for the sorrows	110
	God is good all the time	125
23: 5	He brought me to his banqueting table	152
	I just want to be where you are	207
	The trumpets sound, the angels sing	506
23:6	Take me past the outer courts	467
	You love me as you found me	602
24:1-2	Our God is so great	420
24:3	Can I ascend	63
24:3-4	I will seek your face, O Lord	268
24:7	Lift up your heads	321
24:7-10	Did you feel the mountains tremble?	80
	Open the doors of praise	411
	Welcome the King	549
24:8	King of kings	308
24:8-10	You are my rock	597
25:1-7	To you, O Lord, I lift up my soul	530
25:3	My life is in you, Lord	368
25:4	I want to serve the purpose of God	256
25:5	My life is in you, Lord	368
25:7-8	I cry out for your hand	201
27:1	I will seek you	267
	You are my rock	597
27:4	As I come into your presence	26
	By your side	60
	God of all comfort	129
	How lovely is your dwelling-place	188
	Isn't he beautiful	242
	I will seek your face, O Lord	268
	O Lord, you're beautiful	401
	One thing I ask	407
	Sound the trumpet	461
	Take me past the outer courts	467
	There's no one like you	502

	To be in your presence	524	
	To keep your lovely face	527	
	Turn your eyes upon Jesus	533	
	When I look into your holiness	571	
	You are beautiful	589	
27:5	My Jesus, my Saviour	367	
27:6	Come on and celebrate	75	
	Men of faith	354	
	We are his people	538	
27:7	O Lord, hear my prayer	394	
27:7-9	One thing I ask	407	
27:8	As we seek your face	31	
	Come on, all us singers, sing	74	
	How can I not love you?	184	
	I stand before your throne	245	
	I will change your name	260	
	I will seek you	267	
	I will seek your face, O Lord	268	
	Lord, I come to you	329	
	Lord, you have my heart	341	
	More love, more power	359	
	O Lord, you're beautiful	401	
	Take me past the outer courts	467	
	There's no one like you	502	
	To keep your lovely face	527	
	Turn your eyes upon Jesus	533	
	When I look into your holiness	571	
28:2	Save the people	444	
28:9	Save the people	444	
29:1-3	To God be the glory!	526	
29:1-11	Be glorified	42	
29:2	The crucible for silver	479	
29:9	See his glory	446	
	To God be the glory!	526	
30:2	You have shown me	599	
30:5	Where there once was only hurt	577	
30:5	You make my heart feel glad	603	
30:11	Come on, all us singers, sing	74	
	Jesus put this song into our hearts	292	
30:11-12	Where there once was only hurt	577	
30:12	You have shown me	599	
31:5	Father, I place into your hands	97	
	My spirit rests in you alone	371	
	You are my King	595	
32:7	Almighty God, my Redeemer	17	
	You are my rock	597	
32:8	O, we are more than conquerors	423	
32:11	We rejoice in the goodness of our God	554	
33:3	Almighty God, my Redeemer	17	
33:4	Faithful God	88	
	On this day	409	
33:22	You have shown me	599	
34:1	Almighty God, my Redeemer	17	
	We come into your presence	543	
34:4	We come into your presence	543	
34:5	To keep your lovely face	527	
34:6	I need you more	226	
	We come into your presence	543	
34:8	Have you got an appetite?	145	
	Jesus, Jesus (Holy and anointed one)	286	
34:17-18	I need you more	226	

36:5	Faithful God	88	
	On this day	409	
36:8	Your love flows like a river	607	
36:8-9	Father, we adore you	101	
36:9	How can I not love you?	184	
39:12	O Lord, hear my prayer	394	
40:1	I lift my eyes up to the mountains	211	
	To you, O Lord, I bring my worship	529	
40:2	Father, we adore you, you've drawn us	102	
	Jesus, lover of my soul	290	
	We shall stand	556	
	You make your face to shine on me	604	
40:2-3	Well, I hear they're singing in the streets	550	
40:8	I want to serve the purpose of God	256	
	This is my desire	515	
42:1	No one but you, Lord	373	
42:1-2	As the deer pants (Nystrom)	27	
	As the deer pants (Lewis)	28	
42:7	As the deer pants (Lewis)	28	
	We are his people	538	
	When I feel the touch	570	
42:8	My first love	362	
45:1-7	My heart is full	363	
45:4	The Lord is marching out	482	
45:7	Jesus, Jesus (Holy and anointed one)	286	
46:1	Mighty God	356	
46:1-2	How firm a foundation	186	
46:1-3	Jesus, lover of my soul	290	
46:1-7	Though the earth should tremble	523	
46:2	You make your face to shine on me	604	
46:2-3	This is the time	610	
46:4	There's a river of joy	499	
	Your love flows like a river	607	
	Your mercy flows	608	
46:10	Be still, for the presence of the Lord	47	
	Be still and know	48	
	Be still, my soul	49	
	Dear Lord and Father of mankind	79	
	In the secret	233	
47:1	I'm gonna click	218	
	My Jesus, my Saviour	367	
	Shout, shout for joy	451	
	Shout! The Lord is risen!	452	
	Shout unto God	453	
47:1-2	To God be the glory!	526	
47:5	My Jesus, my Saviour	367	
48:1-2	Great is the Lord and most worthy of praise	137	
48:1	I sing praises	240	
	O Lord, my God	396	
	Thank you for saving me	472	
51:1-2	O Lord, your tenderness	402	
51:1	Save the people	444	
51:2	How can I be free from sin?	183	
51:5	You are merciful to me	593	
51:7	It's your blood	250	
51:10	Change my heart, O God	68	
	Purify my heart	436	
	Turn our hearts	531	
	We have a great priest	546	

PSALMS continued

	When the music fades	576
51:12	How can I be free from sin?	183
51:15	We declare your majesty	544
51:16-17	When the music fades	576
51:17	It's our confession, Lord	248
	I will offer up my life	265
	Let me be a sacrifice	315
	Who sees it all	580
55:22	Higher, higher	170
56:3-4	With all my heart	581
56:4	Be still and know	48
	Jesus, you're my firm foundation	302
56:10	Jesus, you're my firm foundation	302
56:11	Be still and know	48
57:1	Living under the shadow of his wing	323
57:5	Be glorified	42
	To God be the glory!	526
57:8	Wake up, my soul	534
57:11	Be glorified	42
	To God be the glory!	526
60:5	Save the people	444
61:1-3	When my heart is overwhelmed	573
61:3	My Jesus, my Saviour	367
62:1	Jesus! I am resting, resting	280
62:1-2	Our confidence is in the Lord	417
	You are my rock	597
62:5	Jesus! I am resting, resting	280
62:5-6	You are my rock	597
63:1	In the morning when I rise	231
	More than oxygen	361
	My first love	362
	No one but you, Lord	373
63:1-8	You are my passion	596
63:2	Take me past the outer courts	467
63:3	Jesus, your loving kindness	303
	My lips shall praise you	369
63:4	I lift my hands	212
	I love to be in your presence	213
	In moments like these	229
	I will lift my voice	263
	I will praise you all my life	266
	I will wave my hands	269
63:5	My lips shall praise you	369
63:7	How lovely is your dwelling-place	188
63:8	Hold me closer to you	172
	Hold me, Lord	173
67:1-7	God, be gracious	122
67:2	To God be the glory!	526
68:3	I could sing unending songs	200
68:3-6	Let the righteous sing	316
68:5	Lord, my heart cries out	331
	O Father of the fatherless	382
68:5- 6	You have taken the precious	600
68:18	O God, most high	385
68:19	I am standing beneath your wings	193
68:28	Look what the Lord has done	326
	Show your power, O Lord	454
68:35	Our God is an awesome God	418
	Show your power, O Lord	454
69:2	Father, we adore you, you've drawn us	102
69:14	Father, we adore you, you've drawn us	102
71:14	I will praise you all my life	266
72:4	Save the people	444
72:5-8	From the sun's rising	116
72:6	Let it rain	314
	Mercy is falling	355
	There's a wind a-blowing	501
	We are the army of God	540
72:8	Jesus Christ is Lord of all	275
72:11	Jesus, God's righteousness revealed	278
72:13	Save the people	444
73:21-26	When peace like a river	574
73:23	Hold me closer to you	172
	Hold me, Lord	173
73:25	Lord, you are more precious	339
	More than oxygen	361
	My heart will sing to you	364
	This is my desire	515
73:25-26	Father, you are my portion	104
	Jesus, lover of my soul	290
80:2	We serve a God of miracles	555
80:3	As we lift up your name	30
	O Breath of Life	379
	Restore, O Lord	439
	Save the people	444
	We'll walk the land	551
80:7	As we lift up your name	30
	O Breath of Life	379
	Restore, O Lord	439
	Save the people	444
	We'll walk the land	551
80:14	As we lift up your name	30
	O Breath of Life	379
	Restore, O Lord	439
	Save the people	444
	We'll walk the land	551
80:18	As we lift up your name	30
80:19	O Breath of Life	379
	Restore, O Lord	439
	Save the people	444
	We'll walk the land	551
81:1	We are his people	538
81:16	His love	171
84:1	I will seek your face, O Lord	268
84:1-2	Lord, we long to see your glory	338
84:1-12	How lovely is your dwelling-place	188
84:2	As the deer pants (Lewis)	28
	More than oxygen	361
84:10	God's not dead	133
	I will seek your face, O Lord	268
	Lord, we long to see your glory	338
85:4	Restore, O Lord	439
85:4-7	Who can sound the depths of sorrow	579
	Your mercy flows	608
85:6	As we lift up your name	30
	Hear, O Lord, our cry	148
86:1	O Lord, hear my prayer	394
86:1-7	I cry out for your hand	201
86:5-2	Among the gods	19
86:6	O Lord, hear my prayer	394
86:8	There is none like you	493

	There's no one like you	502
	We worship and adore you	564
	You are God, you are great	591
86:11	Soften my heart, Lord	459
	Teach me your ways	470
	To keep your lovely face	527
	Turn our hearts	531
88:1-2	To you, O Lord, I bring my worship	529
89:1	Over the mountains and the sea	421
89:6	You are God, you are great	591
90:1	Lord, for the years	327
90:14	O let the sun of God enfold you	392
91:1	I am standing beneath your wings	193
	Jesus! I am resting, resting	280
	Living under the shadow of his wing	323
	My spirit rests in you alone	371
91:2	Our confidence is in the Lord	417
91:4	I am standing beneath your wings	193
	Living under the shadow of his wing	323
	My spirit rests in you alone	371
92:4	I will enter his gates	262
	My Jesus, my Saviour	367
92:12-15	I want to be a tree that's bearing fruit	254
93:1	King of kings, majesty	309
	Mighty is our God	357
	You are Lord	592
93:3-4	My Jesus, my Saviour	367
93:4	Mighty is our God	357
95:1	I'm gonna click	218
95:3	You are my King	595
95:3-5	O Lord, my God	396
95:6	King of kings, majesty	309
	We worship and adore you	564
95:6-7	You are my King	595
96:1-13	Far and near	90
96:3-10	We declare your majesty	544
96:4	I sing praises	240
96:4-6	Great and mighty is he	135
96:4-8	Great is your name	139
96:4-9	You are beautiful	589
96:9	I will worship	270
	O worship the Lord in the beauty of holiness	426
96:9	The crucible for silver	479
96:11	O give thanks	384
96:12	Joy to the world	305
97:1	The Lord reigns	485
97:3	The Lord reigns	485
97:5-6	The Lord reigns	485
97:9	For thou, O Lord, art high	112
	I have made you too small	205
	The Lord reigns	485
	We worship and adore you	564
98:1-9	Far and near	90
98:4	Shout for joy	449
	Shout for joy and sing	450
98:8	Joy to the world	305
98:9	King of kings	308
99:1	Welcome, King of kings	548
99: 2	I just want to praise you	208
99:2-5	You are mighty	594
99:5-9	Exalt the Lord	87
99:5	I just want to praise you	208
99:9	I just want to praise you	208
100:1-5	All people that on earth do dwell	13
100:1	Make a joyful noise, all ye people	347
	Shout, shout for joy	451
100:1-2	What noise shall we make	569
100:1-5	You are God, you are great	591
100:4	As I come into your presence	26
	I will enter his gates	262
	Shout for joy and sing	450
100:5	God is good	124
	God is good all the time	125
	I'm standing here to testify	223
	Make a joyful noise, all ye people	347
102:1-2	To you, O Lord, I bring my worship	529
102:27	Restore, O Lord	439
103:1	Almighty God, my Redeemer	17
	Bless the Lord, my soul	56
	Exalt the Lord	87
	I love you, Lord, with all of my heart	215
	I will worship	270
	Sing, praise and bless the Lord	458
	This is my desire	515
103:1-4	I could sing unending songs	200
103:1-5	You rescued me	605
103:1-22	Praise, my soul, the King of heaven	433
	Praise the Lord, O my soul	434
103:8	Filled with compassion	105
	We rejoice in the goodness of our God	554
103:8-12	You rescued me	605
103:8-13	How can I be free from sin?	183
103:11	I've got a love song	252
	Overwhelmed by love	422
	There's an awesome sound	497
103:11-12	Because of your love	39
	Here is love	164
	The cross has said it all	478
	You are Lord	592
	You love me as you found me	602
103:13	How deep the Father's love for us	185
103:17	Here is love	164
	You rescued me	605
103:21	Praise God from whom all blessings flow	432
103:22	Sing, praise and bless the Lord	458
104:1-35	All things bright and beautiful	14
	God is great	126
	O Lord, my God	396
	O worship the King	425
105:1-3	O give thanks	384
105:4	God of all comfort	129
106:1	I'm standing here to testify	223
107:1	I'm standing here to testify	223
107:1-43	Beauty for brokenness	37
	For the joys and for the sorrows	110
	Give thanks with a grateful heart	118
	How firm a foundation	186
107:9	O let the sun of God enfold you	392
107:14	O God, most high	385
107:20	I am the God that healeth thee	194

PSALMS continued

	Say the word	445
108:4-5	You alone, Lord, are wonderful	588
108:4-6	I have made you too small	205
110:1	I went to the enemy's camp	257
	Led like a lamb	312
110:3	This is the time	610
115:1	Great is your name	139
	Hold me, Lord	173
	It is to you	247
116:1	In moments like these	229
116:1-2	Father, hear our prayer	93
	I love you, Lord, and I lift my voice	214
116:11	I love your presence	216
116:12-13	Oh, I was made for this	389
116:12-14	I have come to love you	204
	I will offer up my life	265
116:17	We bring the sacrifice of praise	542
118:1	I am so thankful	192
	I'm standing here to testify	223
118:24	I will enter his gates	262
	This is the day that the Lord has made	516
	This is the day	517
118:26	Welcome the King	549
118:28-9	Thank you for your mercy	474
118:29	I am so thankful	192
	I'm standing here to testify	223
119:2	I will seek you	267
119:57	Father, you are my portion	104
119:72	Lord, you are more precious	339
119:74	Jesus, you're my firm foundation	302
119:81	I will seek you	267
	Jesus, you're my firm foundation	302
119:89	Jesus, restore to us again	295
119:103	Jesus, Jesus (Holy and anointed one)	286
119:105	Jesus, Jesus (Holy and anointed one)	286
119:176	O Father of the fatherless	382
121:1-2	I lift my eyes up to the mountains	211
122:1	I love to be in your presence	213
126:1-6	Can we walk upon the water	64
126:1-3	When the Lord brought us back	575
126:2	No one but you, Lord	373
126:2-3	There's a sound of singing	500
	To God be the glory!	526
126:5	We will cross every border	560
130:1-2	I cry out for your hand	201
130:3-4	Only by grace	408
130:4	You make your face to shine on me	604
130:5	Jesus, you're my firm foundation	302
131:1-3	O Lord, my heart is not proud	397
133:1	Turn our hearts	531
	We must work together	553
133:1-3	How good and how pleasant	187
	There is a place of commanded blessing	491
	To every good thing God is doing	525
134:1	From where the sun rises	117
134:1-3	As I come into your presence	26
	I just want to praise you	208
134:2	I will lift my voice	263
	I will wave my hands	269
135:3	I'm standing here to testify	223
136:1	Come on, all us singers, sing	74
	Father, I come to you	95
	I'm standing here to testify	223
	Look what God has done	325
	Restore, O Lord	439
	See his glory	446
	The Lord is marching out	482
139:2	My spirit rests in you alone	371
139:9-10	Though I feel afraid	522
139:11-16	Who sees it all	580
139:15	I'm so secure	221
139:23	Lord, the light of your love	335
142:1	I will lift my voice	263
142:1-7	I cry out for your hand	201
142:6	I need you more	226
143:1	O Lord, hear my prayer	394
144:1	Our God is awesome in power	419
145:1-2	I could sing unending songs	200
145:1-7	God of glory, we exalt your name	130
145:3	I sing praises	240
145:4	Father in heaven, how we love you	96
145:7	Celebrate, celebrate	66
145:8-9	Filled with compassion	105
145:13	Faithful God	88
	I want to serve the purpose of God	256
	On this day	409
146:2	Hail, Jesus, you're my King	140
146:5-6	I will praise you all my life	266
146:6	Faithful God	88
148:1-14	From the ends of the earth	115
149:2-3	I will wave my hands	269
149:3	Come on, all us singers, sing	74
	I'm gonna click	218
149:6	Shout unto God	453
	There is power in the name of Jesus	495
149:6-9	We march to the tune of a love-song	552
150:1-6	Lord, you put a tongue in my mouth	342
150:3	Sound the trumpet	461
150:4	Come on, all us singers, sing	74

PROVERBS

1:7	Come on, all us singers, sing	74
3:5	I will seek you	267
3:5-6	Seek ye first	447
	With all my heart	581
3:14-15	Lord, you are more precious	339
8:11	Lord, you are more precious	339
17:3	The crucible for silver	479
18:10	My Jesus, my Saviour	367
	You are my rock	597
18:24	What a friend I've found	565
30:5	Jesus, you're my firm foundation	302

ECCLESIASTES

4:9-12	On this day of happiness	410

SONG OF SOLOMON

1:3	May the fragrance	352
	You are my passion	596
1:15	This is the mystery	519
2:4	He brought me to his banqueting table	152

	The trumpets sound, the angels sing	506
2:6	You are my passion	596
	You love me as you found me	602
2:10	This is the mystery	519
2:13	This is the mystery	519
2:16	As the deer pants (Lewis)	28
	By your side	60
	He brought me to his banqueting table	152
	I will be yours	258
	My Jesus, I love thee	366
	With my whole heart	582
	You are my passion	596
4:1	This is the mystery	519
4:16	There's a wind a-blowing	501
	With my whole heart	582
5:10	With my whole heart	582
5:16	Jesus, how lovely you are	279
6:4	This is the mystery	519
7:10-12	You are my passion	596
8:3	You love me as you found me	602
8:6-7	With my whole heart	582
	You are my passion	596

ISAIAH

1:18	O the blood of Jesus	412
6:1	O Lord, how majestic is your name	395
6:1-5	I see the Lord	238
6:3-7	In the presence of a holy God	232
6:6	Take me past the outer courts	467
6:6-7	The crucible for silver	479
6:8	Here I am	161
	I, the Lord of sea and sky	246
	I want to serve the purpose of God	256
7:14	He walked where I walked	168
	Immanuel, O Immanuel	219
	Jesus, name above all names	291
	We believe	541
9:2	Mighty God	356
9:6-7	For unto us a child is born	113
9:6	Glory to the King of kings	121
	Isn't he beautiful	242
	I worship you, Almighty God	271
	King of kings and Lord of lords	307
	Lord of lords	332
	Mighty God	356
9:7	And he shall reign	22
	Jesus, God's righteousness revealed	278
12:2-6	The Lord is our strength	484
26:3	Peace, perfect peace	430
33:17	Soon and very soon	460
	There's a blessed time that's coming	496
35:1	My heart will sing to you	364
35:6-7	There's a river of joy	499
35:10	There's a place where the streets shine	498
40:3	Make way, make way	349
	Sound the trumpet	461
	Welcome the King	549
40:6-8	Abide with me	2
40:8	In the morning when I rise	231
	Jesus, you're my firm foundation	302
40:9-11	See, your Saviour comes	448
40:11	You are my passion	596
40:28	They that wait on the Lord	509
40:31	Can we walk upon the water	64
	Lord, I come to you	329
	Men of faith	354
	O, we are more than conquerors	423
	There's a river of joy	499
	They that wait on the Lord	509
	We will run and not grow weary	561
42:1	Thank you for the cross	473
42:1-13	It's rising up	249
42:13	Our God is awesome in power	419
43:1	I will change your name	260
43:1-2	How firm a foundation	186
43:1-7	Have you not said	147
43:5-7	It's rising up	249
43:13	The Lord is marching out	482
	The Lord is moving across this land	483
43:18-21	There's a river of joy	499
43:19	Do something new, Lord	82
43:21	For I'm building a people of power	109
	We are a people of power	536
44:3	Come, Spirit, come	76
	There's a river of joy	499
	We have prayed that you would have mercy	547
44:5	I will change your name	260
44:23	Joy to the world	305
44:24	Shout for joy and sing	450
45:8	Let it rain	314
	There's a wind a-blowing	501
45:22	Turn to me and be saved	532
46:9	There is none like you	493
	There's no one like you	502
47:4	There is a Redeemer	492
48:18	Peace like a river	429
49:8	This love	521
49:13	Joy to the world	305
49:14-16	What a friend I've found	565
50:7	We shall stand	556
51:4	We are his children	537
52:7-10	How lovely on the mountains	189
53:3	My Lord, what love is this	370
	Who can sound the depths of sorrow	579
53:3-5	Holy One of God	179
53:3-7	Man of sorrows	350
53:4	What a friend we have in Jesus	566
53:4-5	Filled with compassion	105
	Hallelujah, my Father	143
	How deep the Father's love for us	185
	The price is paid	487
53:4-6	Who sees it all	580
53:4-7	Led like a lamb	312
53:5	Immanuel, O Immanuel	219
	Thank you for the cross	473
	You laid aside your majesty	601
53:5-6	Come and see	70
53:5-8	He was pierced	169
53:6	Overwhelmed by love	422
53:11	From heaven you came	114
	Say the word	445

ISAIAH continued

	This is my beloved Son	514
54:17	In heavenly armour	228
	I walk by faith	253
	Shout, shout for joy	451
55:1	Just as I am, without one plea	306
	You have taken the precious	600
55:6-7	You are merciful to me	593
55:12	Joy to the world	305
	You shall go out with joy	609
56:5	I will change your name	260
57:15	King of kings, majesty	309
58:6-7	See, your Saviour comes	448
58:12	See, your Saviour comes	448
59:16-19	In heavenly armour	228
59:17	Our God is awesome in power	419
61:1	God of glory, we exalt your name	130
	I give you all the honour	203
	I will change your name	260
	Make way, make way	349
	We march to the tune of a love-song	552
	We will cross every border	560
	Who sees it all	580
61:1-2	We rejoice in the goodness of our God	554
	Where there once was only hurt	577
	Who can sound the depths of sorrow	579
61:1-3	Day of favour	78
	The Spirit of the sovereign Lord	504
	You have shown me	599
61:1-4	See, your Saviour comes	448
61:3	He's given me a garment of praise	166
	You have taken the precious	600
61:10	God of grace	32
	He has clothed us with his righteousness	153
	He's given me a garment of praise	166
	How can I be free from sin?	183
	King of kings, majesty	309
	O Father of the fatherless	382
62:2-4	I will change your name	260
62:3-5	This is the mystery	519
64:6	God of grace	132
	O Father of the fatherless	382
65:19	Great is the darkness	136
	I will be yours	258

JEREMIAH

1:5	Before the world began	40
2:11	Can a nation be changed?	62
10:6-7	There is none like you	493
	There's no one like you	502
18:6	Change my heart, O God	68
23:6	I worship you, Almighty God	271
29:11	Jesus, you're my firm foundation	302
29:13	O come and join the dance	381
31:34	All I once held dear	11
32:17	Be still, for the presence of the Lord	47
32:35	Who can sound the depths of sorrow	579
33:16	I worship you, Almighty God	271

LAMENTATIONS

3:21-23	Yet this will I call to mind	587
3:22-24	Great is thy faithfulness	138
3:22-23	It's our confession, Lord	248
	The steadfast love of the Lord	505
	This is the day that the Lord has made	516
3:23	We rejoice in the goodness of our God	554
3:24	Father, you are my portion	104

EZEKIEL

11:19	Soften my heart, Lord	459
33:1-9	Filled with compassion	105
34:27	We are his people	538
36:26	Soften my heart, Lord	459
36:26-27	Who can sound the depths of sorrow	579
37:1-14	These are the days	503
37:9-10	Breathe on me, Breath of God	57
	Men of faith	354
	O Breath of Life	379
	There's a wind a-blowing	501
37:10	Rejoice!	438
47:1	There's a river of joy	499
	Your love flows like a river	607
47:1-12	Down the mountain the river flows	83

DANIEL

2:24	Though the earth should tremble	523
2:47	Surely our God	466
4:3	Though the earth should tremble	523
6:26	Though the earth should tremble	523
7:9	Streams of worship	464
7:9-14	Blessing and honour	54
7:13	And he shall reign	22
7:14	Though the earth should tremble	523

HOSEA

6:1	Come, let us return	72
6:3	Let it rain	314
6:3	Mercy is falling	355
	Say the word	445
	There's a wind a-blowing	501

JOEL

1:3	One shall tell another	406
2:11	We are the army of God	540
2:23	Say the word	445
	We have prayed that you would have mercy	547
2:25	I'm standing here to testify	223
2:28	All over the world	12
	Lord, we long for you	337
	We have prayed that you would have mercy	547
	Here we stand in total surrender	165
2:28-29	Great is the darkness	136
2:28-32	I believe the promise	196
2:32	He is the Lord	159
	How sweet the name of Jesus sounds	190
	There is power in the name of Jesus	495

AMOS

3:7	I want to serve the purpose of God	256
5:24	O Lord, the clouds are gathering	399
9:13	You have taken the precious	600

JONAH

3:4-5	Turn to me and be saved	532
3:5	Can a nation be changed?	62

MICAH

5:4	We declare your majesty	544
7:18-19	Here is love	164
	Love of Christ, come now	343
	O the deep, deep love of Jesus!	414
	Overwhelmed by love	422

NAHUM

1:13	We are his people	538

HABAKKUK

2:14	God is working his purpose out	128
	This is the time	610
3:2	Restore, O Lord	439
	Show your power, O Lord	454
3:6	Restore, O Lord	439

ZEPHANIAH

3:14	We are his people	538
3:17	Thank you for the cross	473

HAGGAI

2:6-7	Restore, O Lord	439
	You have taken the precious	600

ZECHARIAH

4:6	In heavenly armour	228
	Not by might	376
8:4-5	Let your love come down	319
9:9	See, your Saviour comes	448
10:1	Let it rain	314
	There's a wind a-blowing	501
	We are the army of God	540
	We have prayed that you would have mercy	547
12:10	Lo, he comes with clouds descending	324
	The heavens shall declare	480
13:1	River, wash over me	441

MALACHI

1:11	From the ends of the earth	115
	From the sun's rising	116
	From where the sun rises	117
	May our worship be as fragrance	351
3:2-4	Purify my heart	436
4:2	This Child	511
4:5	These are the days	503
4:6	Turn our hearts	531
	We will turn the hearts	562

MATTHEW

1:21	Jesus, your name is power	304
	Like a candle flame	322
	Save the people	444
1:23	He is here	157
	He walked where I walked	168
	Immanuel, O Immanuel	219

	Like a candle flame	322
2:1-2	O come, all ye faithful	380
2:5-6	Once in royal David's city	404
2:11	At this time of giving	34
	He is here	157
3:1-3	These are the days	503
3:3	Welcome the King	549
3:11	Father, we adore you, you've drawn us	102
	Ruach	442
3:11-12	God of glory	131
	I will never be the same again	264
3:16	Come on, all us singers, sing	74
	Holy Spirit, come	180
	This grace is mine	512
4:4	Seek ye first	447
4:19	Though I feel afraid	522
5:5-6	Say the word	445
5:7-9	Make me a channel of your peace	348
5:11-16	An army of ordinary people	20
5:13-14	Here I am	161
5:14-16	Like a candle flame	322
5:16	One shall tell another	406
	Seek ye first	447
	We'll walk the land	551
6:9-10	Holy, holy, Lord, you're worthy	178
6:10	All heaven waits	9
	Father of creation	99
	Hail, Jesus, you're my King	140
	Hear our cry	149
	Here we stand in total surrender	165
	Jesus, God's righteousness revealed	278
	Let your word go forth	320
	Reign in me	437
6:10	Reign in me	437
	This love	521
6:10-12	O Lord, the clouds are gathering	399
6:12	Come on, all us singers, sing	74
	Here we stand in total surrender	165
	Turn our hearts	531
6:21	Father, you are my portion	104
6:32	I want to serve the purpose of God	256
6:33	In the morning when I rise	231
	Seek ye first	447
7:7	Seek ye first	447
7:13	How can I be free from sin?	183
7:21-23	There's a blessed time that's coming	496
7:24	My hope is built	365
7:24-25	You are my rock	597
7:26	My hope is built	365
8:8	Say the word	445
8:16-17	Look what the Lord has done	326
9:2	Father, here I am	94
9:13	Just as I am, without one plea	306
9:17	One shall tell another	406
9:20	Draw me closer	84
9:35-38	From the sun's rising	116
9:37	Here I am	161
	O Breath of Life	379
9:37-38	Look what God has done	325
	This is my beloved Son	514
	We will cross every border	560

MATTHEW continued

10:1	Come on, all us singers, sing	74
	Is it true today	241
	Open the doors of praise	411
	We serve a God of miracles	555
10:5-8	Come on, all us singers, sing	74
10:7-8	Is it true today	241
	O for a thousand tongues to sing	383
	We must work together	553
	We serve a God of miracles	555
10:8	God forgave my sin	123
	Look what God has done	325
	We are the army of God	540
10:28	Come, let us worship Jesus	73
	Let your word go forth	320
10:32-33	I reach up high	235
11:5	O for a thousand tongues to sing	383
11:14	These are the days	503
11:28	Before the world began	40
	Jesus! I am resting, resting	280
	Just as I am, without one plea	306
	O come and join the dance	381
	Our confidence is in the Lord	417
11:28-30	How firm a foundation	186
	I heard the voice of Jesus say	206
	O Lord, your tenderness	402
	What a friend we have in Jesus	566
11:29	Jesus, how lovely you are	279
	King of kings, majesty	309
	Meekness and majesty	353
	The Word made flesh	507
12:29	We march to the tune of a love-song	552
13:44	Father, you are my portion	104
	My heart will sing to you	364
14:13-21	5000+ hungry folk	107
14:22-23	Can we walk upon the water	64
16:16	I believe in Jesus	195
	Jesus reigns	293
16:18	I will build my church	259
	We are his people	538
	We shall stand	556
16:19	We march to the tune of a love-song	552
17:3	Jesus, restore to us again	295
	These are the days	503
18:1-5	I'm your child	224
18:2-3	My spirit rests in you alone	371
18:18	We march to the tune of a love-song	552
18:18-20	To every good thing God is doing	525
18:19-20	I believe the promise	196
	Where two or three	578
18:20	As we are gathered	29
	God is here, God is present	127
	He is here	157
	I believe in Jesus	195
	Jesus, we enthrone you	300
18:21-22	Turn our hearts	531
19:26	Almighty God, my Redeemer	17
	Rejoice!	438
20:28	From heaven you came	114
21:1-11	Welcome the King	549
21:5	Rejoice!	438
21:9	Hosanna	182
21:15	Hosanna	182
22:1-14	There's a place where the streets shine	498
22:2	The trumpets sound, the angels sing	506
22:8-10	We've had a light	557
22:29	Jesus, restore to us again	295
22:37	More love, more power	359
	My life is in you, Lord	368
24:13	Wake up, my soul	534
24:14	Alleluia, alleluia, give thanks to the risen Lord	4
	God is working his purpose out	128
	Great is the darkness	136
	Let your word go forth	320
	Shout! The Lord is risen!	452
	We will cross every border	560
	You have called us	598
	You're the Lion of Judah	606
24:30	And he shall reign	22
24:35	In the morning when I rise	231
	Jesus, you're my firm foundation	302
24:45-46	Be patient, be ready	46
25:1-13	Sing a song of celebration	457
	There's a place where the streets shine	498
25:6	Jesus, how lovely you are	279
25:13	There's a blessed time that's coming	496
25:21	There's a blessed time that's coming	496
26:26:27	Broken for me	58
	We do not presume	545
	With this bread	583
26:26-29	Here is bread	163
26:39	Abba, Father, let me be	1
	Do something new, Lord	82
	From heaven you came	114
26:42	Abba, Father, let me be	1
	Do something new, Lord	82
26:49	The Word made flesh	507
26:64	And he shall reign	22
27:28-31	Come and see	70
27:32-40	At the foot of the cross	32
27:32-44	Beneath the cross of Jesus	45
	No scenes of stately majesty	375
27:35	I know a place	209
	On a hill far away	403
27:39-44	How deep the Father's love for us	185
27:51	I stand before the presence	244
	Take me past the outer courts	467
27:57-61	No scenes of stately majesty	375
27:59-60	Low in the grave he lay	345
27:60	In the tomb so cold	234
27:66	Low in the grave he lay	345
28:2	Low in the grave he lay	345
28:5-6	Low in the grave he lay	345
28:6	Alleluia, alleluia, give thanks to the risen Lord	4
	Celebrate Jesus	67
	He has risen	155
	In the tomb so cold	234
	Jesus Christ is risen today	276
	Led like a lamb	312
	O, what a morning	424

	Shout! The Lord is risen!	452	14:22-23	Broken for me	58
28:9-10	Thine be the glory	510	14:22-25	Here is bread	163
28:18	Led like a lamb	312	14:22-23	We do not presume	545
	Sound the trumpet	461		With this bread	583
	The price is paid	487	14:36	Abba, Father, let me be	1
28:18-20	Father of creation	99		Do something new, Lord	82
	From the sun's rising	116		From heaven you came	114
	We are his children	537	14:45	The Word made flesh	507
	We will cross every border	560	14:62	And he shall reign	22
	You're the Lion of Judah	606	15:17-20	Come and see	70
28:19	Called to a battle	61	15:21-32	At the foot of the cross	32
	Filled with compassion	105		Beneath the cross of Jesus	45
	Fire	106		No scenes of stately majesty	375
	God forgave my sin	123	15:24	I know a place	209
	Great is the darkness	136		On a hill far away	403
	Shout! The Lord is risen!	452	15:33-34	How deep the Father's love for us	185
	This is my beloved Son	514	15:42-47	No scenes of stately majesty	375
28:20	Abide with me	2	15:46	In the tomb so cold	234
	Be bold, be strong	38	16:6	Alleluia, alleluia, give thanks to the	
	For the joys and for the sorrows	110		risen Lord	4
	He is here	157		Celebrate Jesus	67
	I'm so secure	221		He has risen	155
	Though I feel afraid	522		In the tomb so cold	234
				Jesus Christ is risen today	276
MARK				Led like a lamb	312
1:1-4	These are the days	503		O, what a morning	424
1:1-2	Welcome the King	549		Shout! The Lord is risen!	452
1:3	Make way, make way	349	16:12	Thine be the glory	510
1:10	Come on, all us singers, sing	74	16:17	Open the doors of praise	411
	Holy Spirit, come	180	16:17-18	Jesus is Lord!	284
	This grace is mine	512	16:19	Led like a lamb	312
1:15	Heaven shall not wait	151	16:20	We believe	541
1:17	Though I feel afraid	522			
2:5	Father, here I am	94	**LUKE**		
2:17	Just as I am, without one plea	306	1:17	Turn our hearts	531
2:22	One shall tell another	406		We will turn the hearts	562
5:27	Draw me closer	84	1:29	Turn our hearts	531
6:7	Come on, all us singers, sing	74	1:34-35	We believe	541
	We serve a God of miracles	555	1:38	Let it be to me	313
6:13	We serve a God of miracles	555		Silent, surrendered	456
6:30-44	5000+ hungry folk	107	1:46-55	Tell out, my soul	471
6:45-51	Can we walk upon the water	64	1:51-53	Earth lies spellbound	85
9:4	Jesus, restore to us again	295	1:52-53	This Child	511
	These are the days	503	1:53	The trumpets sound, the angels sing	506
9:24	I believe in Jesus	195	1:76-79	O come and join the dance	81
10:41-45	Make me a channel of your peace	348	1:78-79	This Child	511
10:45	From heaven you came	114	2:1-20	O little town of Bethlehem	393
	He is the mighty God	160	2:4	Once in royal David's city	404
	How can I not love you?	184	2:4-7	Earth lies spellbound	85
	The Word made flesh	507	2:6-7	O come and join the dance	381
	The world is looking for a hero	508		What kind of greatness	567
11:1-11	Welcome the King	549	2:7	Away in a manger	36
11:9-10	Hosanna	182	2:8-20	O come, all ye faithful	380
11:22	I walk by faith	253		Silent night	455
11:22-24	I believe the promise	196	2:8-14	Tonight	528
11:22-25	To every good thing God is doing	525	2:10-14	Heaven invites you to a party	150
12:24	Jesus, restore to us again	295	2:13-14	Earth lies spellbound	85
12:29	I will worship	270		Hark, the herald-angels sing	144
12:30	More love, more power	359		He is here	157
	My life is in you, Lord	368		Like a candle flame	322
13:26	And he shall reign	22	2:14	Gloria	119

LUKE continued

2:29-32	Mighty God	356
3:2-6	These are the days	503
3:4-6	Welcome the King	549
3:16	Father, we adore you, you've drawn us	102
	Ruach	442
3:21	Come on, all us singers, sing	74
3:22	Holy Spirit, come	180
	This grace is mine	512
	This is my beloved Son	514
4:4	Seek ye first	447
4:18	Anointing, fall on me	24
	Beauty for brokenness	37
	Day of favour	78
	God of glory, we exalt your name	130
	Hallelujah, hallelujah	141
	Have you heard the good news	146
	Heaven shall not wait	151
	I give you all the honour	203
	Jesus, the name high over all	298
	Jesus, your name is power	304
	Let your love come down	319
	Make way, make way	349
	Men of faith	354
	Not by might	376
	O for a thousand tongues to sing	383
	Say the word	445
	See, your Saviour comes	448
	Shout! The Lord is risen!	452
	The Spirit of the sovereign Lord	504
	We march to the tune of a love-song	552
	We rejoice in the goodness of our God	554
	We will cross every border	560
	Where there once was only hurt	577
	Who sees it all	580
	You have shown me	599
5:20	Father, here I am	94
5:32	Just as I am, without one plea	306
5:37-39	One shall tell another	406
6:48-49	My hope is built	365
7:7	Say the word	445
7:47	Jesus, Jesus, Jesus	287
8:44	Draw me closer	84
9:1	We serve a God of miracles	555
9:1-2	Come on, all us singers, sing	74
	Is it true today	241
	We must work together	553
9:10-17	5000+ hungry folk	107
9:30	Jesus, restore to us again	295
	These are the days	503
9:51	We shall stand	556
10:2	Here I am	161
	O Breath of Life	379
	These are the days	503
10:5	Peace be to these streets	427
10:8-9	We must work together	553
10:21	Surely our God	466
10:27	I love you, Lord, with all of my heart	215
	More love, more power	359
10:39	To be in your presence	524
11:2	Reign in me	437
11:2-4	O Lord, the clouds are gathering	399
11:4	Turn our hearts	531
12:24	Father, you are my portion	104
14:17	The trumpets sound, the angels sing	506
15:5	Well, I hear they're singing in the streets	550
15:7	Well, I hear they're singing in the streets	550
15:11-24	Oh, I was made for this	389
15:17-24	God is good	124
	O Father of the fatherless	382
15:20	I sing a simple song of love	239
	Just as I am, without one plea	306
15:20-24	Well, I hear they're singing in the streets	550
15:32	Well, I hear they're singing in the streets	550
17:20-21	O, heaven is in my heart	388
17:21	Heaven shall not wait	151
18:27	God will make a new way	134
19:10	Save the people	444
19:28-44	Welcome the King	549
19:38	Hosanna	182
19:38-42	See, your Saviour comes	448
22:14-20	Here is bread	163
22:18	One shall tell another	406
22:19-20	Broken for me	58
	We do not presume	545
	With this bread	583
22:42	Abba, Father, let me be	1
	Do something new, Lord	82
	From heaven you came	114
22:48	The Word made flesh	507
22:63	Come and see	70
23:25	In the tomb so cold	234
23:26-43	At the foot of the cross	32
	Beneath the cross of Jesus	45
	No scenes of stately majesty	375
23:33	I know a place	209
	On a hill far away	403
23:34	Come and see	70
	Meekness and majesty	353
23:42	Jesus, remember me	294
23:50-56	No scenes of stately majesty	375
24:6	Alleluia, alleluia, give thanks to the risen Lord	4
	Celebrate Jesus	67
	He has risen	155
	In the tomb so cold	234
	Jesus Christ is risen today	276
	Led like a lamb	312
	O, what a morning	424
	Shout! The Lord is risen!	452
24:15-16	Thine be the glory	510
24:51	Shout! The Lord is risen!	452

JOHN

1:1	O come, all ye faithful	380
1:1-3	Almighty God, we bring you praise	16
	Jesus is Lord!	284
1:4	Jesus reigns	293

	Jesus, restore to us again	295	
1:4-5	Like a candle flame	322	
1:5	God is good all the time	125	
	Lord, the light of your love	335	
	We'll walk the land	551	
1:9	Like a candle flame	322	
	The Word made flesh	507	
	This Child	511	
1:10	What kind of greatness	567	
1:12	I am so thankful	192	
1:12-13	Joy to the world	305	
	Make way, make way	349	
	O come and join the dance	381	
	O happy day	387	
	O little town of Bethlehem	393	
1:12	We are a people of power	536	
1:14	Meekness and majesty	353	
1:14	O come, all ye faithful	380	
	The Word made flesh	507	
	What kind of greatness	567	
	You are God, you are great	591	
1:29	I worship you, O Lamb of God	272	
	Jesus reigns	293	
	Just as I am, without one plea	306	
	Lamb of God	310	
	There is a Redeemer	492	
2:1-11	On this day of happiness	410	
2:9	The trumpets sound, the angels sing	506	
3:3	God forgave my sin	123	
3:8	Peace like a river	429	
	Ruach	442	
	There's a wind a-blowing	501	
3:14	We want to see Jesus lifted high	559	
3:14-15	Beneath the cross of Jesus	45	
3:14-16	Man of sorrows	350	
	The cross has said it all	478	
3:16	Because of your love	39	
	Give thanks with a grateful heart	118	
	I'm special	222	
	I stand amazed in the presence	243	
	I've got a love song	252	
	Jesus, God's righteousness revealed	278	
	Jesus, your loving kindness	303	
	Just as I am, without one plea	306	
	O Lord, my God	396	
	Such love	465	
	There's an awesome sound	497	
	This grace is mine	512	
3:16-17	This is my beloved Son	514	
3:17	Save the people	444	
3:29	Jesus, how lovely you are	279	
4:13-14	I heard the voice of Jesus say	206	
	There's a river of joy	499	
4:14	Is anyone thirsty?	237	
	Jesus, I am thirsty	281	
	Jesus, Jesus (Holy and anointed one)	286	
	Peace like a river	429	
	River, wash over me	441	
	Say the word	445	
4:23	Father God, we worship you	92	
4:24	O Lord, how majestic is your name	395	
4:28-30	One shall tell another	406	
4:35	Here I am	161	
	O Breath of Life	379	
	These are the days	503	
	We've had a light	557	
	We will cross every border	560	
	This is the time	610	
5:19	Father, I place into your hands	97	
5:22	Come, let us worship Jesus	73	
6:1-15	5000+ hungry folk	107	
6:15-21	Can we walk upon the water	64	
6:27	Jesus, restore to us again	295	
6:44	Father, we adore you, you've drawn us	102	
	God of all comfort	129	
	Only by grace	408	
7:17	Jesus, restore to us again	295	
7:37-38	Hear our cry	149	
	I heard the voice of Jesus say	206	
	Is anyone thirsty?	237	
	I've found a friend	251	
	Jesus, I am thirsty	281	
	Let your living water flow	318	
	Shout! The Lord is risen!	452	
	There's a river of joy	499	
7:38-39	Jesus, Jesus (Holy and anointed one)	286	
8:12	Can you see what we have made	65	
	Colours of day	69	
	I heard the voice of Jesus say	206	
	Lord, the light of your love	335	
8:32	Lord, the light of your love	335	
	Seek ye first	447	
	Thank you for saving me	472	
8:36	Hallelujah! Jesus is alive	142	
	Seek ye first	447	
8:58	We are the army of God	540	
9:6	Draw me closer	84	
9:38	I believe in Jesus	195	
10:11	O let the sun of God enfold you	392	
	Shout for joy and sing	450	
10:14	O let the sun of God enfold you	392	
	Shout for joy and sing	450	
10:27-29	I'm so secure	221	
10:27-30	How firm a foundation	186	
11:27	I believe in Jesus	195	
12:12-19	Welcome the King	549	
12:13	Hosanna	182	
12:28	Father, we love you	103	
12:32	Lord, we lift you high	336	
13:2-5	Heaven shall not wait	151	
13:5	Meekness and majesty	353	
13:34	A new commandment	23	
13:34-35	Let there be love	317	
	We are marching	539	
13:35	Peace, perfect peace	430	
14:1	I believe in Jesus	195	
14:6	Jesus is greater	282	
	Jesus, your name is power	304	
	There is only one Lord	494	
	There's a place where the streets shine	498	
	We want to see Jesus lifted high	559	
14:9-10	The Word made flesh	507	

JOHN continued

14:12	We serve a God of miracles	555
14:16	I love your presence	216
	I've found a friend	251
14:16-18	Jesus, at your name	273
	Though I feel afraid	522
14:17	Holy Spirit, come	180
	Holy Spirit, we welcome you	181
14:23	Father of life, draw me closer	100
	How can I not love you?	184
	I've found a friend	251
	Make way, make way	349
	Though I feel afraid	522
14:26	I love your presence	216
	More about Jesus	358
	Silent, surrendered	456
14:27	Peace I give to you	428
	Peace, perfect peace	430
15:1-8	I want to be a tree that's bearing fruit	254
15:4	Abide with me	2
	How can I not love you?	184
15:5	There is only one Lord	494
15:7	Abide with me	2
15:9	We want to remain in your love	558
15:12	A new commandment	23
15:15	As the deer pants (Nystrom)	27
	I'm special	222
	I'm standing here to testify	223
	I want to serve the purpose of God	256
	I will change your name	260
	I will seek you	267
	King of kings, majesty	309
	There is a place of commanded blessing	491
	What a friend I've found	565
	What a friend we have in Jesus	566
15:16	We shall stand	556
15:26	Jesus, restore to us again	295
16:14	More about Jesus	358
	River, wash over me	441
16:20-24	You make my heart feel glad	603
16:22	Jesus put this song into our hearts	292
17:20	God forgave my sin	123
17:20-21	How good and how pleasant	187
	There is a place of commanded blessing	491
17:22	Yahweh	586
18:5	The Word made flesh	507
19:2	Come and see	70
19:5	Come and see	70
19:16-24	No scenes of stately majesty	375
19:16-27	At the foot of the cross	32
	Beneath the cross of Jesus	45
19:17	Come and see	70
19:18	I know a place	209
	On a hill far away	403
19:30	How deep the Father's love for us	185
	Man of sorrows	350
19:34	O the blood of my Saviour	413
19:38-42	No scenes of stately majesty	375
19:42	In the tomb so cold	234
20:14	Thine be the glory	510
20:16	Led like a lamb	312

20:21-22	Have you not said	147
20:27	From heaven you came	114
20:28	Hail, Jesus, you're my King	140
20:31	Jesus, your name is power	304
21:14	Celebrate Jesus	67
	In the tomb so cold	234
21:15	O let the sun of God enfold you	392

ACTS

1:8	There is a Redeemer	492
	We are marching	539
	We shall stand	556
	We've had a light	557
1:9	Shout! The Lord is risen!	452
1:11	He is the mighty God	160
	This is the time	610
1:14	I believe the promise	196
2:1-3	All honour, all glory	10
2:1-4	Breathe on me, Breath of God	57
	Come down, O Love divine	71
	Come, Spirit, come	76
	Fire	106
	I believe the promise	196
	O God of burning, cleansing flame	386
	O thou who camest from above	416
	Shout! The Lord is risen!	452
	Spirit of the living God (Iverson)	462
	Spirit of the living God (Armstrong)	463
	Therefore we lift our hearts in praise	489
	There's a wind a-blowing	501
	We believe	541
2:2	Peace like a river	429
	Ruach	442
2:2-3	Holy Spirit, we welcome you	181
	As we lift up your name	30
2:4	Anointing, fall on me	24
2:18	Great is the darkness	136
2:21	Every nation, power and tongue	86
	There is power in the name of Jesus	495
2:27	He has risen	155
2:34	Led like a lamb	312
2:39	The promise of the Holy Spirit	488
2:46-47	One shall tell another	406
3:7-8	Make way, make way	349
3:16	I know it	210
4:12	Above the clash of creeds	3
	Every nation, power and tongue	86
	How sweet the name of Jesus sounds	190
	I know it	210
	In Christ alone	225
	Jesus Christ is the Lord of all	277
	Jesus, name above all names	291
	Jesus, your name is power	304
	No other name	374
	There is only one Lord	494
4:30	We serve a God of miracles	555
8:4	One shall tell another	406
8:8	One shall tell another	406
	Well, I hear they're singing in the streets	550
9:35	Well, I hear they're singing in the streets	550

10:44	Anointing, fall on me	24
13:1-3	I want to serve the purpose of God	256
20:35	Make me a channel of your peace	348

ROMANS

1:16	He is the Lord	159
1:17	Jesus, God's righteousness revealed	278
2:4	Hear our cry	149
3:23-25	How can I be free from sin?	183
3:25	Holiness is your life in me	174
	I am so thankful	192
3:26	Alleluia, alleluia, give thanks to the risen Lord	4
5:1-5	Have you heard the good news	146
5:1-11	Amazing grace	18
5:1-2	He has clothed us with his righteousness	153
5:1-11	Lord, I come to you	329
5:2	Father, I come to you	95
	I am a new creation	191
	This grace is mine	512
5:5	Be free	41
	I receive your love	236
	Love divine, all loves excelling	343
	No one but you, Lord	373
5:6-11	And can it be	21
5:8	Above the clash of creeds	3
	At the foot of the cross	32
	God is good all the time	125
	Hallelujah, my Father	143
	He walked where I walked	168
	How can I be free from sin?	183
	I stand amazed in the presence	243
	Just as I am, without one plea	306
	Man of sorrows	350
	My Lord, what love is this	370
	There's an awesome sound	497
	The world is looking for a hero	508
	We worship and adore you	564
5:10	Hallelujah, my Father	143
	Jesus, we celebrate the victory	299
5:15-17	Behold his love	43
6:5-10	How can I be free from sin?	183
6:6	The world is looking for a hero	508
6:9	For this purpose	111
	You are mighty	594
8:1	I am a new creation	191
	I'm accepted, I'm forgiven	217
	The price is paid	487
8:1-2	And can it be	21
8:2	Nothing shall separate us	377
8:3	Jesus, take me as I am	297
8:15	Abba, Father, let me be	1
	Father God, I wonder	91
	Father, I want you to hold me	98
	I'm accepted, I'm forgiven	217
	Jesus, we celebrate the victory	299
	O Father of the fatherless	382
8:15-17	He has clothed us with his righteousness	153
8:17	Righteousness, peace, joy in the Holy Ghost	440

8:18-21	Beauty for brokenness	37
8:19	Father of creation	99
	More of your glory	360
	Shout for joy	449
	Shout! The Lord is risen!	452
8:19-22	The Lord is a mighty King	481
8:22	You have taken the precious	600
8:26	Jesus, restore to us again	295
8:28	When peace like a river	574
8:29	Oh, I was made for this	389
8:31	I could sing unending songs	200
	I walk by faith	253
8:31-32	This is my beloved Son	514
8:32	Nothing shall separate us	377
	There is a Redeemer	492
8:34	All heaven waits	9
	Nothing shall separate us	377
8:35-37	O, we are more than conquerors	423
8:38-39	His love	171
	Nothing shall separate us	377
9:21	Change my heart, O God	68
10:4	Shout for joy	449
10:8-10	Jesus, restore to us again	295
10:9-10	I believe in Jesus	195
	O happy day	387
10:13	He is the Lord	159
	There is power in the name of Jesus	495
11:33	I will offer up my life	265
12:1	As we lift up your name	30
	Come on, all us singers, sing	74
	Fire	106
	From heaven you came	114
	I bow my knee	198
	I will lift my voice	263
	I will offer up my life	265
	King of kings, majesty	309
	Let me be a sacrifice	315
	Lord, prepare me	334
	Lord, you have my heart	341
	Lord, you put a tongue in my mouth	342
	May our worship be as fragrance	351
	On this day	409
	O thou who camest from above	416
	Reign in me	437
	Silent, surrendered	456
	Take my life, and let it be	468
	Teach me to dance	469
	The price is paid	487
	There's a wind a-blowing	501
	This love	521
	What kind of greatness	567
	When I survey the wondrous cross	572
12:1-2	All to Jesus I surrender	15
	I reach up high	235
	You rescued me	605
12:2	Do something new, Lord	82
	Lord, I come to you	329
12:11	As we lift up your name	30
12:15	Look what God has done	325
14:17	I've found a friend	251
	Jesus Christ is Lord of all	275

ROMANS continued

	Righteousness, peace, joy in the Holy Ghost	440
16:20	I went to the enemy's camp	257
	The price is paid	487
	There is power in the name of Jesus	495

1 CORINTHIANS

1:9	Faithful God	88
	On this day	409
1:17-25	I have made you too small	205
1:18-25	This is the message of the cross	518
1:18-30	How deep the Father's love for us	185
1:24-25	Surely our God	466
1:25	In the presence of a holy God	232
	Men of faith	354
	My heart will sing to you	364
1:27	You have taken the precious	600
1:30	Be thou my vision	50
	Jesus, God's righteousness revealed	278
1:30-31	Surely our God	466
2:9	What kind of love is this	568
2:9-10	He has clothed us with his righteousness	153
3:10-11	I want to serve the purpose of God	256
3:11	O, heaven is in my heart	388
	The church's one foundation	477
3:12	There is a louder shout to come	490
3:12-13	Purify my heart	436
3:13	Restore, O Lord	439
4:20	Rejoice!	438
6:19-20	I bow my knee before your throne	197
	Lord, prepare me	334
6:19	O the glory of your presence	415
6:20	O the blood of my Saviour	413
9:26-27	Wake up, my soul	534
10:13	Faithful God	88
11:23-26	Broken for me	58
	Here is bread	163
	With this bread	583
11:23-30	We do not presume	545
12:4	At this time of giving	34
12:12	As we are gathered	29
12:12-27	We must work together	553
13:4-7	We want to remain in your love	558
13:12	He has risen	155
13:13	Bind us together	51
15:3	I know a place	209
15:3-4	Jesus, how lovely you are	279
	Lord, I lift your name on high	330
	Thank you, Jesus	475
	Therefore we lift our hearts in praise	489
	The Word made flesh	507
	We believe	541
15:13-20	He has risen	55
15:15	The Word made flesh	507
15:54	Called to a battle	61
	Holy One of God	179
15:54-58	Thine be the glory	510
15:55	O God, most high	385
15:55-57	Hallelujah! Jesus is alive	142

	Jesus reigns	293
	For all that you've done	108
	Open the doors of praise	411

2 CORINTHIANS

1:3	God of all comfort	129
1:3-4	Peace I give to you	428
1-20	To every good thing God is doing	525
2:14	May the fragrance	352
3:14-16	Hear our cry	149
3:15-18	Can I ascend	63
3:18	Glory to the King of kings	121
	Lord, the light of your love	335
	Love divine, all loves excelling	343
	May the fragrance	352
	More love, more power	359
	My heart will sing to you	364
	See his glory	446
	The Lord is a mighty King	481
	This love	521
	To keep your lovely face	527
	Turn your eyes upon Jesus	533
	We shall stand	556
	Yahweh	586
4:4	Hear our cry	149
4:6	See his glory	446
	To keep your lovely face	527
	Turn your eyes upon Jesus	533
	Yahweh	586
4:7	Rejoice!	438
4:7-11	Men of faith	354
4:7-12	Make me a channel of your peace	48
5:7	I walk by faith	253
	Men of faith	354
5:13	I will dance, I will sing	261
5:14	Jesus' love has got under our skin	289
5:17	I am a new creation	191
5:21	Come and see	70
6:2	This love	521
6:10	Almighty God, my Redeemer	17
8:9	Say the word	445
	This grace is mine	512
9:8	O Lord, you're beautiful	401
9:15	Give thanks with a grateful heart	118
	Thank you, Jesus	475
10:4	Our God is awesome in power	419
	We want to see Jesus lifted high	559
10:4-5	We march to the tune of a love-song	552
12:9	It's our confession, Lord	248
	Say the word	445
	We are marching	539
12:10	Almighty God, my Redeemer	17
12:10	Men of faith	354
12:10	Rejoice!	438
13:14	This is the sweetest mystery	520

GALATIANS

2:20	Alleluia, alleluia, give thanks to the risen Lord	4
	Come on and celebrate	75
	God's not dead	133

	I stand amazed in the presence	243
	This grace is mine	512
	This is the message of the cross	518
	What kind of love is this	568
3:7	We are the army of God	540
3:13	Hallelujah! Jesus is alive	142
3:28	Jesus' love has got under our skin	289
	Jesus put this song into our hearts	292
4:5-6	Father God, I wonder	91
	Father, I want you to hold me	98
4:6	Abba, Father, let me be	1
	I'm accepted, I'm forgiven	217
	O Father of the fatherless	382
5:1	Jesus, we celebrate the victory	299
5:15	Come on, all us singers, sing	74
6:7	Let your love come down	319
6:14	In Christ alone	225
	Oh, lead me	390
	On a hill far away	403
	The cross has said it all	478
	This is the message of the cross	518
	When I survey the wondrous cross	572

EPHESIANS

1:3	My life is in you, Lord	368
	O, we are more than conquerors	423
	Praise God from whom all blessings flow	432
1:4	Before the world began	40
1:4-5	Be free	41
1:5	Father God, I wonder	91
	What kind of love is this	568
1:7	Jesus, how lovely you are	279
	Jesus, name above all names	291
1:9	This is the mystery	519
1:10	The Lord is a mighty King	481
1:12	This is the mystery	519
1:18-19	In every circumstance	227
1:18-20	We are marching	539
1:19	Be free	41
1:19-23	Low in the grave he lay	345
1:20	He is exalted	156
	Jesus is King	283
	Jesus, Jesus (Holy and anointed one)	286
1:20-21	Lift up your heads	321
1:21-23	Meekness and majesty	353
1:22	Jesus reigns	293
1:22-23	I went to the enemy's camp	257
2:1-9	And can it be	21
2:1-10	By his grace	59
2:4-5	You are merciful to me	593
2:8	God of grace	132
	There's a sound of singing	500
	What kind of love is this	568
	You have shown me	599
2:8-9	All hail the power of Jesus' name	7
	Only by grace	408
2:13-18	Turn our hearts	531
2:14	Jesus put this song into our hearts	292
	There is a place of commanded blessing	491
2:14-16	All over the world	12

2:20-22	O, heaven is in my heart	388
2:21-22	For I'm building a people of power	109
	O the glory of your presence	415
2:22	As we are gathered	29
3:14-19	I want to be out of my depth in your love	255
3:14-19	Just as I am, without one plea	306
	More about Jesus	358
3:15	O Father of the fatherless	382
3:16-19	You love me as you found me	602
3:17-19	His love	171
3:18-19	Here is love	164
	Love of Christ, come now	343
	More love, more power	359
	My heart will sing to you	364
	O the deep, deep love of Jesus!	414
	Overwhelmed by love	422
4:3-6	For I'm building a people of power	109
	How good and how pleasant	187
4:3	Let your word go forth	320
	There is a place of commanded blessing	491
4:3-6	One heart, one voice, one mind	405
	We must work together	553
4:4	All heaven waits	9
4:4-6	The church's one foundation	477
4:8	O God, most high	385
4:22-24	Jesus, take me as I am	297
5:2	May the fragrance	352
	My Lord, what love is this	370
5:18	Anointing, fall on me	24
	Hold me, Lord	173
	Jesus is King	283
	Let your living water flow	318
	River, wash over me	441
	Spirit of the living God (Iverson)	462
	Spirit of the living God (Armstrong)	463
5:8-17	Wake up, O sleeper	535
6:7	From heaven you came	114
6:10-18	Be thou my vision	50
6:11	In heavenly armour	228
6:12	Called to a battle	61
	Open the doors of praise	411
	The Lord is moving across this land	483
6:13	We shall stand	556
6:16-17	You're the Lion of Judah	606

PHILIPPIANS

1:6	O, we are more than conquerors	423
	Say the word	445
1:21	Jesus, Jesus, you have the name	288
	More about Jesus	358
	When peace like a river	574
	When the music fades	576
2:1-4	If you are encouraged	202
2:5-11	At the name of Jesus	33
	Celebrate, celebrate	66
2:6-7	What kind of greatness	567
2:6-8	And can it be	21
2:6-9	Meekness and majesty	353
	You laid aside your majesty	601
2:6-11	Jesus Christ	274

PHILIPPIANS continued

	The world is looking for a hero	508
2:7	From heaven you came	114
2:8	Behold his love	43
	I will offer up my life	265
2:9	He is exalted	156
	He that is in us	167
	Jesus, name above all names	291
	There is a Redeemer	492
	We declare your majesty	544
2:9-10	Higher, higher	170
	Jesus, at your name	273
	Jesus is the name we honour	285
2:9-11	He is the mighty God	160
	Here in your presence	162
	How sweet the name of Jesus sounds	190
	Jesus, Jesus, you have the name	288
	Jesus shall take the highest honour	296
	Jesus, the name high over all	298
	Jesus, your name is power	304
	Lord of the heavens	333
	Mighty is our God	357
	No other name	374
	O God, most high	385
	Shout! The Lord is risen!	452
	The heavens shall declare	480
	Therefore we lift our hearts in praise	489
	There is only one Lord	494
	There is power in the name of Jesus	495
	There's a sound of singing	500
2:10-11	He is Lord	158
	I will build my church	259
	We believe	541
2:11	Jesus Christ is Lord of all	275
	Jesus Christ is the Lord of all	277
	Jesus is Lord!	284
	Shout for joy and sing	450
	Welcome, King of kings	548
3:7	Jesus, Jesus, you have the name	288
3:7-11	All I once held dear	11
	All to Jesus I surrender	15
3:8	Turn your eyes upon Jesus	533
	When I survey the wondrous cross	572
3:10	In the morning when I rise	231
	More love, more power	359
	More of your glory	360
3:10-14	In the secret	233
3:13-14	Wake up, my soul	534
3:20	The Word made flesh	507
4:4	We rejoice in the goodness of our God	554
4:6-7	What a friend we have in Jesus	566
4:8	Hold me closer to you	172
4:12-13	Be thou my vision	50
	Say the word	445
	When peace like a river	574
4:13	In Christ alone	225
	My life is in you, Lord	368
4:19	Be thou my vision	50
	My spirit rests in you alone	371

COLOSSIANS

1:14	Thank you for the cross	473

1:16	The Lord is a mighty King	481
1:17	O Lord our God	398
1:19-20	When I survey the wondrous cross	572
1:19-22	Turn our hearts	531
1:26	Shout for joy	449
1:27	Rejoice!	438
	Surely our God	466
	This love	521
2:3	Surely our God	466
2:6-7	I want to be a tree that's bearing fruit	254
	Thank you for saving me	472
2:9-10	God of grace	132
	Jesus, what a beautiful name	301
	This love	521
2:13-15	Beneath the cross of Jesus	45
	I know a place	209
	I will offer up my life	265
	No scenes of stately majesty	375
2:14-15	O Lord, the clouds are gathering	399
2:14-15	The Lord is moving across this land	483
	The world is looking for a hero	508
	This is the message of the cross	518
2:15	The price is paid	487
3:3	My life is in you, Lord	368
3:4	See his glory	446
3:5	Jesus, take me as I am	297
3:14	Bind us together	51
3:15-17	Father of life, draw me closer	100
3:17	I reach up high	235
3:17	Lord, we lift you high	336

1 THESSALONIANS

4:14	Man of sorrows	350
4:16-17	All heaven waits	9
4:16	He has risen	155
	My hope is built	365
	O, heaven is in my heart	388
	O Lord, my God	396
	These are the days	503
	The Word made flesh	507
	We believe	541
4:16-17	He is the mighty God	160
4:17	Lo, he comes with clouds descending	324
5:18	For all that you've done	108
	Give thanks with a grateful heart	118
5:24	Faithful God	88
	On this day	409

2 THESSALONIANS

1:7	The Word made flesh	507
1:12	In my life, Lord	230
2:8	All heaven waits	9

1 TIMOTHY

1:14	Therefore we lift our hearts in praise	489
1:17	Immortal, invisible, God only wise	220
	Now unto the King	378
2:6	Jesus is Lord!	284
4:16	Be patient, be ready	46
6:15	All hail King Jesus!	5
	King of kings	308
	Lord of lords	332

2 TIMOTHY

1:6	O thou who camest from above	416
	Ruach	442
1:12	Blessed assurance, Jesus is mine	52
	I cannot tell	199
	O Jesus, I have promised	391
2:12	O Jesus, I have promised	391

TITUS

2:11	Therefore we lift our hearts in praise	489

HEBREWS

1:1-2	Above the clash of creeds	3
1:3	Jesus, God's righteousness revealed	278
	Jesus is the name we honour	285
	We believe	541
	You are crowned with many crowns	590
1:8-9	My heart is full	363
1:12	Restore, O Lord	439
1:13	I went to the enemy's camp	257
2:9	This is my beloved Son	514
	You are crowned with many crowns	590
2:9-10	How deep the Father's love for us	185
2:10	Meekness and majesty	353
2:14	He walked where I walked	168
3:12	Restore, O Lord	439
4:11	Jesus! I am resting, resting	280
4:14	Jesus is King	283
4:14-16	What a friend we have in Jesus	566
4:15	He walked where I walked	168
	Immanuel, O Immanuel	219
	Meekness and majesty	353
4:16	I just want to be where you are	207
	Jesus, we celebrate the victory	299
	Our confidence is in the Lord	417
	Thank you for your mercy	474
5:8	Meekness and majesty	353
5:11-14	Have you got an appetite?	145
6:18-19	Jesus is King	283
6:19	Jesus, you're my firm foundation	302
	My hope is built	365
7:25	All heaven waits	9
	Jesus is King	283
	Thank you for the cross	473
9:11	Take me past the outer courts	467
9:24	Take me past the outer courts	467
10:19-22	O, heaven is in my heart	388
	Take me past the outer courts	467
	The price is paid	487
10:19-23	We have a great priest	546
12:1-2	In the secret	233
	I will never be the same again	264
	Wake up, my soul	534
12:1-3	Be patient, be ready	46
12:2	Led like a lamb	312
12:22	Alleluia, alleluia, give thanks to the risen Lord	4
12:24	Alleluia, alleluia, give thanks to the risen Lord	4
12:26-27	Be patient, be ready	46
	We are his children	537

12:28	Be still, for the presence of the Lord	47
13:8	Abide with me	2
	For all that you've done	108
	For the joys and for the sorrows	110
	Look what the Lord has done	326
13:15	I bow my knee before your throne	197
	There's a sound of singing	500
	We bring the sacrifice of praise	542
	When the music fades	576

JAMES

2:23	I'm standing here to testify	223
	I will change your name	260
4:7-8	I'm standing here to testify	223
4:8	Oh, lead me	390

1 PETER

1:3	Jesus, you're my firm foundation	302
1:6-7	Purify my heart	436
1:8	I am a new creation	191
1:10-12	All hail the power of Jesus' name	7
1:15	We are his children	537
1:15-16	I will never be the same again	264
	O God of burning, cleansing flame	386
1:18-19	Almighty God, we bring you praise	16
	By his grace	59
	Great and mighty is he	135
	Man of sorrows	350
	Thank you for saving me	472
	The Lord is a mighty King	481
	The price is paid	487
1:19	Lord, you are more precious	339
	Lord, you are so precious to me	340
	Only by grace	408
	O the blood of Jesus	412
	O the blood of my Saviour	413
2:2-3	Have you got an appetite?	145
2:4	Lord, you are more precious	339
	Lord, you are so precious to me	340
2:6	Lord, you are more precious	339
	Lord, you are so precious to me	340
2:9	This is the mystery	519
	We are his children	537
	You have called us	598
2:24	For this purpose	111
	I stand amazed in the presence	243
	Thank you for the cross	473
	The price is paid	487
3:18	Therefore we lift our hearts in praise	489
	What kind of love is this	568
5:4	See his glory	446
5:7	Higher, higher	170
	Let your living water flow	318

2 PETER

1:3-4	My Jesus, my Saviour	367
1:19	Almighty God, we bring you praise	16
3:9	Filled with compassion	105
	See, your Saviour comes	448
3:12	Great is the darkness	136
	I want to serve the purpose of God	256
3:13	Joy to the world	305

1 JOHN

1:1-2	Jesus, restore to us again	295
	There's a sound of singing	500
1:5	This, in essence, is the message	513
	We'll walk the land	551
1:7	Holiness is your life in me	174
	I bow my knee	198
	It's your blood	250
	Lamb of God	310
	Only by grace	408
	O the blood of Jesus	412
	Purify my heart	436
	We are marching	539
	We'll walk the land	551
	Who can sound the depths of sorrow	579
1:7-9	Father, here I am	94
1:9	Thank you for saving me	472
2:2	Can you see what we have made	65
	Holiness is your life in me	174
	I know a place	209
	I know it	210
	Lamb of God	310
	Man of sorrows	350
2:8	Colours of day	69
2:12	I know it	210
3:1	Father God, I wonder	91
	Father, I want you to hold me	98
	How deep the Father's love for us	185
	I'm your child	224
3:3	There's a place where the streets shine	498
3:5	Be still, for the presence of the Lord	47
3:8	For this purpose	111
4:4	He that is in us	167
4:7	Let there be love	317
4:14	Hallelujah, my Father	143
4:16	I want to be out of my depth in your love	255
	We want to remain in your love	558
4:18	I want to be out of my depth in your love	255
	Jesus, we celebrate the victory	299
	Let your love come down	319
	My lips shall praise you	369
4:19	Father, I come to you	95
	Father, we adore you, you've drawn us	102
	How can I not love you?	184
	Jesus put this song into our hearts	292
	Lord, you are so precious to me	340
	My Jesus, I love thee	366
	O come, all ye faithful	380

REVELATION

1:5	Crown him with many crowns	77
1:5-6	There's a place where the streets shine	498
1:6	Lord, my heart cries out	331
	Lord of lords	332
	This grace is mine	512
1:7	Every nation, power and tongue	86
	Lo, he comes with clouds descending	324
1:8	Behold his love	43
	Father in heaven, how we love you	96

1:12	The heavens shall declare	480
1:13	And he shall reign	22
1:14	Be still, for the presence of the Lord	47
1:14-18	At your feet we fall	35
	Behold the Lord	44
1:15	All heaven waits	9
1:16	Be still, for the presence of the Lord	47
	To keep your lovely face	527
1:17	As we seek your face	31
	King of kings, majesty	309
1:17-18	Hallelujah! Jesus is alive	142
	He is the mighty God	160
	Lord of the heavens	333
1:18	God's not dead	133
	Sound the trumpet	461
2:4	My first love	362
2:4-5	O Lord, you're beautiful	401
2:17	I will change your name	260
3:7	God will make a new way	134
3:12	I will change your name	260
3:15	God of grace	132
3:17	Just as I am, without one plea	306
3:18	Don't let my love grow cold	81
4:1	Come on, all us singers, sing	74
4:2	I stand before your throne	245
4:6-8	Holy, holy, Lord God Almighty	177
4:6-11	Holy, holy, holy! Lord God Almighty	176
4:8	As we seek your face	31
	Behold the Lord	44
	Father in heaven, how we love you	96
	Holy, holy, Lord, you're worthy	178
	Streams of worship	464
4:8-10	In the presence of a holy God	232
4:11	All honour, all glory	10
	Holy, holy, Lord, you're worthy	178
	Lord of the heavens	333
	My heart is full	363
	Worthy, O worthy are you, Lord	585
5:5	Hail, Jesus, you're my King	140
	Hallelujah, hallelujah	141
	King of kings	308
5:5-6	Jesus reigns	293
	You're the Lion of Judah	606
5:6	All heaven declares	8
	I worship you, O Lamb of God	272
	Lo, he comes with clouds descending	324
5:8	Hear our cry	149
	May our worship be as fragrance	351
5:9	Every nation, power and tongue	86
	Filled with compassion	105
	Jesus Christ is the Lord of all	277
	Jesus' love has got under our skin	289
	King of kings, majesty	309
	Lord of the heavens	333
	O the blood of my Saviour	413
	Sing a song of celebration	457
	Take me past the outer courts	467
	The church's one foundation	477
	The price is paid	487
	There's an awesome sound	497
	This is my beloved Son	514

	We will cross every border	560
5:9-10	All hail the power of Jesus' name	7
	Come, let us worship Jesus	73
5:9-13	You're the Lion of Judah	606
5:9-14	Streams of worship	464
	There is a louder shout to come	490
5:11	Holy One of God	179
	Praise God from whom all blessings flow	432
5:11-12	O for a thousand tongues to sing	383
5:11-14	Crown him with many crowns	77
	The angels, Lord, they sing	476
5:12	All hail the Lamb	6
	All heaven declares	8
	Come and see	70
	Glory to the King of kings	121
	Here in your presence	162
	Lamb of God	310
	Living under the shadow of his wing	323
	My heart is full	363
	No other name	374
	There's an awesome sound	497
	This is my beloved Son	514
	Worthy is the Lamb	584
5:12-13	Blessing, honour, glory to the Lamb	55
	Lord of the heavens	333
	This grace is mine	512
	We will worship the Lamb of glory	563
	Worthy, O worthy are you, Lord	585
5:13	Glory	120
	Hail, Jesus, you're my King	140
	Jesus shall take the highest honour	296
	Majesty	346
	O Lord our God	398
6:9-10	All hail the power of Jesus' name	7
6:10	Shout! The Lord is risen!	452
6:16	Lo, he comes with clouds descending	324
7:10	Salvation belongs to our God	443
7:12	Lord, my heart cries out	331
	Lord of lords	332
	Salvation belongs to our God	443
7:14	These are the days	503
	We are the army of God	540
10:3	It's rising up	249
10:11	Shout, shout for joy	451
11:15	And he shall reign	22
	From the sun's rising	116
	Joy to the world	305
	Restore, O Lord	39
	Shout! The Lord is risen!	452
	There's a blessed time that's coming	496
12:10	For this purpose	111
12:10-11	Called to a battle	61
12:10-12	The Lord is moving across this land	483
12:11	May our worship be as fragrance	351
	O Lord, the clouds are gathering	399
	Only by grace	408
	O, we are more than conquerors	423
	There is only one Lord	494
	We march to the tune of a love-song	552
13:8	I worship you, O Lamb of God	272
14:2	Streams of worship	464
	What noise shall we make	569
17:14	All hail King Jesus!	5
	He that is in us	167
	King of kings	308
	Lord of lords	332
	The crucible for silver	479
	Welcome, King of kings	548
19:1	Man of sorrows	350
19:1	We march to the tune of a love-song	552
19:6	Hallelujah, hallelujah	141
	Lo, he comes with clouds descending	324
	Streams of worship	464
	We march to the tune of a love-song	552
	What noise shall we make	569
	You're the Lion of Judah	606
19:7	Lord, my heart cries out	331
	Lord of lords	332
19:7-8	This is the mystery	519
19:7-9	This is my beloved Son	514
19:8	Shout for joy	449
19:9	The trumpets sound, the angels sing	506
19:11	Be patient, be ready	46
	Faithful God	88
	Great is your name	139
	On this day	409
	Rejoice!	438
	The Lord is marching out	482
	The Lord is moving across this land	483
	He has fire in his eyes	154
	We march to the tune of a love-song	552
19:11-12	These are the days	503
19:11-14	He has risen	155
19:12	All hail the power of Jesus' name	7
	Crown him with many crowns	77
	There's a blessed time that's coming	496
	You are crowned with many crowns	590
19:13	King of kings	308
19:16	All hail King Jesus!	5
	All hail the power of Jesus' name	7
	He has fire in his eyes	154
	He is the mighty God	160
	Jesus Christ is Lord of all	275
	Jesus reigns	293
	King of kings and Lord of lords	307
	King of kings	308
	Lord of lords	332
	The crucible for silver	479
	The world is looking for a hero	508
	Welcome, King of kings	548
	We will worship the Lamb of glory	563
19:17	Hail, Jesus, you're my King	140
19:19	We are the army of God	540
21:1-4	There's a place where the streets shine	498
21:2	Sing a song of celebration	457
	The church's one foundation	477
	There's a blessed time that's coming	496
	With my whole heart	582
21:2-3	Shout for joy	449
	This is my beloved Son	514
21:3-4	Great is the darkness	136

REVELATION continued

	I will be yours	258
21:3	Take me past the outer courts	467
21:4	Let your love come down	319
	Soon and very soon	460
21:5	Do something new, Lord	82
	Joy to the world	305
21:21	There's a place where the streets shine	498
21:23	There's a place where the streets shine	498
21:24	Come, let us worship Jesus	73
22:1	River, wash over me	441
22:1-2	Down the mountain the river flows	83
	Lord, the light of your love	335
	Peace be to these streets	427
	There's a river of joy	499
	Your love flows like a river	607
22:4	Sing a song of celebration	457
	Soon and very soon	460
	Take me past the outer courts	467
	There is a Redeemer	492
	There's a place where the streets shine	498

	This is my beloved Son	514
	To keep your lovely face	527
	We shall stand	556
22:5	All hail King Jesus!	5
	And he shall reign	22
22:16	All hail King Jesus!	5
	Almighty God, we bring you praise	16
	I will seek you	267
22:16-17	Jesus, how lovely you are	279
22:17	O, heaven is in my heart	388
	This is the mystery	519
	With my whole heart	582
	You have taken the precious	600
22:20	Be patient, be ready	46
	Great is the darkness	136
	Hear our cry	149
	Shout! The Lord is risen!	452
	Soon and very soon	460
	There's a blessed time that's coming	496
	The Word made flesh	507
	This is the mystery	519
	We are his children	537

Key Word Index

The key word categories appear alphabetically and are cross-referenced to make it as easy as possible for worship leaders to find songs and hymns suitable for various themes and occasions.

ADORATION AND PRAISE – GODHEAD

All people that on earth do dwell	13
All things bright and beautiful	14
Almighty God, we bring you praise	16
Almighty God, my Redeemer	17
Among the gods	19
Ascribe greatness	25
As I come into your presence	26
As the deer pants (Lewis)	28
As we seek your face	31
Be glorified	42
Be still, for the presence of the Lord	47
Blessing and honour	54
Bless the Lord, my soul	56
Exalt the Lord	87
Faithful God	88
Father, I come to you	95
Father in heaven, how we love you	96
For thou, O Lord, art high	112
From the ends of the earth	115
Gloria	119
God is good	124
God is good all the time	125
God is great	126
God of glory, we exalt your name	130
God's not dead	133
Great and mighty is he	135
Great is the Lord and most worthy of praise	137
Great is your name	139
Hallelujah, hallelujah	141
He's given me a garment of praise	166
Holy, holy, Lord God Almighty	177
Holy, holy, Lord, you're worthy	178
How lovely is your dwelling-place	188
I am standing beneath your wings	193
I give you all the honour	203
I have come to love you	204
I have made you too small	205
I just want to be where you are	207
I just want to praise you	208
I love to be in your presence	213
I'm gonna click	218
Immortal, invisible, God only wise	220
In heavenly armour	228
In the presence of a holy God	232

I sing praises	240
I stand before your throne	245
I will enter his gates	262
I will praise you all my life	266
I will wave my hands	269
I worship you, Almighty God	271
Let the righteous sing	316
Look what God has done	325
Lord, for the years	327
Lord, my heart cries out	331
Lord of lords	332
Lord, we long to see your glory	338
Lord, you are more precious	339
Lord, you are so precious to me	340
Lord, you have my heart	341
Lord, you put a tongue in my mouth	342
Make a joyful noise, all ye people	347
May our worship be as fragrance	351
Mighty is our God	357
More love, more power	359
My heart will sing to you	364
Now unto the King	378
O give thanks	384
O Lord, how majestic is your name	395
O Lord our God	398
On this day	409
O the glory of your presence	415
Our God is an awesome God	418
O worship the King	425
O worship the Lord in the beauty of holiness	426
Praise, my soul, the King of heaven	433
Praise the Lord, O my soul	434
Salvation belongs to our God	443
See his glory	446
Sing, praise and bless the Lord	458
Streams of worship	464
Surely our God	466
Teach me to dance	469
Tell out, my soul	471
Thank you for your mercy	474
The angels, Lord, they sing	476
The Lord is our strength	484
The Lord reigns	485
Therefore we lift our hearts in praise	489
There is none like you	493
The steadfast love of the Lord	505
They that wait on the Lord	509
This is my desire	515

This is the day that the Lord has made	516
This is the day	517
Though the earth should tremble	523
To every good thing God is doing	525
To God be the glory!	526
To keep your lovely face	527
Tonight	528
To you, O Lord, I bring my worship	529
We bring the sacrifice of praise	542
We declare your majesty	544
We rejoice in the goodness of our God	554
What noise shall we make	569
When I feel the touch	570
When I look into your holiness	571
Yahweh	586
You alone, Lord, are wonderful	588
You are beautiful	589
You are God, you are great	591
You are Lord	592
You are merciful to me	593
You are my rock	597
You rescued me	605

ADORATION AND PRAISE – JESUS CHRIST

Alleluia, alleluia, give thanks to the risen Lord	4
All hail King Jesus!	5
All hail the Lamb	6
All hail the power of Jesus' name	7
All heaven declares	8
All I once held dear	11
Almighty God, we bring you praise	16
Almighty God, my Redeemer	17
And he shall reign	22
As the deer pants (Nystrom)	27
At the foot of the cross	32
At the name of Jesus	33
At your feet we fall	35
Behold his love	43
Behold the Lord	44
Blessed be the name of the Lord	53
Blessing, honour, glory to the Lamb	55
By his grace	59
By your side	60
Come and see	70
Come, let us worship Jesus	73
Come on, all us singers, sing	74

Crown him with many crowns 77
Every nation, power and tongue 86
Far and near 90
Father, you are my portion 104
For all that you've done 108
From heaven you came 114
From the sun's rising 116
From where the sun rises 117
Glory 120
Glory to the King of kings 121
Hail, Jesus, you're my King 140
Hallelujah! Jesus is alive 142
Hallelujah, my Father 143
He is exalted 156
He is here 157
He is Lord 158
Here in your presence 162
Higher, higher 170
Holy One of God 179
Hosanna 182
How can I not love you? 184
How deep the Father's love for us 185
How sweet the name of Jesus sounds 190
I am a new creation 191
I am so thankful 192
I bow my knee before your throne 197
I lift my hands 212
I love you, Lord, and I lift my voice 214
I love you, Lord, with all of my heart 215
I love your presence 216
I'm accepted, I'm forgiven 217
Immanuel, O Immanuel 219
I'm special 222
In Christ alone 225
In moments like these 229
I reach up high 235
I sing a simple song of love 239
Isn't he beautiful 242
I stand amazed in the presence 243
I stand before the presence 244
I've got a love song 252
I will dance, I will sing 261
I will lift my voice 263
I will offer up my life 265
I will worship 270
I worship you, O Lamb of God 272
Jesus, at your name 273
Jesus Christ 274
Jesus Christ is risen today 276
Jesus Christ is the Lord of all 277
Jesus, God's righteousness revealed 278
Jesus, how lovely you are 279
Jesus! I am resting, resting 280
Jesus is greater 282
Jesus is King 283

Jesus is Lord! 284
Jesus is the name we honour 285
Jesus, Jesus (Holy and anointed one) 286
Jesus, Jesus, you have the name 288
Jesus, lover of my soul 290
Jesus, name above all names 291
Jesus shall take the highest honour 296
Jesus, what a beautiful name 301
Jesus, your loving kindness 303
Jesus, your name is power 304
King of kings, majesty 309
Lamb of God 310
Led like a lamb 312
Lift up your heads 321
Living under the shadow of his wing 323
Lo, he comes with clouds descending 324
Look what the Lord has done 326
Lord, I lift your name on high 330
Lord of the heavens 333
Lord, the light of your love 335
Lord, we lift you high 336
Majesty 346
Make way, make way 349
Man of sorrows 350
May the fragrance 352
Meekness and majesty 353
My heart is full 363
My Jesus, I love thee 366
My Jesus, my Saviour 367
My life is in you, Lord 368
My lips shall praise you 369
My Lord, what love is this 370
No one but you, Lord 373
No other name 374
No scenes of stately majesty 375
O for a thousand tongues to sing 383
O let the sun of God enfold you 392
O Lord our God 398
O Lord, you're beautiful 401
O the deep, deep love of Jesus! 414
O, what a morning 424
Praise the name of Jesus 435
Shout for joy 449
Shout for joy and sing 450
Sing a song of celebration 457
Sound the trumpet 461
Streams of worship 464
Such love 465
Thank you for saving me 472
Thank you for the cross 473
Thank you, Jesus 475
The heavens shall declare 480
The price is paid 487
There is a louder shout to come 490
There is only one Lord 494

There is power in the name of Jesus 495
There's an awesome sound 497
There's a sound of singing 500
The trumpets sound, the angels sing 506
The world is looking for a hero 508
Thine be the glory 510
This Child 511
This is my beloved Son 514
To every good thing God is doing 525
To God be the glory! 526
Tonight 528
We come into your presence 543
Welcome the King 549
Well, I hear they're singing in the streets 550
We will cross every border 560
We will worship the Lamb of glory 563
We worship and adore you 564
What kind of greatness 567
When the music fades 576
With my whole heart 582
Worthy is the Lamb 584
Worthy, O worthy are you, Lord 585
You are crowned with many crowns 590
You are mighty 594
You are my King 595
You are my passion 596
You are my rock 597
You have called us 598
You laid aside your majesty 601
You make my heart feel glad 603
You're the Lion of Judah 606

ADORATION AND PRAISE – THE FATHER

Father God, I wonder 91
Father, we adore you 101
Father, you are my portion 104
God is good 124
Hallelujah, my Father 143
How deep the Father's love for us 185
It is to you 247
No one but you, Lord 373
O Father of the fatherless 382
Surely our God 466
We come into your presence 543

ADORATION AND PRAISE – TRINITY

All honour, all glory 10
Father God, we worship you 92
Father, we adore you, you've drawn us 102
Father, we love you 103

Holy, holy, holy! Lord God
   Almighty 176
I'm your child 224
Lead us, heavenly Father, lead us 311
Let your living water flow 318
Praise God from whom all
   blessings flow 432
River, wash over me 441
There is a Redeemer 492
This is the sweetest mystery 520
We believe 541

ADVENT

See **Jesus – Advent and Birth**

ASCENSION

See **Jesus – Ascension**

ASSURANCE

Blessed assurance, Jesus is mine 52
I am a new creation 191
I know it 210
I'm so secure 221
In heavenly armour 228
Jesus, we celebrate the victory 299
Jesus, you're my firm foundation 302
My Jesus, my Saviour 367
My life is in you, Lord 368
My lips shall praise you 369
Nothing shall separate us 377
Our confidence is in the Lord 417
Salvation belongs to our God 443
There is only one Lord 494
This grace is mine 512
This is the day that the Lord
   has made 516
Though I feel afraid 522
Though the earth should tremble 523
We are a people of power 536
We have a great priest 546
You make your face to shine
   on me 604

ATONEMENT

See **Jesus – Atonement, Suffering
and Death**

BENEDICTIONS

See **Closing of Service**

CALL TO WORSHIP

As I come into your presence 26
As we are gathered 29
Be glorified 42
Blessed be the name of the Lord 53
Celebrate, celebrate 66
Come on, all us singers, sing 74
Come on and celebrate 75
Crown him with many crowns 77

Exalt the Lord 87
Far and near 90
For this purpose 111
From the ends of the earth 115
Glory 120
God is good 124
God is here, God is present 127
God of all comfort 129
Hail, Jesus, you're my King 140
Heaven invites you to a party 150
Here in your presence 162
He's given me a garment of praise 166
Holy, holy, holy! Lord God
   Almighty 176
Hosanna 182
I believe in Jesus 195
I have come to love you 204
I will enter his gates 262
Jesus is Lord! 284
Jesus, the name high over all 298
Joy to the world 305
King of kings and Lord of lords 307
King of kings 308
Lift up your heads 321
Lord, I lift your name on high 330
Lord of lords 332
Lord, you put a tongue in my
   mouth 342
Make a joyful noise, all ye
   people 347
Make way, make way 349
My lips shall praise you 369
O, heaven is in my heart 388
Oh, I was made for this 389
On this day 409
Praise God from whom all
   blessings flow 432
Praise, my soul, the King of
   heaven 433
Praise the Lord, O my soul 434
Rejoice! 438
Righteousness, peace, joy in
   the Holy Ghost 440
Shout for joy 449
Shout for joy and sing 450
Sing, praise and bless the Lord 458
Sound the trumpet 461
Tell out, my soul 471
The Lord is marching out 482
We are marching 539
We believe 541
We bring the sacrifice of praise 542
We come into your presence 543
Welcome, King of kings 548

CELEBRATION

Celebrate, celebrate 66
Celebrate Jesus 67
Come on, all us singers, sing 74
Come on and celebrate 75

Down the mountain the river
   flows 83
Far and near 90
From where the sun rises 117
God is good 124
Great and mighty is he 135
Hail, Jesus, you're my King 140
Hallelujah! Jesus is alive 142
Heaven invites you to a party 150
He has clothed us with his
   righteousness 153
He is the Lord 159
He's given me a garment of
   praise 166
I am a new creation 191
I could sing unending songs 200
In the tomb so cold 234
I reach up high 235
I will wave my hands 269
Jesus' love has got under
   our skin 289
Jesus, we celebrate the victory 299
Joy to the world 305
Let the righteous sing 316
Look what the Lord has done 326
Lord of lords 332
Lord, you put a tongue in my
   mouth 342
Low in the grave he lay 345
Make way, make way 349
O come and join the dance 381
O give thanks 384
O, heaven is in my heart 388
Oh, I was made for this 389
O, what a morning 424
Righteousness, peace, joy in
   the Holy Ghost 440
Shout for joy 449
Shout for joy and sing 450
Shout, shout for joy 451
Shout! The Lord is risen! 452
Shout unto God 453
Sing a song of celebration 457
Teach me to dance 469
Tell out, my soul 471
The Lord is marching out 482
The Lord is our strength 484
The price is paid 487
There's a sound of singing 500
The trumpets sound, the
   angels sing 506
This is the day that the Lord
   has made 516
This is the day 517
Welcome, King of kings 548
Welcome the King 549
Well, I hear they're singing in
   the streets 550
What noise shall we make 569
Where there once was only hurt 577
You shall go out with joy 609

CHILDREN AND FAMILY WORSHIP

All things bright and beautiful	14
Be bold, be strong	38
Earth lies spellbound	85
Father God, I wonder	91
5000+ hungry folk	107
God's not dead	133
Have you got an appetite?	145
Heaven invites you to a party	150
Higher, higher	170
I'm gonna click	218
I'm special	222
I'm your child	224
I reach up high	235
I've got a love song	252
I want to be a tree that's bearing fruit	254
I will wave my hands	269
Jesus put this song into our hearts	292
Like a candle flame	322
Lord, we lift you high	336
Lord, you put a tongue in my mouth	342
O come and join the dance	381
O give thanks	384
Once in royal David's city	404
Our God is so great	420
Righteousness, peace, joy in the Holy Ghost	440
Seek ye first	447
Teach me to dance	469
The promise of the Holy Spirit	488
This Child	511
We are marching	539
We will turn the hearts	562
What noise shall we make	569

CHRISTINGLE

Can you see what we have made	65

CHRISTMAS

At this time of giving	34
Away in a manger	36
Earth lies spellbound	85
Gloria	119
Hark, the herald-angels sing	144
Heaven invites you to a party	150
He is here	157
Immanuel, O Immanuel	219
Like a candle flame	322
O come, all ye faithful	380
O come and join the dance	381
O little town of Bethlehem	393
Once in royal David's city	404
Silent night	455
This Child	511
Tonight	528
What kind of greatness	567

CHURCH – FELLOWSHIP AND UNITY

All over the world	12
An army of ordinary people	20
A new commandment	23
As we are gathered	29
Bind us together	51
Called to a battle	61
Did you feel the mountains tremble?	80
God is here, God is present	127
God of all comfort	129
He brought me to his banqueting table	152
Here is bread	163
How good and how pleasant	187
I believe in Jesus	195
If you are encouraged	202
I love to be in your presence	213
Jesus put this song into our hearts	292
Jesus, restore to us again	295
Let there be love	317
Let your word go forth	320
Living under the shadow of his wing	323
Look what God has done	325
May the fragrance	352
One heart, one voice, one mind	405
O the glory of your presence	415
Peace I give to you	428
Rejoice!	438
Righteousness, peace, joy in the Holy Ghost	440
The church's one foundation	477
There is a place of commanded blessing	491
To every good thing God is doing	525
Turn our hearts	531
We are his people	538
We are marching	539
We must work together	553
We want to remain in your love	558
We will turn the hearts	562
Where two or three	578

CHURCH – IN PRAYER

All heaven waits	9

CHURCH – NATURE

An army of ordinary people	20
As we are gathered	29
For I'm building a people of power	109
Here I am	161
I went to the enemy's camp	257
I will build my church	259
Jesus put this song into our hearts	292

Jesus, we enthrone you	300
Look what God has done	325
May the fragrance	352
O, heaven is in my heart	388
One heart, one voice, one mind	405
O the glory of your presence	415
Our God is awesome in power	419
Rejoice!	438
Shout for joy	449
Show your power, O Lord	454
The church's one foundation	477
We are marching	539
We are the army of God	540
We must work together	553
You have called us	598
Your mercy flows	608

CLOSING OF SERVICE

Be patient, be ready	46
In my life, Lord	230
Now unto the King	378
O Jesus, I have promised	391
Peace to you	431
The steadfast love of the Lord	505
This is the sweetest mystery	520
To every good thing God is doing	525

COMFORT AND ENCOURAGEMENT

See **Faith and Hope**

COMMITMENT AND CONSECRATION

Abba, Father, let me be	1
All I once held dear	11
All to Jesus I surrender	15
A new commandment	23
At the name of Jesus	33
Be thou my vision	50
Blessed assurance, Jesus is mine	52
Breathe on me, Breath of God	57
By your side	60
Can I ascend	63
Change my heart, O God	68
Come and see	70
Come, let us return	72
Come on, all us singers, sing	74
Do something new, Lord	82
Draw me closer	84
Father, hear our prayer	93
Fire	106
From heaven you came	114
God is here, God is present	127
Have you got an appetite?	145
Have you not said	147
He has fire in his eyes	154
Here I am	161
Here we stand in total surrender	165
How can I be free from sin?	183

How can I not love you? 184
I bow my knee before your throne 197
I bow my knee 198
I have come to love you 204
I lift my hands 212
I love you, Lord, with all of my heart 215
In the morning when I rise 231
I reach up high 235
Is it true today 241
I, the Lord of sea and sky 246
I want to be a tree that's bearing fruit 254
I want to be out of my depth in your love 255
I want to serve the purpose of God 256
I will be yours 258
I will lift my voice 263
I will never be the same again 264
I will offer up my life 265
I will praise you all my life 266
I will worship 270
Jesus! I am resting, resting 280
Jesus, Jesus, you have the name 288
Jesus, lover of my soul 290
Jesus, take me as I am 297
Jesus, your loving kindness 303
Just as I am, without one plea 306
King of kings, majesty 309
Lamb of God 310
Let it be to me 313
Let me be a sacrifice 315
Let your word go forth 320
Lord, for the years 327
Lord, I come to you 329
Lord, my heart cries out 331
Lord, prepare me 334
Lord, the light of your love 335
Lord, you are more precious 339
Lord, you have my heart 341
May our worship be as fragrance 351
More about Jesus 358
More love, more power 359
More of your glory 360
My Jesus, I love thee 366
O happy day 387
O Jesus, I have promised 391
O Lord, my heart is not proud 397
O Lord, you're beautiful 401
One thing I ask 407
On this day 409
O thou who camest from above 416
Purify my heart 436
Reign in me 437
Restore, O Lord 439
River, wash over me 441
Ruach 442
Seek ye first 447

Show your power, O Lord 454
Silent, surrendered 456
Spirit of the living God (Iverson) 462
Take me past the outer courts 467
Take my life, and let it be 468
Teach me to dance 469
Teach me your ways 470
Thank you for saving me 472
The crucible for silver 479
There's a sound of singing 500
There's a wind a-blowing 501
There's no one like you 502
This is my desire 515
This is the sweetest mystery 520
This love 521
Though I feel afraid 522
To every good thing God is doing 525
To keep your lovely face 527
Wake up, my soul 534
Wake up, O sleeper 535
We are a people of power 536
We shall stand 556
We've had a light 557
We will run and not grow weary 561
When I look into your holiness 571
When I survey the wondrous cross 572
When the music fades 576
With my whole heart 582
You are my King 595

COMMUNION

As we are gathered 29
Broken for me 58
Here is bread 163
We do not presume 545
With this bread 583

CONFESSION

See **Repentance and Forgiveness**

CREATION

See **God – Creation**

CREEDS

The Lord is a mighty King 481
We believe 541

DELIVERANCE

I give you all the honour 203
I know it 210
O God, most high 385
O the blood of my Saviour 413
This is the message of the cross 518
We are his people 538
When the Lord brought us back 575

DESIRE FOR GOD

Abba, Father, let me be 1
All I once held dear 11
Anointing, fall on me 24
As the deer pants (Nystrom) 27
As the deer pants (Lewis) 28
As we seek your face 31
Be still, for the presence of the Lord 47
Be thou my vision 50
Blessed assurance, Jesus is mine 52
By your side 60
Can I ascend 63
Change my heart, O God 68
Come down, O Love divine 71
Come, let us return 72
Come on, all us singers, sing 74
Come, Spirit, come 76
Dear Lord and Father of mankind 79
Don't let my love grow cold 81
Draw me closer 84
Father, here I am 94
Father, I want you to hold me 98
Father of life, draw me closer 100
Father, you are my portion 104
God of all comfort 129
He brought me to his banqueting table 152
Hold me closer to you 172
Hold me, Lord 173
Holiness unto the Lord 175
Holy Spirit, come 180
Holy Spirit, we welcome you 181
How lovely is your dwelling-place 188
I bow my knee before your throne 197
I bow my knee 198
I cry out for your hand 201
I just want to be where you are 207
I just want to praise you 208
I lift my eyes up to the mountains 211
I love to be in your presence 213
I love you, Lord, with all of my heart 215
I love your presence 216
Immanuel, O Immanuel 219
I'm special 222
I need you more 226
In my life, Lord 230
In the morning when I rise 231
In the secret 233
I receive your love 236
Is anyone thirsty? 237
I sing a simple song of love 239
Isn't he beautiful 242
I stand before your throne 245
I want to be a tree that's bearing fruit 254

I want to be out of my depth
in your love 255
I want to serve the purpose
of God 256
I will never be the same again 264
I will seek your face, O Lord 268
I will worship 270
Jesus! I am resting, resting 280
Jesus, I am thirsty 281
Jesus, Jesus, Jesus 287
Jesus, Jesus, you have the name 288
Jesus, lover of my soul 290
Jesus, take me as I am 297
Jesus, your loving kindness 303
Just as I am, without one plea 306
Let your living water flow 318
Lord, I come to you 329
Lord, the light of your love 335
Lord, we long for you 337
Lord, we long to see your glory 338
Lord, you are more precious 339
Lord, you are so precious to me 340
Lord, you have my heart 341
Love divine, all loves excelling 343
Love of Christ, come now 343
May the fragrance 352
More about Jesus 358
More love, more power 359
More of your glory 360
More than oxygen 361
My first love 362
My heart is full 363
My heart will sing to you 364
My spirit rests in you alone 371
Nearer, my God, to thee 372
No one but you, Lord 373
O Breath of Life 379
O Father of the fatherless 382
O God of burning, cleansing
flame 386
Oh, lead me 390
O Jesus, I have promised 391
O let the sun of God enfold you 392
O Lord, hear my prayer 394
O Lord, you're beautiful 401
O Lord, your tenderness 402
One thing I ask 407
O thou who camest from above 416
Over the mountains and the sea 421
Peace like a river 429
Purify my heart 436
Righteousness, peace, joy in
the Holy Ghost 440
River, wash over me 441
Ruach 442
Silent, surrendered 456
Soften my heart, Lord 459
Spirit of the living God
(Iverson) 462
Spirit of the living God
(Armstrong) 463

Take me past the outer courts 467
Teach me to dance 469
Teach me your ways 470
Thank you for the cross 473
The crucible for silver 479
There's a wind a-blowing 501
There's no one like you 502
This is my desire 515
This is the mystery 519
This love 521
To be in your presence 524
To keep your lovely face 527
To you, O Lord, I bring my
worship 529
Turn your eyes upon Jesus 533
Wake up, my soul 534
Wake up, O sleeper 535
We have a great priest 546
We want to remain in your love 558
What a friend I've found 565
When I feel the touch 570
When I look into your holiness 571
When the music fades 576
With my whole heart 582
Yahweh 586
You are merciful to me 593
You are my King 595
You are my passion 596
You laid aside your majesty 601
Your love flows like a river 607

DISCIPLESHIP

See **Commitment and Consecration**

EASTER

At the foot of the cross 32
Beneath the cross of Jesus 45
Celebrate Jesus 67
Come and see 70
For this purpose 111
From heaven you came 114
Hallelujah! Jesus is alive 142
Hallelujah, my Father 143
He has risen 155
He is Lord 158
He is the mighty God 160
Here is love 164
He was pierced 169
Holy One of God 179
How can I be free from sin? 183
How deep the Father's love for us 185
I am so thankful 192
I believe in Jesus 195
I know a place 209
In the tomb so cold 234
I stand amazed in the presence 243
It's your blood 250
I will offer up my life 265
I worship you, O Lamb of God 272
Jesus Christ 274

Jesus Christ is risen today 276
Jesus is Lord! 284
Lamb of God 310
Led like a lamb 312
Low in the grave he lay 345
Man of sorrows 350
Meekness and majesty 353
My Lord, what love is this 370
No scenes of stately majesty 375
On a hill far away 403
Only by grace 408
O the blood of Jesus 412
O the blood of my Saviour 413
O, what a morning 424
Thank you for saving me 472
Thank you for the cross 473
Thank you, Jesus 475
The cross has said it all 478
The price is paid 487
There is a Redeemer 492
The Word made flesh 507
Thine be the glory 510
This is my beloved Son 514
This is the message of the cross 518
To God be the glory! 526
What kind of love is this 568
When I survey the wondrous
cross 572
You laid aside your majesty 601

ETERNAL LIFE

Called to a battle 61
This grace is mine 512

EVANGELISM

See **Mission**

FAITH AND HOPE

Almighty God, my Redeemer 17
And can it be 21
Be bold, be strong 38
Beneath the cross of Jesus 45
Be still, my soul 49
Called to a battle 61
Can we walk upon the water 64
Draw me closer 84
Faithful God 88
Faithful One 89
Father in heaven, how we love
you 96
Father, I place into your hands 97
For the joys and for the sorrows 110
Give thanks with a grateful
heart 118
God is good all the time 125
Great is thy faithfulness 138
Have you heard the good news 146
Have you not said 147
He is the Lord 159
He that is in us 167

He walked where I walked 168
His love 171
How can I be free from sin? 183
How firm a foundation 186
I am standing beneath your wings 193
I believe the promise 196
I heard the voice of Jesus say 206
I lift my eyes up to the mountains 211
In Christ alone 225
I need you more 226
In every circumstance 227
Is it true today 241
I've found a friend 251
I walk by faith 253
I will be yours 258
I will change your name 260
I will never be the same again 264
I will praise you all my life 266
Jesus, God's righteousness revealed 278
Jesus, you're my firm foundation 302
Let your love come down 319
Living under the shadow of his wing 323
Men of faith 354
My life is in you, Lord 368
O Jesus, I have promised 391
O Lord, you lead me 400
One thing I ask 407
Our confidence is in the Lord 417
Our God is awesome in power 419
O, we are more than conquerors 423
Peace I give to you 428
Peace, perfect peace 430
Salvation belongs to our God 443
Say the word 445
Soon and very soon 460
Tell out, my soul 471
The Lord is moving across this land 483
The Lord is our strength 484
The Lord's my shepherd 486
There is a louder shout to come 490
There is only one Lord 494
There is power in the name of Jesus 495
There's a place where the streets shine 498
The Word made flesh 507
The world is looking for a hero 508
They that wait on the Lord 509
Thine be the glory 510
This grace is mine 512
This is the day that the Lord has made 516
This is the time 610
This love 521
To every good thing God is doing 525

To you, O Lord, I lift up my soul 530
Wake up, my soul 534
We are his people 538
We are the army of God 540
We march to the tune of a love-song 552
We must work together 553
We serve a God of miracles 555
We will run and not grow weary 561
We will turn the hearts 562
When peace like a river 574
Where two or three 578
With all my heart 581
Yet this will I call to mind 587
You are Lord 592
You are my rock 597
You have taken the precious 600
You love me as you found me 602
You make your face to shine on me 604

FELLOWSHIP OF BELIEVERS

See **Church – Fellowship and Unity**

FELLOWSHIP WITH GOD

See **Desire for God** and **God – Presence**

FORGIVENESS

See **Repentance and Forgiveness**

GOD – CREATION

All things bright and beautiful 14
From the ends of the earth 115
God is great 126
He is the Lord 159
I, the Lord of sea and sky 246
Jesus is Lord! 284
Mighty is our God 357
No scenes of stately majesty 375
O give thanks 384
O Lord, my God 396
Our God is so great 420
O worship the King 425
The heavens shall declare 480
The Lord is a mighty King 481
We believe 541

GOD – FAITHFULNESS

All people that on earth do dwell 13
Almighty God, my Redeemer 17
Ascribe greatness 25
Be bold, be strong 38
Faithful God 88
Faithful One 89
Great is thy faithfulness 138
Have you not said 147
I am standing beneath your wings 193

I'm so secure 221
I'm standing here to testify 223
In every circumstance 227
I walk by faith 253
I will be yours 258
I will praise you all my life 266
Look what God has done 325
My Jesus, my Saviour 367
O Lord, you lead me 400
On this day 409
O the deep, deep love of Jesus! 414
Our confidence is in the Lord 417
O, we are more than conquerors 423
The Lord's my shepherd 486
There is none like you 493
The steadfast love of the Lord 505
To you, O Lord, I lift up my soul 530
We have a great priest 546
We rejoice in the goodness of our God 554
We shall stand 556
What a friend I've found 565
What a friend we have in Jesus 566
When peace like a river 574
When the Lord brought us back 575
Where two or three 578
With all my heart 581
Yahweh 586
Yet this will I call to mind 587
You alone, Lord, are wonderful 588
You love me as you found me 602

GOD – FATHER

Abba, Father, let me be 1
Father God, I wonder 91
Father God, we worship you 92
Father, hear our prayer 93
Father, I come to you 95
Father, I place into your hands 97
Father, I want you to hold me 98
Father, we adore you 101
God is good 124
I'm accepted, I'm forgiven 217
I'm your child 224
O Father of the fatherless 382
One shall tell another 406
Praise, my soul, the King of heaven 433
We will turn the hearts 562
Where two or three 578

GOD – GLORY

Be glorified 42
Be still, for the presence of the Lord 47
Father, we adore you, you've drawn us 102
Glory to the King of kings 121
God of glory, we exalt your name 130

God of glory	131
Great and mighty is he	135
Here in your presence	162
I love you, Lord, with all of my heart	215
Immortal, invisible, God only wise	220
In my life, Lord	230
I sing praises	240
Lord, my heart cries out	331
Lord of lords	332
Lord of the heavens	333
Lord, we long to see your glory	338
Now unto the King	378
O Lord, how majestic is your name	395
O the glory of your presence	415
Praise God from whom all blessings flow	432
Salvation belongs to our God	443
See his glory	446
There's no one like you	502
This grace is mine	512
This, in essence, is the message	513
We declare your majesty	544
When I look into your holiness	571
Yahweh	586

GOD – GRACE

Amazing grace	18
And can it be	21
Behold his love	43
By his grace	59
Father, I come to you	95
For the joys and for the sorrows	110
God, be gracious	122
God of grace	132
He brought me to his banqueting table	152
He has clothed us with his righteousness	153
Here is bread	163
How can I not love you?	184
I am a new creation	191
I could sing unending songs	200
I cry out for your hand	201
I heard the voice of Jesus say	206
In the presence of a holy God	232
I will change your name	260
Jesus, what a beautiful name	301
Just as I am, without one plea	306
Look what God has done	325
Love divine, all loves excelling	343
Love of Christ, come now	343
Make me a channel of your peace	348
Meekness and majesty	353
O Lord, you're beautiful	401
O Lord, your tenderness	402
One shall tell another	406

Only by grace	408
O worship the Lord in the beauty of holiness	426
Peace be to these streets	427
Praise, my soul, the King of heaven	433
Such love	465
Surely our God	466
Thank you for your mercy	474
The cross has said it all	478
Therefore we lift our hearts in praise	489
There's an awesome sound	497
The Spirit of the sovereign Lord	504
The trumpets sound, the angels sing	506
This grace is mine	512
This is the message of the cross	518
Turn to me and be saved	532
We rejoice in the goodness of our God	554
We worship and adore you	564
What kind of love is this	568
You rescued me	605

GOD – HOLINESS

Ascribe greatness	25
Holiness is your life in me	174
Holiness unto the Lord	175
Holy, holy, holy! Lord God Almighty	176
Holy, holy, Lord God Almighty	177
Holy, holy, Lord, you're worthy	178
I love you, Lord, with all of my heart	215
In the presence of a holy God	232
I see the Lord	238
I will seek your face, O Lord	268
Lord, we long to see your glory	338
O God of burning, cleansing flame	386
O worship the Lord in the beauty of holiness	426
The crucible for silver	479
The heavens shall declare	480
This, in essence, is the message	513
We declare your majesty	544
You are mighty	594

GOD – JUDGEMENT

O Lord, the clouds are gathering	399
Tell out, my soul	471
The Lord reigns	485
We believe	541
Who can sound the depths of sorrow	579
Who sees it all	580
Your mercy flows	608

GOD – MAJESTY AND POWER

Among the gods	19
Ascribe greatness	25
As the deer pants (Lewis)	28
Be glorified	42
Be still, for the presence of the Lord	47
Did you feel the mountains tremble?	80
Father, we adore you, you've drawn us	102
Glory to the King of kings	121
God of glory, we exalt your name	130
Great and mighty is he	135
He is the Lord	159
I have made you too small	205
Immortal, invisible, God only wise	220
In the presence of a holy God	232
I see the Lord	238
I sing praises	240
King of kings, majesty	309
Lo, he comes with clouds descending	324
Majesty	346
Meekness and majesty	353
Mighty is our God	357
My heart is full	363
My Jesus, my Saviour	367
Now unto the King	378
O God, most high	385
O Lord, how majestic is your name	395
O Lord our God	398
Our God is an awesome God	418
Our God is so great	420
O worship the King	425
Rejoice!	438
Salvation belongs to our God	443
Shout! The Lord is risen!	452
Show your power, O Lord	454
Streams of worship	464
Surely our God	466
Tell out, my soul	471
Thank you for saving me	472
The Lord is our strength	484
The Lord reigns	485
They that wait on the Lord	509
This grace is mine	512
Though the earth should tremble	523
We are his people	538
We are the army of God	540
We declare your majesty	544
We serve a God of miracles	555
What kind of greatness	567
What noise shall we make	569
You alone, Lord, are wonderful	588
You are God, you are great	591
You are Lord	592

You are mighty   594
You are my rock   597
You make my heart feel glad   603
You're the Lion of Judah   606

GOD – MERCY

And can it be   21
Come, let us return   72
Day of favour   78
Father, hear our prayer   93
Father, here I am   94
Hear, O Lord, our cry   148
Hear our cry   149
It's our confession, Lord   248
I will seek your face, O Lord   268
Jesus, take me as I am   297
Just as I am, without one plea   306
Lamb of God   310
Let it rain   314
Lord, have mercy   328
Love of Christ, come now   343
Mercy is falling   355
O Lord, the clouds are gathering   399
O Lord, your tenderness   402
Restore, O Lord   439
Save the people   444
See his glory   446
See, your Saviour comes   448
Soften my heart, Lord   459
Take me past the outer courts   467
Tell out, my soul   471
Thank you for the cross   473
Thank you for your mercy   474
The cross has said it all   478
There is none like you   493
There's an awesome sound   497
The steadfast love of the Lord   505
This is the message of the cross   518
To you, O Lord, I lift up
  my soul   530
Turn to me and be saved   532
We do not presume   545
We have prayed that you
  would have mercy   547
We rejoice in the goodness
  of our God   554
We worship and adore you   564
What kind of love is this   568
Who can sound the depths
  of sorrow   579
Who sees it all   580
You are merciful to me   593
You have shown me   599
Your mercy flows   608

GOD – PRESENCE

Abide with me   2
As I come into your presence   26
As we are gathered   29
As we seek your face   31

At your feet we fall   35
Be bold, be strong   38
Be still, for the presence of
  the Lord   47
Be still and know   48
By your side   60
Can I ascend   63
Come down, O Love divine   71
Dear Lord and Father of
  mankind   79
Down the mountain the river
  flows   83
Draw me closer   84
Father, I want you to hold me   98
Father, we adore you   101
For the joys and for the sorrows   110
God is here, God is present   127
God of all comfort   129
He brought me to his
  banqueting table   152
He has fire in his eyes   154
He is here   157
Here is bread   163
He walked where I walked   168
Hold me closer to you   172
Hold me, Lord   173
How lovely is your
  dwelling-place   188
I believe in Jesus   195
I have come to love you   204
I heard the voice of Jesus say   206
I just want to be where you are   207
I love to be in your presence   213
I love your presence   216
Immanuel, O Immanuel   219
I'm your child   224
I need you more   226
In every circumstance   227
In the morning when I rise   231
In the presence of a holy God   232
In the secret   233
I receive your love   236
I sing a simple song of love   239
I stand before the presence   244
I stand before your throne   245
I've found a friend   251
I will be yours   258
I will seek your face, O Lord   268
Lift up your heads   321
Like a candle flame   322
Living under the shadow of
  his wing   323
Lord, I come to you   329
My first love   362
My heart will sing to you   364
My Jesus, I love thee   366
My spirit rests in you alone   371
Nearer, my God, to thee   372
No one but you, Lord   373
O, heaven is in my heart   388
Oh, I was made for this   389

Oh, lead me   390
O Lord, hear my prayer   394
O Lord, my heart is not proud   397
O Lord, you lead me   400
One thing I ask   407
Only by grace   408
O the glory of your presence   415
Peace be to these streets   427
See his glory   446
Take me past the outer courts   467
Thank you for your mercy   474
The angels, Lord, they sing   476
The crucible for silver   479
There's a place where the
  streets shine   498
There's a wind a-blowing   501
There's no one like you   502
This grace is mine   512
This is the mystery   519
Though I feel afraid   522
Though the earth should
  tremble   523
To be in your presence   524
To keep your lovely face   527
To you, O Lord, I bring my
  worship   529
We come into your presence   543
We have a great priest   546
Welcome, King of kings   548
We want to remain in your love   558
We will run and not grow weary   561
What a friend I've found   565
What a friend we have in Jesus   566
When I feel the touch   570
When my heart is overwhelmed   573
Yahweh   586
You love me as you found me   602
You make your face to shine
  on me   604

**GOD – PROTECTION, CARE
AND GUIDANCE**

Abide with me   2
All people that on earth do dwell   13
Amazing grace   18
Because of your love   39
Be free   41
Be still and know   48
Be still, my soul   49
Father, I place into your hands   97
Father, I want you to hold me   98
God is good all the time   125
God will make a new way   134
His love   171
How firm a foundation   186
I cry out for your hand   201
I lift my eyes up to the
  mountains   211
I'm so secure   221
I'm your child   224

In heavenly armour 228
I will change your name 260
I will praise you all my life 266
Jesus, you're my firm foundation 302
Lead us, heavenly Father, lead us 311
Living under the shadow of
  his wing 323
My life is in you, Lord 368
My spirit rests in you alone 371
O Jesus, I have promised 391
O Lord, you lead me 400
O the deep, deep love of Jesus! 414
Our confidence is in the Lord 417
O, we are more than conquerors 423
O worship the King 425
Rejoice! 438
Say the word 445
The Lord's my shepherd 486
There is none like you 493
This is the day that the Lord
  has made 516
Though I feel afraid 522
Though the earth should
  tremble 523
To you, O Lord, I lift up
  my soul 530
We come into your presence 543
What a friend we have in Jesus 566
When my heart is overwhelmed 573
You are my rock 597
You make your face to shine
  on me 604

GOD – PROVISION

Father, we adore you 101
He brought me to his
  banqueting table 152
Lead us, heavenly Father, lead us 311
My spirit rests in you alone 371
O give thanks 384
Say the word 445
The Lord's my shepherd 486
The trumpets sound, the
  angels sing 506
This is the day that the Lord
  has made 516
We rejoice in the goodness
  of our God 554
We will run and not grow weary 561
Where two or three 578

HARVEST

O give thanks 384

HEALING

Be still and know 48
For this purpose 111
Here is bread 163
Holy Spirit, come 180

I am the God that healeth thee 194
I believe in Jesus 195
I know it 210
I love your presence 216
Look what the Lord has done 326
Lord, we long for you 337
Make way, make way 349
O let the sun of God enfold
  you 392
One shall tell another 406
Peace like a river 429
Say the word 445
Thank you for the cross 473
There is none like you 493
This is the message of the cross 518
This love 521
To every good thing God is
  doing 525
We serve a God of miracles 555
Where there once was only hurt 577
Who sees it all 580
You are Lord 592
You have shown me 599
You make my heart feel glad 603
You rescued me 605
Your love flows like a river 607

HEAVEN

Abide with me 2
All hail the power of Jesus' name 7
He has risen 155
I will be yours 258
O, heaven is in my heart 388
O the deep, deep love of Jesus! 414
Soon and very soon 460
Streams of worship 464
The angels, Lord, they sing 476
There is a louder shout to come 490
There's a place where the
  streets shine 498
This is my beloved Son 514
This is the mystery 519
You're the Lion of Judah 606

HOLINESS AND PURITY

All to Jesus I surrender 15
Be still, for the presence of
  the Lord 47
Can I ascend 63
Come down, O Love divine 71
God of glory 131
Hold me, Lord 173
Holiness is your life in me 174
Holiness unto the Lord 175
Holy, holy, holy! Lord God
  Almighty 176
Holy, holy, Lord God Almighty 177
How can I be free from sin? 183
Lamb of God 310
Lord, prepare me 334

Lord, the light of your love 335
O God of burning, cleansing
  flame 386
Only by grace 408
O the blood of Jesus 412
Purify my heart 436
Take me past the outer courts 467
Teach me your ways 470
The crucible for silver 479

**HOLY SPIRIT – PRESENCE
AND POWER**

All honour, all glory 10
All over the world 12
Anointing, fall on me 24
As we lift up your name 30
Breathe on me, Breath of God 57
Come down, O Love divine 71
Come, Spirit, come 76
Down the mountain the river
  flows 83
Father God, we worship you 92
Hold me, Lord 173
Holy Spirit, come 180
Holy Spirit, we welcome you 181
I believe the promise 196
I love your presence 216
I'm your child 224
I receive your love 236
Is anyone thirsty? 237
I've found a friend 251
I will never be the same again 264
Jesus, restore to us again 295
Lord, we long for you 337
More of your glory 360
O Breath of Life 379
O God of burning, cleansing
  flame 386
O thou who camest from above 416
Peace like a river 429
Ruach 442
Silent, surrendered 456
Spirit of the living God
  (Iverson) 462
Spirit of the living God
  (Armstrong) 463
The promise of the Holy Spirit 488
Therefore we lift our hearts in
  praise 489
There's an awesome sound 497
There's a wind a-blowing 501
The Spirit of the sovereign Lord 504
We are marching 539

HOLY SPIRIT – GIFTS

I've found a friend 251
O thou who camest from above 416

HOPE

See **Faith and Hope**

INTERCESSION

See **Prayer**

INTIMACY

See **Desire for God**

JESUS – ADVENT AND BIRTH

At this time of giving	34
Away in a manger	36
Earth lies spellbound	85
For unto us a child is born	113
Hark, the herald-angels sing	144
Heaven invites you to a party	150
He is here	157
I cannot tell	199
Immanuel, O Immanuel	219
Joy to the world	305
King of kings	308
Let it be to me	313
Like a candle flame	322
Mighty God	356
O come, all ye faithful	380
O come and join the dance	381
O little town of Bethlehem	393
Once in royal David's city	404
Silent night	455
This Child	511
Tonight	528
What kind of greatness	567

JESUS – ASCENSION

Lift up your heads	321
Lord, I lift your name on high	330
Nothing shall separate us	377
Shout! The Lord is risen!	452
Therefore we lift our hearts in praise	489

JESUS – ATONEMENT, SUFFERING AND DEATH

At the foot of the cross	32
At the name of Jesus	33
Beneath the cross of Jesus	45
Broken for me	58
Come and see	70
Filled with compassion	105
For this purpose	111
From heaven you came	114
Hallelujah, my Father	143
He is the mighty God	160
Here is love	164
He walked where I walked	168
He was pierced	169
Holiness is your life in me	174
Holy One of God	179
How can I be free from sin?	183
How deep the Father's love for us	185
I am so thankful	192
I believe in Jesus	195

I cannot tell	199
I know a place	209
Immanuel, O Immanuel	219
I stand amazed in the presence	243
It's your blood	250
I will offer up my life	265
I worship you, O Lamb of God	272
Jesus Christ	274
Jesus Christ is risen today	276
Jesus is Lord!	284
Jesus, remember me	294
Lamb of God	310
Led like a lamb	312
Lord, I lift your name on high	330
Man of sorrows	350
Meekness and majesty	353
My Lord, what love is this	370
No scenes of stately majesty	375
Nothing shall separate us	377
O Lord, my God	396
On a hill far away	403
Only by grace	408
O the blood of Jesus	412
O the blood of my Saviour	413
Thank you for saving me	472
Thank you for the cross	473
Thank you, Jesus	475
The cross has said it all	478
The Lord is a mighty King	481
The price is paid	487
Therefore we lift our hearts in praise	489
There is a Redeemer	492
The Word made flesh	507
This is my beloved Son	514
This is the message of the cross	518
To God be the glory!	526
What kind of love is this	568
When I survey the wondrous cross	572
With this bread	583
You laid aside your majesty	601

JESUS – INCARNATION

Behold his love	43
Let it be to me	313
Meekness and majesty	353
Mighty God	356
O come, all ye faithful	380
O come and join the dance	381
O little town of Bethlehem	393
Silent night	455
The Word made flesh	507
This Child	511
What kind of greatness	567
You are God, you are great	591

JESUS – KINGSHIP AND KINGDOM

All heaven waits	9
And he shall reign	22

At the name of Jesus	33
Beauty for brokenness	37
Behold the Lord	44
Blessed be the name of the Lord	53
Blessing and honour	54
Can we walk upon the water	64
Come, let us worship Jesus	73
Come on, all us singers, sing	74
Come on and celebrate	75
Crown him with many crowns	77
Day of favour	78
Did you feel the mountains tremble?	80
Every nation, power and tongue	86
Father God, we worship you	92
Father of creation	99
Filled with compassion	105
For I'm building a people of power	109
From the sun's rising	116
God forgave my sin	123
God is working his purpose out	128
God of glory, we exalt your name	130
Great is the darkness	136
Hallelujah, hallelujah	141
Have you not said	147
Heaven shall not wait	151
He has fire in his eyes	154
He is exalted	156
How lovely on the mountains	189
I cannot tell	199
Is it true today	241
It's rising up	249
I want to serve the purpose of God	256
I will build my church	259
I will worship	270
Jesus Christ is Lord of all	275
Jesus, God's righteousness revealed	278
Jesus is King	283
Jesus is the name we honour	285
Jesus' love has got under our skin	289
Jesus put this song into our hearts	292
Jesus reigns	293
Jesus, remember me	294
Jesus, we enthrone you	300
Jesus, what a beautiful name	301
Joy to the world	305
King of kings and Lord of lords	307
King of kings	308
King of kings, majesty	309
Let it rain	314
Let the righteous sing	316
Let your love come down	319
Lift up your heads	321
Lord, we lift you high	336
Majesty	346

Make me a channel of your peace 348
Make way, make way 349
Meekness and majesty 353
Men of faith 354
My heart is full 363
No scenes of stately majesty 375
Not by might 376
O for a thousand tongues
to sing 383
O God, most high 385
O, heaven is in my heart 388
Oh, I was made for this 389
Once in royal David's city 404
One shall tell another 406
Open the doors of praise 411
Our God is awesome in power 419
Peace I give to you 428
Peace, perfect peace 430
Reign in me 437
Rejoice! 438
Restore, O Lord 439
Righteousness, peace, joy in
the Holy Ghost 440
See, your Saviour comes 448
Shout for joy 449
Shout for joy and sing 450
Shout! The Lord is risen! 452
Shout unto God 453
Show your power, O Lord 454
Sing a song of celebration 457
Sound the trumpet 461
The Lord is marching out 482
The Lord is moving across
this land 483
There is a place of commanded
blessing 491
There is power in the name
of Jesus 495
There's a blessed time that's
coming 496
There's a place where the
streets shine 498
These are the days 503
The Spirit of the sovereign Lord 504
The trumpets sound, the
angels sing 506
This love 521
Though the earth should
tremble 523
We are a people of power 536
We are his children 537
We are the army of God 540
We believe 541
Welcome the King 549
Well, I hear they're singing
in the streets 550
We'll walk the land 551
We march to the tune of a
love-song 552
We must work together 553
We serve a God of miracles 555

We've had a light 557
We will cross every border 560
Where there once was only hurt 577
You are my King 595
You have called us 598
You have taken the precious 600
You laid aside your majesty 601
You're the Lion of Judah 606
You shall go out with joy 609

JESUS – LIFE

5000+ hungry folk 107
He walked where I walked 168
Hosanna 182
I cannot tell 199
Immanuel, O Immanuel 219
Once in royal David's city 404
Welcome the King 549

JESUS – LORDSHIP

All hail King Jesus! 5
All hail the Lamb 6
All to Jesus I surrender 15
A new commandment 23
At the name of Jesus 33
At your feet we fall 35
Come, let us worship Jesus 73
Do something new, Lord 82
From the sun's rising 116
Heaven shall not wait 151
He is Lord 158
He is the mighty God 160
He that is in us 167
I lift my hands 212
I'm your child 224
In the tomb so cold 234
I want to be out of my depth
in your love 255
I went to the enemy's camp 257
I will build my church 259
Jesus, at your name 273
Jesus Christ is Lord of all 275
Jesus Christ is the Lord of all 277
Jesus is greater 282
Jesus is King 283
Jesus is Lord! 284
Jesus is the name we honour 285
Jesus, Jesus, you have the name 288
Jesus shall take the highest
honour 296
Jesus, the name high over all 298
Jesus, we enthrone you 300
King of kings and Lord of lords 307
King of kings 308
King of kings, majesty 309
Led like a lamb 312
Majesty 346
Men of faith 354
My heart is full 363
No other name 374
O God, most high 385

O Lord, how majestic is your
name 395
O Lord our God 398
Open the doors of praise 411
Shout for joy 449
Shout, shout for joy 451
Silent, surrendered 456
Sound the trumpet 461
Take my life, and let it be 468
The world is looking for a hero 508
We believe 541
Welcome, King of kings 548
We want to see Jesus lifted high 559
We will worship the Lamb
of glory 563
When the music fades 576
You are crowned with many
crowns 590

JESUS – NAME AND GLORY

All heaven declares 8
Almighty God, we bring you
praise 16
At the name of Jesus 33
At your feet we fall 35
Behold the Lord 44
Blessing, honour, glory to the
Lamb 55
Celebrate, celebrate 66
Come, let us worship Jesus 73
Crown him with many crowns 77
For unto us a child is born 113
He is exalted 156
Holy One of God 179
How sweet the name of Jesus
sounds 190
Jesus, Jesus (Holy and
anointed one) 286
Jesus, restore to us again 295
Jesus shall take the highest
honour 296
Jesus, the name high over all 298
Jesus, your name is power 304
Mighty God 356
More about Jesus 358
No other name 374
Shout for joy and sing 450
Shout! The Lord is risen! 452
Streams of worship 464
There is a Redeemer 492
There is only one Lord 494
The world is looking for a hero 508
Turn your eyes upon Jesus 533
We want to see Jesus lifted high 559
You are crowned with many
crowns 590
You laid aside your majesty 601

JESUS – RESURRECTION

Alleluia, alleluia, give thanks
to the risen Lord 4

Blessing, honour, glory to the
   Lamb   55
Celebrate Jesus   67
For this purpose   111
Hallelujah! Jesus is alive   142
He has risen   155
He is Lord   158
He is the mighty God   160
Holy One of God   179
In the tomb so cold   234
Jesus is Lord!   284
Jesus, we celebrate the victory   299
Led like a lamb   312
Lord, I lift your name on high   330
Low in the grave he lay   345
Nothing shall separate us   377
O God, most high   385
O, what a morning   424
Shout! The Lord is risen!   452
Thank you, Jesus   475
Therefore we lift our hearts in
   praise   489
Thine be the glory   510
You are mighty   594
You laid aside your majesty   601

JESUS – SAVIOUR

Above the clash of creeds   3
For all that you've done   108
For the joys and for the sorrows   110
How firm a foundation   186
I went to the enemy's camp   257
Jesus, Jesus, Jesus   287
Jesus, lover of my soul   290
Jesus reigns   293
Jesus, what a beautiful name   301
Jesus, your name is power   304
Men of faith   354
My Jesus, I love thee   366
My Jesus, my Saviour   367
O for a thousand tongues to sing   383
Oh, I was made for this   389
Oh, lead me   390
Save the people   444
See, your Saviour comes   448
Shout for joy and sing   450
There's a place where the
   streets shine   498
The Word made flesh   507
This is the message of the cross   518
We believe   541
We have a great priest   546
Well, I hear they're singing in
   the streets   550
Who can sound the depths of
   sorrow   579
You rescued me   605
Your love flows like a river   607

JESUS – SECOND COMING

All heaven waits   9

And he shall reign   22
At the name of Jesus   33
Be patient, be ready   46
Great is the darkness   136
He has fire in his eyes   154
He has risen   155
He is the mighty God   160
I cannot tell   199
Joy to the world   305
King of kings   308
Lo, he comes with clouds
   descending   324
Man of sorrows   350
O Lord, my God   396
Sing a song of celebration   457
Soon and very soon   460
Sound the trumpet   461
The heavens shall declare   480
There's a blessed time that's
   coming   496
These are the days   503
The Word made flesh   507
This is the mystery   519
This is the time   610
We are his children   537
We believe   541
We will cross every border   560
You have taken the precious   600
You're the Lion of Judah   606

JOY

Down the mountain the river
   flows   83
God is good   124
Hallelujah! Jesus is alive   142
Heaven invites you to a party   150
He has clothed us with his
   righteousness   153
He's given me a garment of
   praise   166
I could sing unending songs   200
In every circumstance   227
In the tomb so cold   234
I've found a friend   251
I've got a love song   252
I will enter his gates   262
I will wave my hands   269
Jesus' love has got under
   our skin   289
Jesus put this song into
   our hearts   292
Jesus, we celebrate the victory   299
Joy to the world   305
Let the righteous sing   316
Lord, I lift your name on high   330
Make a joyful noise, all ye
   people   347
Make way, make way   349
My first love   362
O come and join the dance   381
O happy day   387

O, heaven is in my heart   388
Oh, I was made for this   389
One shall tell another   406
Over the mountains and the sea   421
O, what a morning   424
Peace be to these streets   427
Peace I give to you   428
Peace like a river   429
Peace, perfect peace   430
Rejoice!   438
Righteousness, peace, joy in
   the Holy Ghost   440
Shout for joy   449
Shout for joy and sing   450
Shout, shout for joy   451
Sing a song of celebration   457
Teach me to dance   469
The Lord is marching out   482
The Lord is our strength   484
There's a sound of singing   500
The trumpets sound, the
   angels sing   506
This is the day that the Lord
   has made   516
This is the day   517
Well, I hear they're singing in
   the streets   550
We rejoice in the goodness of
   our God   554
When the Lord brought us back   575
Where there once was only hurt   577
With my whole heart   582
You are mighty   594
You make my heart feel glad   603
You shall go out with joy   609

JUSTICE

Beauty for brokenness   37
Have you heard the good news   146
Heaven shall not wait   151
Make me a channel of your
   peace   348
O Lord, the clouds are gathering   399
See, your Saviour comes   448
Who can sound the depths
   of sorrow   579

LORD'S SUPPER

See **Communion**

LOVE – GOD'S LOVE

And can it be   21
A new commandment   23
Because of your love   39
Before the world began   40
Be free   41
Behold his love   43
Bind us together   51
Come on, all us singers, sing   74
Father, I come to you   95

Father, I want you to hold me 98
Filled with compassion 105
God is good 124
Here is love 164
His love 171
How can I not love you? 184
How deep the Father's love
　for us 185
I am so thankful 192
I'm special 222
I receive your love 236
I stand amazed in the presence 243
I've got a love song 252
I want to be out of my depth
　in your love 255
Jesus! I am resting, resting 280
Jesus, Jesus, Jesus 287
Jesus' love has got under
　our skin 289
Jesus, your loving kindness 303
Let it rain 314
Let there be love 317
Let your love come down 319
Look what God has done 325
Lord, I come to you 329
Lord, you are so precious to me 340
Love divine, all loves excelling 343
Love of Christ, come now 343
Make me a channel of your
　peace 348
My heart will sing to you 364
My Lord, what love is this 370
Nothing shall separate us 377
O give thanks 384
Oh, I was made for this 389
O Lord, your tenderness 402
One shall tell another 406
O the deep, deep love of Jesus! 414
Over the mountains and the sea 421
Overwhelmed by love 422
Peace be to these streets 427
Peace I give to you 428
Peace, perfect peace 430
Righteousness, peace, joy in
　the Holy Ghost 440
Soften my heart, Lord 459
Such love 465
Thank you for your mercy 474
Thank you, Jesus 475
The cross has said it all 478
The Lord is marching out 482
There's an awesome sound 497
The steadfast love of the Lord 505
This grace is mine 512
To you, O Lord, I lift up
　my soul 530
We are marching 539
We march to the tune of a
　love-song 552
We rejoice in the goodness of
　our God 554

We want to remain in your love 558
What a friend I've found 565
What kind of love is this 568
With my whole heart 582
Yet this will I call to mind 587
You alone, Lord, are wonderful 588
You are my passion 596
You love me as you found me 602
Your love flows like a river 607
Your mercy flows 608

LOVE – OUR LOVE FOR
OTHERS

A new commandment 23
Bind us together 51
Filled with compassion 105
Let there be love 317
Make me a channel of your peace 348
Peace I give to you 428
Righteousness, peace, joy in
　the Holy Ghost 440
We are marching 539
We want to remain in your love 558

MARCH FOR JESUS

And he shall reign 22
Celebrate, celebrate 66
Come, let us worship Jesus 73
Far and near 90
From where the sun rises 117
Hail, Jesus, you're my King 140
I will build my church 259
Jesus Christ is Lord of all 275
Jesus' love has got under
　our skin 289
Jesus put this song into our
　hearts 292
King of kings 308
Lift up your heads 321
Make way, make way 349
O give thanks 384
O, heaven is in my heart 388
Peace be to these streets 427
The Lord is marching out 482
Welcome the King 549

MARRIAGE

On this day of happiness 410

MISSION

Above the clash of creeds 3
All over the world 12
As we lift up your name 30
At this time of giving 34
Before the world began 40
Colours of day 69
Come on, all us singers, sing 74
Day of favour 78
Did you feel the mountains
　tremble? 80

Every nation, power and tongue 86
Far and near 90
Father of creation 99
Filled with compassion 105
Fire 106
From the sun's rising 116
God forgave my sin 123
Great is the darkness 136
Have you heard the good news 146
Have you not said 147
Heaven invites you to a party 150
He is the Lord 159
Here I am 161
Here we stand in total surrender 165
How lovely on the mountains 189
I heard the voice of Jesus say 206
I'm standing here to testify 223
Is anyone thirsty? 237
Is it true today 241
I, the Lord of sea and sky 246
It's rising up 249
I want to serve the purpose
　of God 256
Just as I am, without one plea 306
Let your word go forth 320
Lord, the light of your love 335
Lord, we lift you high 336
Make way, make way 349
Not by might 376
O Breath of Life 379
O Father of the fatherless 382
O for a thousand tongues to sing 383
O God of burning, cleansing
　flame 386
Oh, I was made for this 389
One shall tell another 406
O thou who camest from above 416
Peace be to these streets 427
Rejoice! 438
Show your power, O Lord 454
The Lord is moving across
　this land 483
These are the days 503
The Spirit of the sovereign Lord 504
This is my beloved Son 514
This is the message of the cross 518
This is the time 610
To God be the glory! 526
Turn to me and be saved 532
We are his children 537
We are the army of God 540
We believe 541
Well, I hear they're singing in
　the streets 550
We'll walk the land 551
We march to the tune of a
　love-song 552
We've had a light 557
We will cross every border 560
You have called us 598
You're the Lion of Judah 606

NATURE

See **God – Creation**

OFFERING

Give thanks with a grateful heart 118

OPENING OF SERVICE

See **Call to Worship**

PALM SUNDAY

See **Jesus – Life**

PEACE

Father, we adore you	101
Here is bread	163
Hold me closer to you	172
Jesus! I am resting, resting	280
Make me a channel of your peace	348
O Lord, my heart is not proud	397
Peace be to these streets	427
Peace I give to you	428
Peace like a river	429
Peace, perfect peace	430
Peace to you	431
Righteousness, peace, joy in the Holy Ghost	440
To be in your presence	524
You shall go out with joy	609

PENTECOST

All honour, all glory	10
All over the world	12
Anointing, fall on me	24
As we lift up your name	30
Breathe on me, Breath of God	57
Come down, O Love divine	71
Come, Spirit, come	76
Down the mountain the river flows	83
Holy Spirit, come	180
Holy Spirit, we welcome you	181
I believe the promise	196
Is anyone thirsty?	237
I've found a friend	251
Jesus, restore to us again	295
Lord, we long for you	337
More of your glory	360
O Breath of Life	379
O God of burning, cleansing flame	386
O thou who camest from above	416
Peace like a river	429
Ruach	442
Spirit of the living God (Iverson)	462
Spirit of the living God (Armstrong)	463
The promise of the Holy Spirit	488

Therefore we lift our hearts in praise	489
There's an awesome sound	497
There's a wind a-blowing	501
The Spirit of the sovereign Lord	504

PERSEVERANCE AND DETERMINATION

All I once held dear	11
Be bold, be strong	38
Be patient, be ready	46
Called to a battle	61
Far and near	90
Fire	106
For I'm building a people of power	109
For this purpose	111
Give thanks with a grateful heart	118
Hail, Jesus, you're my King	140
Have you got an appetite?	145
He has fire in his eyes	154
He that is in us	167
How can I be free from sin?	183
I need you more	226
In the morning when I rise	231
Is it true today	241
I walk by faith	253
I want to serve the purpose of God	256
I went to the enemy's camp	257
I will never be the same again	264
O Jesus, I have promised	391
On this day	409
O thou who camest from above	416
Salvation belongs to our God	443
They that wait on the Lord	509
Wake up, my soul	534
We shall stand	556
We've had a light	557
We want to see Jesus lifted high	559
We will cross every border	560

PRAISE

See **Adoration and Praise**

PRAYER

All heaven waits	9
Be thou my vision	50
Can a nation be changed?	62
Draw me closer	84
Father, hear our prayer	93
Father, here I am	94
Father of creation	99
Father of life, draw me closer	100
God, be gracious	122
God of glory	131
Hear, O Lord, our cry	148
Hear our cry	149
Here we stand in total surrender	165

Holy Spirit, come	180
I cry out for your hand	201
I lift my eyes up to the mountains	211
In my life, Lord	230
Let it rain	314
Let me be a sacrifice	315
Let there be love	317
Let your living water flow	318
Let your love come down	319
Let your word go forth	320
Lord, have mercy	328
Lord, the light of your love	335
Lord, we long for you	337
Love of Christ, come now	343
Make me a channel of your peace	348
May the fragrance	352
More love, more power	359
More of your glory	360
Oh, lead me	390
O Lord, hear my prayer	394
One thing I ask	407
Peace be to these streets	427
Restore, O Lord	439
Ruach	442
Save the people	444
See, your Saviour comes	448
Soften my heart, Lord	459
Teach me your ways	470
There's a wind a-blowing	501
To every good thing God is doing	525
Turn our hearts	531
Turn to me and be saved	532
We are his people	538
We have prayed that you would have mercy	547
We'll walk the land	551
We want to see Jesus lifted high	559
We will turn the hearts	562
What a friend we have in Jesus	566
When my heart is overwhelmed	573
Where two or three	578
Who can sound the depths of sorrow	579
Your mercy flows	608

PROCLAMATION

Above the clash of creeds	3
Be glorified	42
Blessed be the name of the Lord	53
Celebrate, celebrate	66
Come, let us worship Jesus	73
Day of favour	78
Every nation, power and tongue	86
Far and near	90
Father in heaven, how we love you	96
For I'm building a people of power	109

For this purpose 111
From the ends of the earth 115
From the sun's rising 116
Glory to the King of kings 121
God is good all the time 125
Great is thy faithfulness 138
Hail, Jesus, you're my King 140
Hallelujah, hallelujah 141
Hallelujah! Jesus is alive 142
Have you heard the good news 146
He has clothed us with his
  righteousness 153
He is the Lord 159
He is the mighty God 160
He that is in us 167
How lovely on the mountains 189
I am a new creation 191
I believe in Jesus 195
I'm standing here to testify 223
In every circumstance 227
In heavenly armour 228
In the tomb so cold 234
It's rising up 249
I walk by faith 253
I will build my church 259
Jesus, at your name 273
Jesus Christ is Lord of all 275
Jesus Christ is the Lord of all 277
Jesus, God's righteousness
  revealed 278
Jesus is greater 282
Jesus is Lord! 284
Jesus reigns 293
Jesus, we celebrate the victory 299
Jesus, you're my firm foundation 302
Jesus, your name is power 304
Joy to the world 305
King of kings and Lord of lords 307
King of kings 308
Led like a lamb 312
Lift up your heads 321
Lord of lords 332
Lord of the heavens 333
Low in the grave he lay 345
Make way, make way 349
Men of faith 354
Mighty God 356
Mighty is our God 357
My life is in you, Lord 368
Nothing shall separate us 377
O God, most high 385
One heart, one voice, one mind 405
Open the doors of praise 411
Our God is an awesome God 418
O, we are more than conquerors 423
Salvation belongs to our God 443
See his glory 446
Seek ye first 447
Shout, shout for joy 451
Shout! The Lord is risen! 452
Shout unto God 453

Tell out, my soul 471
The cross has said it all 478
The Lord is a mighty King 481
The Lord is marching out 482
The Lord is moving across
  this land 483
The Lord is our strength 484
The Lord reigns 485
The price is paid 487
There is a place of commanded
  blessing 491
There is a Redeemer 492
There is only one Lord 494
There is power in the name
  of Jesus 495
The world is looking for a hero 508
This, in essence, is the message 513
This is my beloved Son 514
This is the message of the cross 518
To every good thing God is doing 525
We are marching 539
We are the army of God 540
We believe 541
We declare your majesty 544
Welcome, King of kings 548
We serve a God of miracles 555
We shall stand 556
We want to see Jesus lifted high 559
We will cross every border 560
We will run and not grow weary 561
You are crowned with many
  crowns 590
You are God, you are great 591
You are mighty 594
You are my King 595
You are my rock 597
You're the Lion of Judah 606

RENEWAL

All over the world 12
Don't let my love grow cold 81
Do something new, Lord 82
Down the mountain the river
  flows 83
How lovely on the mountains 189
Is anyone thirsty? 237
It's our confession, Lord 248
I've found a friend 251
Jesus, restore to us again 295
Let it rain 314
Lord, have mercy 328
Love of Christ, come now 343
May the fragrance 352
Men of faith 354
Mercy is falling 355
More of your glory 360
My first love 362
Not by might 376
O Breath of Life 379
Oh, lead me 390

O let the sun of God enfold you 392
O Lord, the clouds are
  gathering 399
Restore, O Lord 439
River, wash over me 441
Ruach 442
Show your power, O Lord 454
Spirit of the living God
  (Iverson) 462
Spirit of the living God
  (Armstrong) 463
There's a wind a-blowing 501
These are the days 503
The Spirit of the sovereign Lord 504
They that wait on the Lord 509
Turn our hearts 531
We are his people 538
We will turn the hearts 562
When the Lord brought us back 575
You have shown me 599
You have taken the precious 600
Your love flows like a river 607
Your mercy flows 608

REVIVAL

As we lift up your name 30
Can a nation be changed? 62
Can we walk upon the water 64
Don't let my love grow cold 81
Down the mountain the river
  flows 83
God of glory 131
Great is the darkness 136
Hear, O Lord, our cry 148
Hear our cry 149
Here we stand in total surrender 165
I believe the promise 196
Is it true today 241
It's rising up 249
Let it rain 314
Lord, we long for you 337
Not by might 376
O Breath of Life 379
O God of burning, cleansing
  flame 386
O Lord, the clouds are gathering 399
Save the people 444
See, your Saviour comes 448
There's an awesome sound 497
There's a wind a-blowing 501
These are the days 503
The Spirit of the sovereign Lord 504
This is the time 610
We are his people 538
We are the army of God 540
We have prayed that you
  would have mercy 547
We'll walk the land 551
You have taken the precious 600
Your mercy flows 608

REPENTANCE AND FORGIVENESS

And can it be · 1
Come and see · 70
Come, let us return · 72
Come on, all us singers, sing · 74
Dear Lord and Father of mankind · 79
Father, here I am · 94
God forgave my sin · 123
God of grace · 132
Here we stand in total surrender · 165
Holiness is your life in me · 174
Holy Spirit, come · 180
I believe in Jesus · 195
I bow my knee · 198
I have made you too small · 205
I know a place · 209
I'm special · 222
I'm standing here to testify · 223
It's our confession, Lord · 248
I worship you, O Lamb of God · 272
Just as I am, without one plea · 306
Lamb of God · 310
Lord, have mercy · 328
My Lord, what love is this · 370
O Father of the fatherless · 382
Oh, I was made for this · 389
O Lord, the clouds are gathering · 399
O Lord, you're beautiful · 401
Only by grace · 408
O the blood of Jesus · 412
O the blood of my Saviour · 413
Restore, O Lord · 439
Soften my heart, Lord · 459
The cross has said it all · 478
This is the message of the cross · 518
Turn our hearts · 531
Turn to me and be saved · 532
We have a great priest · 546
We have prayed that you would have mercy · 547
Well, I hear they're singing in the streets · 550
We will turn the hearts · 562
What kind of love is this · 568
With this bread · 583
You are merciful to me · 593
You rescued me · 605

ROUNDS/ANTIPHONAL SONGS

From the ends of the earth · 115
Glory · 120
Hail, Jesus, you're my King · 140
Hear our cry · 149
Heaven invites you to a party · 150
I believe in Jesus · 195
I'm standing here to testify · 223
In the tomb so cold · 234

I will worship · 270
I worship you, O Lamb of God · 272
Jesus Christ is Lord of all · 275
Jesus' love has got under our skin · 289
Jesus, you're my firm foundation · 302
King of kings and Lord of lords · 307
Led like a lamb · 312
Lord, you have my heart · 341
Make way, make way · 349
My heart is full · 363
O, heaven is in my heart · 388
O Lord, the clouds are gathering · 399
The Lord is a mighty King · 481
The Spirit of the sovereign Lord · 504
Turn to me and be saved · 532
You are merciful to me · 593

SALVATION AND REDEMPTION

Above the clash of creeds · 3
Amazing grace · 18
And can it be · 21
At the foot of the cross · 32
Because of your love · 39
Before the world began · 40
Beneath the cross of Jesus · 45
Come and see · 70
Crown him with many crowns · 77
Did you feel the mountains tremble? · 80
Filled with compassion · 105
God of grace · 132
Hallelujah, my Father · 143
He has clothed us with his righteousness · 153
He is the Lord · 159
Here is love · 164
He's given me a garment of praise · 166
He was pierced · 169
Holiness is your life in me · 174
How lovely on the mountains · 189
How sweet the name of Jesus sounds · 190
I am a new creation · 191
I believe in Jesus · 195
I could sing unending songs · 200
I cry out for your hand · 201
I give you all the honour · 203
I heard the voice of Jesus say · 206
I know a place · 209
I know it · 210
I'm accepted, I'm forgiven · 217
I'm special · 222
I stand amazed in the presence · 243
I stand before the presence · 244
I, the Lord of sea and sky · 246
It's your blood · 250

I went to the enemy's camp · 257
I will change your name · 260
I will offer up my life · 265
I worship you, O Lamb of God · 272
Jesus! I am resting, resting · 280
Jesus, the name high over all · 298
Jesus, what a beautiful name · 301
Jesus, your name is power · 304
Just as I am, without one plea · 306
Like a candle flame · 322
Meekness and majesty · 353
Mighty God · 356
My Jesus, I love thee · 366
My lips shall praise you · 369
My Lord, what love is this · 370
O Father of the fatherless · 382
O for a thousand tongues to sing · 383
O happy day · 387
O, heaven is in my heart · 388
Oh, I was made for this · 389
O Lord, my God · 396
O Lord, your tenderness · 402
O the blood of my Saviour · 413
Overwhelmed by love · 422
Peace be to these streets · 427
Praise, my soul, the King of heaven · 433
See, your Saviour comes · 448
Shout! The Lord is risen! · 452
Such love · 465
Thank you for saving me · 472
Thank you for the cross · 473
The cross has said it all · 478
The Lord is a mighty King · 481
The price is paid · 487
The promise of the Holy Spirit · 488
There is a Redeemer · 492
There's a place where the streets shine · 498
There's a sound of singing · 500
The trumpets sound, the angels sing · 506
The Word made flesh · 507
The world is looking for a hero · 508
This is my beloved Son · 514
This is the message of the cross · 518
This love · 521
To every good thing God is doing · 525
To God be the glory! · 526
Turn to me and be saved · 532
We believe · 541
We rejoice in the goodness of our God · 554
We serve a God of miracles · 555
What kind of love is this · 568
Where there once was only hurt · 577
Who sees it all · 580
With this bread · 583
Yet this will I call to mind · 587

You are Lord 592
You have called us 598
You have shown me 599
You laid aside your majesty 601
You rescued me 605

SANCTIFICATION

All I once held dear 11
All to Jesus I surrender 15
As we lift up your name 30
At the name of Jesus 33
Breathe on me, Breath of God 57
Can I ascend 63
Change my heart, O God 68
Come down, O Love divine 71
Come, let us return 72
Come, Spirit, come 76
Do something new, Lord 82
Father, here I am 94
God of glory 131
Hold me, Lord 173
Holiness is your life in me 174
Holiness unto the Lord 175
Holy Spirit, come 180
Holy Spirit, we welcome you 181
How can I be free from sin? 183
I bow my knee before your throne 197
I bow my knee 198
If you are encouraged 202
In my life, Lord 230
It's your blood 250
I will never be the same again 264
Jesus, take me as I am 297
Lamb of God 310
Lord, I come to you 329
Lord, prepare me 334
Lord, the light of your love 335
Nothing shall separate us 377
O God of burning, cleansing flame 386
O Jesus, I have promised 391
Purify my heart 436
Reign in me 437
Teach me your ways 470
This is the message of the cross 518
This love 521
Wake up, O sleeper 535
We shall stand 556

SECOND COMING

See **Jesus – Second Coming**

SOCIAL CONCERN

Beauty for brokenness 37
Can a nation be changed? 62
Heaven shall not wait 151
I, the Lord of sea and sky 246
Let your love come down 319
Lord, for the years 327
Lord, we long for you 337

Make me a channel of your peace 348
O Lord, the clouds are gathering 399
One shall tell another 406
Peace be to these streets 427
Save the people 444
See, your Saviour comes 448
The Spirit of the sovereign Lord 504
We'll walk the land 551
Who can sound the depths of sorrow 579
Who sees it all 580
Your mercy flows 608

SPIRITUAL WARFARE

All heaven waits 9
Called to a battle 61
Can a nation be changed? 62
In heavenly armour 228
I went to the enemy's camp 257
I will build my church 259
Open the doors of praise 411
Our God is awesome in power 419
The Lord is moving across this land 483
The price is paid 487
There is power in the name of Jesus 495
We march to the tune of a love-song 552
We shall stand 556
We want to see Jesus lifted high 559
You're the Lion of Judah 606

SUBMISSION TO GOD

All to Jesus I surrender 15
By your side 60
Come down, O Love divine 71
Come, let us return 72
Do something new, Lord 82
Father, I place into your hands 97
God is here, God is present 127
Here I am 161
Here we stand in total surrender 165
I bow my knee before your throne 197
I bow my knee 198
Jesus! I am resting, resting 280
King of kings, majesty 309
Let it be to me 313
Let me be a sacrifice 315
O Lord, my heart is not proud 397
Reign in me 437
River, wash over me 441
Silent, surrendered 456
Take my life, and let it be 468
To keep your lovely face 527

TEMPTATIONS AND TRIALS

Be patient, be ready 46

For the joys and for the sorrows 110
How firm a foundation 186
When peace like a river 574

THANKSGIVING

Alleluia, alleluia, give thanks to the risen Lord 4
For all that you've done 108
Give thanks with a grateful heart 118
Great is the Lord and most worthy of praise 137
Great is thy faithfulness 138
He has clothed us with his righteousness 153
How can I not love you? 184
I am so thankful 192
I could sing unending songs 200
I give you all the honour 203
Immanuel, O Immanuel 219
I'm special 222
I sing a simple song of love 239
Jesus Christ 274
Look what God has done 325
Look what the Lord has done 326
Lord, for the years 327
O give thanks 384
Oh, I was made for this 389
Teach me to dance 469
Thank you for saving me 472
Thank you for the cross 473
Thank you for your mercy 474
Thank you, Jesus 475
The Lord is marching out 482
The Lord is our strength 484
The price is paid 487
Therefore we lift our hearts in praise 489
There's a sound of singing 500
The trumpets sound, the angels sing 506
Thine be the glory 510
This Child 511
When the Lord brought us back 575

TRINITY

See **Adoration and Praise**

TRUST

Almighty God, my Redeemer 17
Because of your love 39
Be still and know 48
Be still, my soul 49
Bless the Lord, my soul 56
Can we walk upon the water 64
Faithful God 88
Faithful One 89
Father, I place into your hands 97
For the joys and for the sorrows 110
God is good all the time 125
God will make a new way 134

Great is the Lord and most worthy of praise 137
Great is thy faithfulness 138
Have you not said 147
He walked where I walked 168
Higher, higher 170
His love 171
Hold me closer to you 172
How firm a foundation 186
I am standing beneath your wings 193
I cry out for your hand 201
I lift my eyes up to the mountains 211
I'm so secure 221
I'm your child 224
In Christ alone 225
I need you more 226
In every circumstance 227
In heavenly armour 228
I walk by faith 253
I will praise you all my life 266
I will worship 270
Jesus! I am resting, resting 280
Jesus, lover of my soul 290
Jesus, you're my firm foundation 302
Lead us, heavenly Father, lead us 311
Let your living water flow 318
Living under the shadow of his wing 323
My Jesus, my Saviour 367
My life is in you, Lord 368
My lips shall praise you 369
My spirit rests in you alone 371
O Jesus, I have promised 391
O Lord, you lead me 400
One thing I ask 407
Our confidence is in the Lord 417
Praise the name of Jesus 435
Say the word 445
Tell out, my soul 471
Thank you for your mercy 474
The Lord's my shepherd 486
There is none like you 493
They that wait on the Lord 509
This grace is mine 512
This is the day that the Lord has made 516
Though I feel afraid 522

Though the earth should tremble 523
To you, O Lord, I lift up my soul 530
What a friend we have in Jesus 566
When my heart is overwhelmed 573
When peace like a river 574
With all my heart 581
You are my rock 597
You love me as you found me 602
You make your face to shine on me 604

UNITY

See **Church**

VICTORY

Be bold, be strong 38
Called to a battle 61
Father of creation 99
For this purpose 111
Hallelujah! Jesus is alive 142
He that is in us 167
Higher, higher 170
I am a new creation 191
In every circumstance 227
In heavenly armour 228
I went to the enemy's camp 257
Nothing shall separate us 377
O God, most high 385
Open the doors of praise 411
Our God is awesome in power 419
O, we are more than conquerors 423
Rejoice! 438
Shout, shout for joy 451
Shout unto God 453
The Lord is moving across this land 483
The price is paid 487
There is only one Lord 494
There is power in the name of Jesus 495
The world is looking for a hero 508
Thine be the glory 510
We are a people of power 536
We are the army of God 540
We march to the tune of a love-song 552
We must work together 553

VISION

Can we walk upon the water 64
Don't let my love grow cold 81
Father of creation 99
Great is the darkness 136
I believe the promise 196
I see the Lord 238
Is it true today 241
It's rising up 249
I want to serve the purpose of God 256
I will change your name 260
I will never be the same again 264
Jesus, God's righteousness revealed 278
Men of faith 354
No scenes of stately majesty 375
Rejoice! 438
Soon and very soon 460
There is a louder shout to come 490
These are the days 503
The Spirit of the sovereign Lord 504
The world is looking for a hero 508
This is my beloved Son 514
Wake up, my soul 534
We are a people of power 536
We are the army of God 540
We must work together 553
We want to see Jesus lifted high 559
We will turn the hearts 562
You have taken the precious 600
You're the Lion of Judah 606

WORD OF GOD

Have you got an appetite? 145
Jesus, restore to us again 295
Jesus, you're my firm foundation 302
Let your word go forth 320
Say the word 445
Seek ye first 447
Silent, surrendered 456
The Lord is a mighty King 481

WORSHIP

See **Adoration and Praise**

Index of First Lines and Titles

*This index gives the first line of each hymn. If a hymn is known by an
alternative title, this is also given, but indented and in italics.*

A

Abba, Father, let me be 1
Abide with me 2
Above the clash of creeds 3
Acts chapter 2, verse 39 488
A living sacrifice 351
Alleluia, alleluia, give thanks to
the risen Lord 4
All hail King Jesus! 5
All hail the Lamb 6
All hail the power of Jesus' name 7
All heaven declares 8
All heaven waits 9
All honour, all glory 10
All I know 522
All I once held dear 11
All I want 231
All over the world 12
All people that on earth do dwell 13
All the earth shall worship 102
All the glory 363
All things are possible 17
All things bright and beautiful 14
All to Jesus I surrender 15
Almighty God, we bring you
praise 16
Almighty God, my Redeemer 17
Amazing grace 18
Amazing love 370
Amen 525
Among the gods 19
An army of ordinary people 20
Ancient of Days 54
And can it be 21
And he shall reign 22
And his love goes on and on 325
*And that my soul knows
very well* 604
A new commandment 23
Anointing, fall on me 24
Arms of love 239
Army of God 540
Ascribe greatness 25
As I come into your presence 26
As the deer pants (Nystrom) 27
As the deer pants (Lewis) 28
As we are gathered 29
As we lift up your name 30
As we seek your face 31
At the cross 209
At the foot of the cross 32
At the name of Jesus 33
At this time of giving 34
At your feet we fall 35
Away in a manger 36

Awesome God 418
Awesome in this place 26

B

Beauty for brokenness 37
Be bold, be strong 38
Because of the Lord's great love 587
Because of you 498
Because of your love 39
Before the world began 40
Be free 41
Be glorified 42
Behold his love 43
Behold the Lord 44
Be magnified 205
Beneath the cross of Jesus 45
Be patient, be ready 46
Be still, for the presence of
the Lord 47
Be still and know 48
Be still, my soul 49
Be thou my vision 50
Better is one day 188
Bind us together 51
Blessed assurance, Jesus is mine 52
*Blessed be the Lord God
Almighty* 96
Blessed be the name 193
Blessed be the name of the Lord 53
Blessing and honour 54
Blessing, honour, glory to the
Lamb 55
Bless the Lord, my soul 56
Break dividing walls 491
Breathe on me, Breath of God 57
Broken for me 58
By his grace 59
By your side 60

C

Called to a battle 61
Can a nation be changed? 62
Can I ascend 63
Can we walk upon the water 64
Can you see what we have made 65
Cast your burdens 170
Celebrate 75
Celebrate, celebrate 66
Celebrate Jesus 67
Champion 508
Change my heart, O God 68
*Christ is risen! (In the tomb
so cold)* 234
*Christ is risen (O, what a
morning)* 424

Colours of day 69
Come and see 70
Come down, O Love divine 71
Come, let us return 72
Come, let us worship Jesus 73
Come, Lord Jesus 136
Come on, all us singers, sing 74
Come on and celebrate 75
Come, Spirit, come 76
Come to the light 223
Creation creed 481
Cross every border 560
Crown him with many crowns 77

D

Day of favour 78
Days of Elijah 503
Dear Lord and Father of
mankind 79
Did you feel the mountains
tremble? 80
Distant thunder 610
Don't let my love grow cold 81
Do something new, Lord 82
Down the mountain the river
flows 83
Draw me closer 84

E

Earth lies spellbound 85
Enemy's camp 257
Eternity 258
Every nation, power and tongue 86
Exalt the Lord 87

F

Faithful God 88
Faithful One 89
Far and near 90
Father God, I wonder 91
Father God, we worship you 92
Father, hear our prayer 93
Father, here I am 94
Father, I come to you 95
Father in heaven, how we love you 96
Father, I place into your hands 97
Father, I want you to hold me 98
Father of creation 99
*Father of creation (We come
into your presence)* 543
Father of life, draw me closer 100
Father me 382
Father, we adore you 101
Father, we adore you, you've
drawn us 102

Father, we love you 103
Father, you are my portion 104
Filled with compassion 105
Fill us up and send us out 147
Fire 106
Fire of God's glory 131
Firm foundation 302
5000+ hungry folk 107
For all that you've done 108
For all the people who live on earth 105
For I'm building a people of power 109
For the joys and for the sorrows 110
For this I have Jesus 110
For this purpose 111
For thou, O Lord, art high 112
For unto us a child is born 113
Fountain of life 101
Freely, freely 123
From heaven you came 114
From the ends of the earth 115
From the sun's rising 116
From where the sun rises 117

G

Give thanks with a grateful heart 118
Gloria 119
Glorify your name 103
Glory 120
Glory to God 528
Glory to the King 331
Glory to the King of kings 121
Glory to the Lamb 55
God, be gracious 122
God forgave my sin 123
God is good 124
God is good all the time 125
God is great 126
God is here, God is present 127
God is light 513
God is working his purpose out 128
God of all comfort 129
God of glory, we exalt your name 130
God of glory 131
God of grace 132
God of the poor 37
God's not dead 133
God will make a new way 134
God with us 168
Go forth in his name 537
Good to me 201
Great and mighty is he 135
Great is the darkness 136
Great is the Lord and most worthy of praise 137
Great is thy faithfulness 138
Great is your mercy 474
Great is your name 139
Great love 364

H

Hail, Jesus, you're my King 140
Hallelujah, hallelujah 141
Hallelujah! Jesus is alive 142
Hallelujah, my Father 143
Hark, the herald-angels sing 144
Hallowed be your name 178
Have faith in God 400
Have you got an appetite? 145
Have you heard the good news 146
Have you not said 147
Heal our nation 337
Hear, O Lord, our cry 148
Hear our cry 149
Hearts on fire 288
Heaven invites you to a party 150
Heaven is in my heart 388
Heaven shall not wait 151
He brought me to his banqueting table 152
He has clothed us with his righteousness 153
He has fire in his eyes 154
He has made me glad 262
He has risen 155
He is exalted 156
He is here 157
He is Lord 158
He is the Lord 159
He is the mighty God 160
Here I am 161
Here I am, Lord 246
Here in your presence 162
Here is bread 163
Here is love 164
Here we stand in total surrender 165
He's given me a garment of praise 166
He that is in us 167
He walked where I walk 168
He was pierced 169
Higher, higher 170
His banner over me is love 152
His love 171
History maker 241
Hold me closer to you 172
Hold me, Lord 173
Holiness is your life in me 174
Holiness unto the Lord 175
Holy and anointed one 286
Holy, holy, holy! Lord God Almighty 176
Holy, holy, Lord God Almighty 177
Holy, holy, Lord, you're worthy 178
Holy is your name 215
Holy One of God 179
Holy Spirit, come 180
Holy Spirit, we welcome you 181
Hosanna 182
How can I be free from sin? 183
How can I not love you? 184

How deep the Father's love for us 185
How firm a foundation 186
How good and how pleasant 187
How great thou art 396
How lovely is your dwelling-place 188
How lovely on the mountains 189
How majestic 395
How sweet the name of Jesus sounds 190

I

I am a new creation 191
I am so thankful 192
I am standing beneath your wings 193
I am the God that healeth thee 194
I believe in Jesus 195
I believe the promise 196
I bow my knee before your throne 197
I bow my knee 198
I cannot tell 199
I could sing of your love for ever 421
I could sing unending songs 200
I cry out for your hand 201
I exalt thee 112
If you are encouraged 202
I give thanks 599
I give you all the honour 203
I give you my heart 515
I have come to love you 204
I have made you too small 205
I heard the voice of Jesus say 206
I just want to be where you are 207
I just want to praise you 208
I know a place 209
I know it 210
I lift my eyes up to the mountains 211
I lift my hands 212
I'll love you more 198
I love to be in your presence 213
I love you, Lord, and I lift my voice 214
I love you, Lord, with all of my heart 215
I love your presence 216
I'm accepted, I'm forgiven 217
I'm coming up the mountain 63
I'm gonna click 218
Immanuel, O Immanuel 219
Immortal, invisible, God only wise 220
I'm so secure 221
I'm special 222
I'm standing here to testify 223
I'm your child 224

In Christ alone 225
I need you more 226
In every circumstance 227
In heavenly armour 228
In moments like these 229
In my generation 256
In my life, Lord 230
In the morning when I rise 231
In the presence of a holy God 232
In the secret 233
In the tomb so cold 234
In your hands 221
I reach up high 235
I really want to worship you, my Lord 601
I receive your love 236
Is anyone thirsty? 237
I see the Lord 238
I sing a simple song of love 239
I sing praises 240
Is it true today 241
Isn't he beautiful 242
I stand amazed in the presence 243
I stand before the presence 244
I stand before your throne 245
I stand complete in you 132
I stand in awe 589
I surrender all 15
I, the Lord of sea and sky 246
It is to you 247
It's our confession, Lord 248
It's rising up 249
It's your blood 250
I've found a friend 251
I've found Jesus 550
I've got a love song 252
I walk by faith 253
I want to be a blooming tree 254
I want to be a tree that's bearing fruit 254
I want to be out of my depth in your love 255
I want to serve the purpose of God 256
I was made for this 389
I went to the enemy's camp 257
I will be yours 258
I will build my church 259
I will change your name 260
I will dance, I will sing 261
I will enter his gates 262
I will lift my voice 263
I will never be the same again 264
I will offer up my life 265
I will praise you all my life 266
I will seek you 267
I will seek your face, O Lord 268
I will serve no foreign god 212
I will sing your praises 91
I will wave my hands 269
I will worship 270

I worship you (I give you all the honour) 203
I worship you, Almighty God 271
I worship you, eternal God 523
I worship you, O Lamb of God 272

J
Jesus, at your name 273
Jesus Christ 274
Jesus Christ is Lord of all 275
Jesus Christ is risen today 276
Jesus Christ is the Lord of all 277
Jesus, friend for ever 565
Jesus, God's righteousness revealed 278
Jesus, how lovely you are 279
Jesus! I am resting, resting 280
Jesus, I am thirsty 281
Jesus is alive 142
Jesus is greater 282
Jesus is King 283
Jesus is Lord! 284
Jesus is our battle cry 275
Jesus is our God 285
Jesus is the name we honour 285
Jesus, Jesus (Holy and anointed one) 286
Jesus, Jesus, Jesus 287
Jesus, Jesus, you have the name 288
Jesus' love has got under our skin 289
Jesus, lover of my soul 290
Jesus, name above all names 291
Jesus put this song into our hearts 292
Jesus reigns 293
Jesus, remember me 294
Jesus, restore to us again 295
Jesus shall take the highest honour 296
Jesus, take me as I am 297
Jesus, the name high over all 298
Jesus, we celebrate the victory 299
Jesus, we enthrone you 300
Jesus, what a beautiful name 301
Jesus, you're my firm foundation 302
Jesus, your loving kindness 303
Jesus, your name is power 304
Joy in the Holy Ghost 251
Joy to the world 305
Just as I am, without one plea 306

K
King of kings and Lord of lords 307
King of kings 308
King of kings, majesty 309
King of the nations 73
Knowing you 11

L
Lamb of God 310
Laudate Dominum 458

Lead me to the cross 183
Lead me to the rock 573
Lead us, heavenly Father, lead us 311
Led like a lamb 312
Let forgiveness flow 94
Let it be to me 313
Let it rain 314
Let it rain (We have prayed …) 547
Let me be a sacrifice 315
Let the bride say, 'Come' 519
Let the flame burn brighter 551
Let the peace of God reign 100
Let the righteous sing 316
Let there be love 317
Let your glory fall 99
Let your living water flow 318
Let your love come down 319
Let your word go forth 320
Lift up your heads 321
Light the fire again 81
Light up the fire 69
Like a candle flame 322
Like a child 362
Like a lamb 169
Lion of Judah 606
Living under the shadow of his wing 323
Living water 318
Lo, he comes with clouds descending 324
Look what God has done 325
Look what the Lord has done 326
Lord, be glorified 230
Lord, for the years 327
Lord, have mercy 328
Lord, I come to you 329
Lord, I lift your name on high 330
Lord most high 115
Lord, my heart cries out 331
Lord of lords 332
Lord of the heavens 333
Lord of the years 327
Lord, prepare me 334
Lord, the light of your love 335
Lord, we lift you high 336
Lord, we long for you 337
Lord, we long to see your glory 338
Lord, you are more precious 339
Lord, you are so precious to me 340
Lord, you have my heart 341
Lord, you put a tongue in my mouth 342
Love divine, all loves excelling 343
Love of Christ, come now 344
Low in the grave he lay 345

M
Majesty 346
Make a joyful noise, all ye people 347
Make me a channel of your peace 348

Make way, make way	349	O let the Son of God enfold you	392	*Psalm 121*	211
Man of sorrows	350	O little town of Bethlehem	393	*Psalm 126*	575
May I never lose sight of you	172	O Lord, hear my prayer	394	Purify my heart	436
May our worship be as fragrance	351	O Lord, how majestic is your		*Purify my heart (Teach me*	
May the fragrance	352	name	395	*your ways)*	470
Meekness and majesty	353	O Lord, my God	396		
Men of faith	354	O Lord, my heart is not proud	397	**R**	
Mercy is falling	355	O Lord our God	398	*Refiner's fire*	436
Mighty God	356	O Lord, the clouds are		Reign in me	437
Mighty is our God	357	gathering	399	Rejoice!	438
More about Jesus	358	O Lord, you lead me	400	*Release my soul*	529
More of you	281	O Lord, you're beautiful	401	Restore, O Lord	439
More love, more power	359	O Lord, your tenderness	402	*Restorer of my soul*	369
More of your glory	360	On a hill far away	403	*Revealer of mysteries*	466
More than oxygen	361	*Once again*	274	*Revival fire, fall*	30
Mourning into dancing	577	Once in royal David's city	404	*Revive us again*	148
My delight	104	One heart, one voice, one mind	405	Righteousness, peace, joy in	
My desire	524	One shall tell another	406	the Holy Ghost	440
My first love	362	One thing I ask	407	River, wash over me	441
My God is so big	420	Only by grace	408	Ruach	442
My heart is full	363	*Only the blood*	174		
My heart will sing to you	364	*Only you*	373	**S**	
My hope is built	365	*Only you deserve the glory*	139	Salvation belongs to our God	443
My Jesus, I love thee	366	On this day	409	*Sanctuary*	334
My Jesus, my Saviour	367	On this day of happiness	410	Save the people	444
My life is in you, Lord	368	Open the doors of praise	411	*Say it loud*	90
My lips shall praise you	369	O the blood of Jesus	412	Say the word	445
My Lord, what love is this	370	O the blood of my Saviour	413	See his glory	446
My spirit rests in you alone	371	O the deep, deep love of Jesus!	414	Seek ye first	447
		O the glory of your presence	415	See, your Saviour comes	448
N		O thou who camest from above	416	*Send revival*	497
Nearer, my God, to thee	372	Our confidence is in the Lord	417	*Send the fire*	386
No one but you, Lord	373	Our God is an awesome God	418	*Seven reasons to celebrate*	66
No other name	374	Our God is awesome in power	419	*Shadow of your wings*	371
No other way	3	Our God is so great	420	*Shine, Jesus, shine*	335
No scenes of stately majesty	375	*Our God reigns*	189	Shout for joy	449
Not by might	376	Over the mountains and the sea	421	Shout for joy and sing	450
Nothing shall separate us	377	Overwhelmed by love	422	Shout, shout for joy	451
Now is the time	521	O, we are more than conquerors	423	Shout! The Lord is risen!	452
Now unto the King	378	O, what a morning	424	*Shout to the Lord (My Jesus,*	
		O worship the King	425	*my Saviour)*	367
O		O worship the Lord in the		*Shout to the Lord (We are*	
O Breath of Life	379	beauty of holiness	426	*his people)*	538
O come, all ye faithful	380	*O you gates*	321	*Shout to the North*	354
O come and join the dance	381			Shout unto God	453
O faithful God	266	**P**		*Show your power*	159
O Father of the fatherless	382	Peace be to these streets	427	Show your power, O Lord	454
O for a thousand tongues		Peace I give to you	428	Silent night	455
to sing	383	Peace like a river	429	Silent, surrendered	456
O give thanks	384	Peace, perfect peace	430	Sing a song of celebration	457
O give thanks (The Lord is		Peace to you	431	*Singers' song*	74
marching out)	482	*People just like us*	86	Sing, praise and bless the	
O God, most high	385	*Power of your love*	329	Lord	458
O God of burning, cleansing		Praise God from whom all		*So come*	600
flame	386	blessings flow	432	Soften my heart, Lord	459
O happy day	387	Praise, my soul, the King of		Soon and very soon	460
O, heaven is in my heart	388	heaven	433	*Song for Christingle*	65
O I love you, Lord	473	Praise the Lord, O my soul	434	Sound the trumpet	461
Oh, I was made for this	389	Praise the name of Jesus	435	*So you would come*	40
Oh, lead me	390	*Prayer of humble access*	545	Spirit of the living God	
O Jesus, I have promised	391	*Prayer song*	328	(Iverson)	462

Spirit of the living God (Armstrong) 463
Spirit of the sovereign Lord 504
Spirit song 392
Streams of worship 464
Such love 465
Surely our God 466
Surely the time has come 557
Sweet mercies 248
Sweet wind 501

T

Take me in 467
Take me past the outer courts 467
Take my life, and let it be 468
Teach me to dance 469
Teach me your ways 470
Tell out, my soul 471
Thank you for saving me 472
Thank you for the cross 473
Thank you for your mercy 474
Thank you, Jesus 475
Thank you, Lord 108
That the Lamb who was slain 514
The angels, Lord, they sing 476
The battle belongs to the Lord 228
The candle song 322
The church's one foundation 477
The cross has said it all 478
The crucible for silver 479
The day of his power 452
The feast is ready 506
The giving song 34
The happy song 200
The heart of worship 576
The heavens shall declare 480
The King of glory comes 308
The Lord Almighty reigns 141
The Lord is a mighty King 481
The Lord is marching out 482
The Lord is moving across this land 483
The Lord is our strength 484
The Lord reigns 485
The Lord's my shepherd 486
The old rugged cross 403
The power and the glory 512
The price is paid 487
The promise of the Holy Spirit 488
Therefore we lift our hearts in praise 489
There is a louder shout to come 490
There is a place of commanded blessing 491
There is a Redeemer 492
There is none like you 493
There is only one Lord 494
There is power in the name of Jesus 495
There's a blessed time that's coming 496

There's an awesome sound 497
There is a place where the streets shine 498
There's a river of joy 499
There's a sound of singing 500
There's a wind a-blowing 501
There's no one like you 502
The river is here 83
These are the days 503
The Servant King 114
The solid Rock 365
The Spirit of the sovereign Lord 504
The steadfast love of the Lord 505
The strong name of Jesus 494
The trees of the field 609
The trumpets sound, the angels sing 506
The wine of the kingdom 406
The Word made flesh 507
The world is looking for a hero 508
They that wait on the Lord 509
Thine be the glory 510
This Child 511
This grace is mine 512
This, in essence, is the message 513
This is my beloved Son 514
This is my desire 515
This is the day that the Lord has made 516
This is the day 517
This is the message of the cross 518
This is the mystery 519
This is the sweetest mystery 520
This is the time 610
This is your God 353
This kingdom 278
This love 521
This thankful heart 265
Though I feel afraid 522
Though the earth should tremble 523
Three part harmony 410
Thunder in the skies 61
To be in your presence 524
To every good thing God is doing 525
To God be the glory! 526
To keep your lovely face 527
Tonight 528
To seek your face 129
To you, O Lord, I bring my worship 529
To you, O Lord, I lift up my soul 530
Turn our hearts 531
Turn the hearts 562
Turn to me and be saved 532
Turn your eyes upon Jesus 533

U

Under our skin 289
Undignified 261

Unending love 95
Unto the King 378

V

Victory chant 140

W

Wake up, my soul 534
Wake up, O sleeper 535
Warrior 419
We are a people of power 536
We are his children 537
We are his people 538
We are marching 539
We are the army of God 540
We await a Saviour from Heaven 507
We believe 541
We bring the sacrifice of praise 542
We come into your presence 543
We declare your majesty 544
We do not presume 545
We have a great priest 546
We have prayed that you would have mercy 547
Welcome, King of kings 548
Welcome the King 549
We lift up a shout 552
Well, I hear they're singing in the streets 550
We'll see it all 553
We'll walk the land 551
We march to the tune of a love-song 552
We must work together 553
We're in God's army 483
We rejoice in the goodness of our God 554
We rejoice in the grace of God 153
We serve a God of miracles 555
We serve a God of power 555
We shall see the King 496
We shall stand 556
We've had a light 557
We want to remain in your love 558
We want to see Jesus lifted high 559
We will cross every border 560
We will dance 457
We will magnify 398
We will ride 154
We will run and not grow weary 561
We will turn the hearts 562
We will wait 561
We will worship the Lamb of glory 563
We worship and adore you 564
We worship at your feet 70
What a friend I've found 565
What a friend we have in Jesus 566
What kind of greatness 567
What kind of love is this 568

What noise shall we make	569	
When I feel the touch	570	
When I look into your holiness	571	
When I survey the wondrous cross	572	
When my heart is overwhelmed	573	
When peace like a river	574	
When the Lord brought us back	575	
When the music fades	576	
Where there once was only hurt	577	
Where two or three	578	
White horse	46	
Who can sound the depths of sorrow	579	
Who sees it all	580	
With all my heart	581	
With my whole heart	582	
With this bread	583	
Worship the Lord	347	

Worthy is the Lamb	584
Worthy, O worthy are you, Lord	585

Y

Yahweh	586
Yet this will I call to mind	587
You alone are God	19
You alone are worthy of my praise	270
You alone, Lord, are wonderful	588
You are beautiful	589
You are crowned with many crowns	590
You are God, you are great	591
You are Lord	592
You are merciful to me	593
You are mighty	594
You are my King	595
You are my passion	596
You are my rock	597

You are the Christ	273
You came from heaven to earth	330
You have broken the chains	385
You have called us	598
You have shown me	599
You have taken the precious	600
You laid aside your majesty	601
You loved me as you found me	602
You make my heart feel glad	603
You make your face to shine on me	604
You're alive	312
You rescued me	605
You're the Lion of Judah	606
Your love	303
Your love flows like a river	607
Your love keeps following me	602
Your mercy flows	608
Your waves of love	28
You shall go out with joy	609

the source is being developed into a major resource for the churches. It is already available in the following editions

- **Complete Music Book**

- **Words Only**

- **Arrangements for Music Groups**

- **Acetate Masters**

- **Guitarist Edition**

- **CD-Rom**

If you would like to be kept informed,
please let us have your name and address.

Write to us   Kevin Mayhew Ltd
Buxhall
Stowmarket
Suffolk
IP14 3BW

or

phone   01449 737978

fax   01449 737834

e-mail   info@kevinmayhewltd.com

● the source
new
songs 1

Compiled by
Graham Kendrick

● **the source new songs 1** presents a selection of the best of new worship material – over eighty songs of praise, thanksgiving, worship and adoration drawn from all the corners of the globe.

The Full Music edition contains arrangements for piano or keyboard with guitar chords, acetate masters and a guitarist's section with just the lyrics and chords.

| 1470106 | Full Music | £15.99 | 1 84003 380 0 |

the source — the definitive worship recordings
available from Alliance Music on cassette and CD

Volume 1

Above the clash of creeds
As the deer pants
Before the world began
Father of creation
From the ends of the earth
I'm so secure
I need you more
I went to the enemy's camp
Jesus Christ (Once again)
My first love
Oh, lead me
Over the mountains and the sea
There is a place of commanded blessing
These are the days
The Spirit of the sovereign Lord
This grace is mine
To be in your presence
To every good thing God is doing
To you, O Lord, I lift up my soul
When peace like a river

Catalogue No.   CD   1901372
                Cassette 1901374

Volume 2

All I once held dear
Be thou my vision
Can a nation be changed?
Down the mountain the river flows
Glory to the King of kings
I could sing unending songs
Is anyone thirsty?
It's our confession, Lord
It's rising up
I want to be out of my depth
    in your love
I will seek you
Jesus, lover of my soul
King of kings, majesty
Lord, I come to you
Mighty is our God
More of your glory
Praise God from whom all
    blessings flow
There is a louder shout to come
There is a place where the streets shine
There's an awesome sound

Catalogue No.   CD   1901382
                Cassette 1901384

Volume 3

All over the world
As we lift up your name
Far and near
Father of life, draw me closer
Fire
God is good all the time
God of glory
How can I not love you?
How good and how pleasant
I see the Lord
Jesus, Jesus, you have the name
Jesus, what a beautiful name
Lamb of God
Lord, I lift your name on high
My heart is full
My Jesus, my Saviour
Overwhelmed by love
Well, I hear they're singing in the streets
We will worship the Lamb of glory
When I survey the wondrous cross

Catalogue No.   CD   1901392
                Cassette 1901394

Volume 4

Among the gods
Be glorified
Celebrate, celebrate
Did you feel the mountains tremble?
Have you not said?
Here we stand in total surrender
I am so thankful
I bow my knee
In Christ alone
I've found a friend
Jesus' love has got under our skin
Let your love come down
O for a thousand tongues to sing
O God of burning, cleansing flame
Sing a song of celebration
Soon and very soon
Teach me to dance
We've had a light
You make your face to shine on me
Your love flows like a river

Catalogue No.   CD   1901402
                Cassette 1901404

Volume 5

Almighty God, my redeemer
And he shall reign
Can I ascend
Come on, all us singers, sing
Great is your name
Hail, Jesus, you're my King
Hallelujah! Jesus is alive
He has clothed us with his righteousness
Holy, holy, holy! Lord God Almighty
I walk by faith
I will offer up my life
Jesus, God's righteousness revealed
Lord, my heart cries out
May our worship be as fragrance
O Lord, how majestic is your name
Our God is an awesome God
Our God is awesome in power
Save the people
The Lord is moving across this land
Who sees it all

Catalogue No.   CD   1901412
                Cassette 1901414

the source recordings are produced in
partnership with Alliance Media and are
available from all good Christian retailers
or, in the event of difficulty, from

Alliance Media
Waterside House
Woodley Headland
Peartree Bridge
Milton Keynes
MK6 3BY

● kidsource

Compiled by
Capt. Alan Price, CA

Someone once said something like this: 'I don't mind the theology, as long as I can write the hymns'. The speaker was referring to the fact that many Christians seem to learn their theology from what they sing, rather than from any other source. For better or worse, it is the hymns and songs learnt from childhood that form the basis of faith for many.

●**kidsource** is a brand-new collection of praise and worship songs for children, and is probably the most significant and comprehensive children's song collection published for a number of years. It is compiled by one of the country's favourite children's worship leaders, Capt. Alan Price, known to kids as Captain Alan of Captain's Crew, and contains over 400 songs from the UK's most renowned children's songwriters, like Doug Horley, Ishmael, Sammy Horner, Richard Hubbard, Paul Field, Ian White and Capt. Alan himself, as well as a significant number of well-known 'adult' praise and worship songs from writers such as Matt Redman, Graham Kendrick and Darlene Zschech.

All of the keyboard accompaniments have been arranged for maximum clarity and ease of use, with much consideration given to the pitch of the tunes and their suitability for young voices. Guitar chords are given for every song.

●**kidsource** contains a multiplicity of useful indexes, including a Key Word Cross-reference Index, making the selection of suitable songs as straightforward and effective as possible. A comprehensive Guitar Chord Index is also included.

Words Only	1470151	£2.99	1 84003 311 8
Full Music	1470154	£17.99	1 84003 310 X

CHRISTMAS 2001

K Kathleen Smith
17 Mearns Drive
Stonehaven
01569 763111